Course	Introduction to Animal Biology
Course Number	**ZO 200**
	Timothy Judd
	Southeast Missouri State University
	Biology

http://create.mheducation.com

ISBN-10: 0390667161   ISBN-13: 9780390667168

Contents

1. Laboratory Safety Procedures 1
2. Tissue Structure and Function 3
3. Gametogenesis and Embryology 21
4. The Sponges 43
5. The Radiate Animals 51
6. The Flatworms 69
7. The Annelids 89
8. The Molluscs 105
9. The Crustacean Arthropods 123
10. The Chelicerate Arthropods 135
11. The Arthropods 141
12. Five Small Protostome Phyla 165
13. The Echinoderms 177
14. Phylum Chordata: A Deuterostome Group 195
15. The Fishes—Lampreys, Sharks, and Bony Fishes 205
16. The Amphibians 227
17. The Nonavian Reptiles 249
18. The Birds 255
19. The Mammals 261
20. Photo Credits 299
21. Definitions 300

Credits

1. Laboratory Safety Procedures: *Chapter from Laboratory Studies in Integrated Principles of Zoology, 14th Edition by Hickman, Kats, Keen, 2008* 1

2. Tissue Structure and Function: *Chapter 4 from Laboratory Studies in Integrated Principles of Zoology, 14th Edition by Hickman, Kats, Keen, 2008* 3

3. Gametogenesis and Embryology: *Chapter 3 from Laboratory Studies in Integrated Principles of Zoology, 14th Edition by Hickman, Kats, Keen, 2008* 21

4. The Sponges: *Chapter 7 from Laboratory Studies in Integrated Principles of Zoology, 14th Edition by Hickman, Kats, Keen, 2008* 43

5. The Radiate Animals: *Chapter 8 from Laboratory Studies in Integrated Principles of Zoology, 14th Edition by Hickman, Kats, Keen, 2008* 51

6. The Flatworms: *Chapter 9 from Laboratory Studies in Integrated Principles of Zoology, 14th Edition by Hickman, Kats, Keen, 2008* 69

7. The Annelids: *Chapter 12 from Laboratory Studies in Integrated Principles of Zoology, 14th Edition by Hickman, Kats, Keen, 2008* 89

8. The Molluscs: *Chapter 11 from Laboratory Studies in Integrated Principles of Zoology, 14th Edition by Hickman, Kats, Keen, 2008* 105

9. The Crustacean Arthropods: *Chapter 14 from Laboratory Studies in Integrated Principles of Zoology, 14th Edition by Hickman, Kats, Keen, 2008* 123

10. The Chelicerate Arthropods: *Chapter 13 from Laboratory Studies in Integrated Principles of Zoology, 14th Edition by Hickman, Kats, Keen, 2008* 135

11. The Arthropods: *Chapter 15 from Laboratory Studies in Integrated Principles of Zoology, 14th Edition by Hickman, Kats, Keen, 2008* 141

12. Five Small Protostome Phyla: *Chapter 10 from Laboratory Studies in Integrated Principles of Zoology, 14th Edition by Hickman, Kats, Keen, 2008* 165

13. The Echinoderms: *Chapter 16 from Laboratory Studies in Integrated Principles of Zoology, 14th Edition by Hickman, Kats, Keen, 2008* 177

14. Phylum Chordata: A Deuterostome Group: *Chapter 17 from Laboratory Studies in Integrated Principles of Zoology, 14th Edition by Hickman, Kats, Keen, 2008* 195

15. The Fishes—Lampreys, Sharks, and Bony Fishes: *Chapter 18 from Laboratory Studies in Integrated Principles of Zoology, 14th Edition by Hickman, Kats, Keen, 2008* 205

16. The Amphibians: *Chapter 19 from Laboratory Studies in Integrated Principles of Zoology, 14th Edition by Hickman, Kats, Keen, 2008* 227

17. The Nonavian Reptiles: *Chapter 20 from Laboratory Studies in Integrated Principles of Zoology, 14th Edition by Hickman, Kats, Keen, 2008* 249

18. The Birds: *Chapter 21 from Laboratory Studies in Integrated Principles of Zoology, 14th Edition by Hickman, Kats, Keen, 2008* 255

19. The Mammals: *Chapter 22 from Laboratory Studies in Integrated Principles of Zoology, 14th Edition by Hickman, Kats, Keen, 2008* 261
20. Photo Credits: *Chapter from Laboratory Studies in Integrated Principles of Zoology, 14th Edition by Hickman, Kats, Keen, 2008* 299
21. Definitions: *Chapter from Laboratory Studies in Integrated Principles of Zoology, 14th Edition by Hickman, Kats, Keen, 2008* 300

LABORATORY SAFETY PROCEDURES

1. Keep your work area uncluttered. Place unnecessary books, backpacks, purses, and so on somewhere other than on your desktop.

2. Avoid contact with embalming fluids. Wear rubber or disposable plastic gloves when working with preserved specimens.

3. Wear eyeglasses or safety glasses to protect your eyes from splattered embalming fluid.

4. Keep your hands away from your mouth and face while in the laboratory. Moisten labels with tap water, not your tongue.

5. Sponge down your work area and wash all laboratory instruments at the end of the period.

6. Wash your hands with soap and water at the end of the period.

EXERCISE 4

Tissue Structure and Function

A **tissue** is an aggregation of cells and cell products of similar structure and embryonic origin that perform a common function. Tissues represent specializations of the properties that all protoplasm possesses, such as irritability, contractility, conductivity, absorption, and excretion. The study of tissues, especially their structure and arrangement, is called **histology.**

However complex an animal may be, its cells fall into one of four major groups of tissues. These basic tissues are named **epithelial** tissue, **connective** tissue, **muscle** tissue, and **nervous** tissue.

An **organ** is an aggregation of tissues organized into a larger functional unit, such as heart or kidney. Organs work together as functional units called **systems.**

The following study is made on vertebrate tissue, but invertebrate tissues are built similarly and may be substituted at the discretion of the instructor.

 Read the general description of the tissues (pp. 49–59) to familiarize yourself with the general types, their functions, and where they are found. As you do, look at slides showing examples of the various tissues to familiarize yourself with their appearance. Later, because tissues are usually found working together with other tissues in organs, you will study some sections through certain organs, each of which will contain several types of tissues.

General Description of Basic Tissue Types

Epithelial Tissue

An **epithelium** is a sheetlike layer of cells with close cell-to-cell contact that covers surfaces and lines cavities. Epithelia also often contain glandular cells that function in fluid secretion. Where epithelium lines the inner surface of the heart, blood vessels, and lymphatic vessels, it is given a special name: **endothelium.** Epithelial surfaces may be large (outer layer of the skin and lining of the digestive tract) or small (sebaceous glands and microscopic tubules). One surface of the epithelium is free, and the other usually rests on a bed

> **General Description of Basic Tissue Types**
> Epithelial tissue
> Connective tissue
> Muscle tissue
> Nervous tissue
>
> **EXERCISE 4A**
> Tissues Combined into Organs

of vascular connective tissue. Between the epithelium and underlying connective tissue, there is usually a thin basement membrane of intercellular substance (not easily seen in many preparations). Epithelial tissue lacks a blood supply; it receives its nourishment by diffusion from the blood supply of underlying connective tissue. All epithelia have the capacity for renewal by mitosis, the rate of renewal varying with location of the epithelium and amount of wear and tear it receives.

Epithelial tissues are derived from all three embryonic layers.

The chief function of an epithelium is protection, but the cells are also variously specialized for secretion, excretion, absorption, lubrication, and sensory perception.

Epithelial tissue may be classified according to the number of layers of cells (simple or stratified) or according to the shape of the cells on the free surface (squamous, cuboidal, or columnar).

Drawings

 On pp. 65 and 66, you will find places to sketch the various types of tissues that you study as assigned by your instructor. A number of the tissues can be identified by studying sections of skin, intestine, artery, nerve, and trachea (pp. 61–63). You will find the rest on special slides.

Draw only tissues that you actually see. Do not copy photographs or drawings. Where possible, show the shape of the cells and size and location of the nuclei. Indicate under each drawing (1) in what organ the tissue was seen; (2) from what animal the tissue was taken, if that information is indicated on the slide; and (3) the magnification of the specimen.

Simple Epithelium. Simple epithelium is made up of a single layer of epithelial cells. It is found where there is not much wear and tear or where diffusion or absorption occurs through a membrane.

1. *Simple squamous epithelium.* Simple squamous epithelium is composed of thin, flat cells with round or oval nuclei (Figure 4-1A). The cells appear hexagonal in surface view; in side view or cut section, they appear extremely thin, bulging a bit where the nucleus is located. Are all cells anchored together, or are there gaps between adjacent cells? _____

   Simple squamous epithelium is found in areas specialized for diffusion, such as the inside walls of blood vessels (endothelium), body cavity, and lungs.

2. *Simple cuboidal epithelium.* Simple cuboidal cells are usually six-sided, but they appear square in side view and polygonal or hexagonal in surface view (Figure 4-1B). Simple cuboidal tissue lines small ducts and tubules, such as kidney tubules, salivary glands, and mucous glands. Cuboidal epithelium of some tissues—kidney tubules, for example—have surfaces densely populated with **microvilli,** short, delicate processes that greatly

increase the surface area of the cells. Are there microvilli on the cells of your preparation? _____ Cilia? _____

3. *Simple columnar epithelium.* Simple columnar cells are taller than they are wide and are closely packed, like the chambers of a honeycomb (Figure 4-2A). In surface view they appear hexagonal; in vertical section they appear as a row of rectangles, with nuclei frequently all at the same level, usually in the lower part of the cell. Are all cells attached to the basement membrane? _____ Do all cells reach to the surface of the tissue? _____

   Simple columnar epithelium is found on highly absorptive surfaces, such as the lining of the small intestine, and on secretory surfaces, such as lining of the stomach, oviduct, and many glands. Columnar cells may be specialized for secretion, such as single-celled glands of the intestine, called **goblet cells** (Figure 4-2B).

4. *Pseudostratified columnar epithelium.* Pseudostratified columnar cells are actually simple epithelium with all cells resting on a basement membrane, a fragile noncellular layer that secures the epithelium. The cells have the

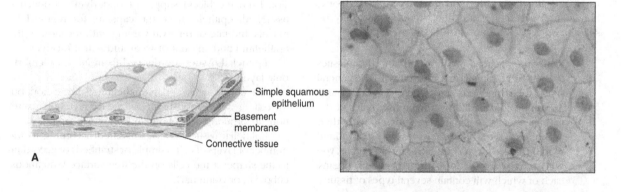

Simple squamous epithelium

Basement membrane

Connective tissue

A

Simple cuboidal epithelium

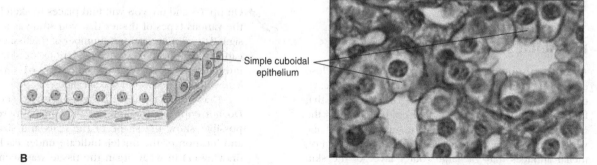

B

Figure 4-1

A, Simple squamous epithelium, composed of flattened, irregularly shaped cells forming a continuous, pavementlike surface.
B, Simple cuboidal epithelium.

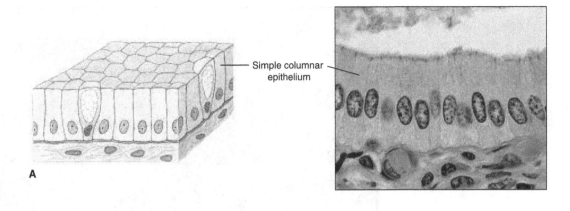

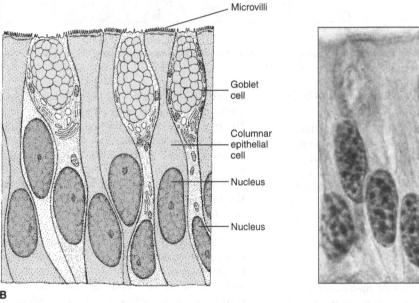
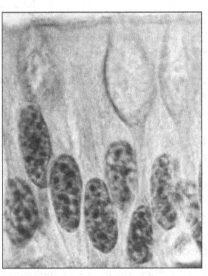

Figure 4-2

A, Simple columnar epithelium is similar to simple cuboidal, but the cells are taller. **B,** Simple columnar epithelial cells of vertebrate intestine, showing position of epithelial and goblet cells.

appearance of stratified epithelium because they are not all the same height and their nuclei are located at different levels (Figure 4-3). Some cells do not reach the surface. Pseudostratified columnar cells line the trachea (windpipe), bronchi, and male urethra. From what tissue was your slide prepared? _____

Stratified Epithelium. Stratified epithelium is composed of two or more layers of cells. It is found where abuse is severe—often where surface cells are being continually sloughed off. It is not adapted for absorption or secretion.

1. *Stratified squamous epithelium.* Stratified squamous epithelium consists of several layers of cells that change from a cuboidal basal layer to extremely flattened layers at the free surface (Figure 4-4A). It is found in areas subjected to moderate mechanical abrasion; these include lining of the mouth, pharynx, esophagus, anal canal, and vagina. The surface of the skin is a specialized form of stratified squamous epithelium that is adapted to withstand constant abrasion and drying. As surface cells age and die, they become **keratinized,** forming a tough, noncellular layer of the protein keratin. From what tissue was your slide

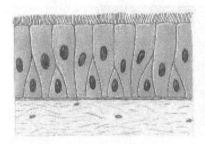

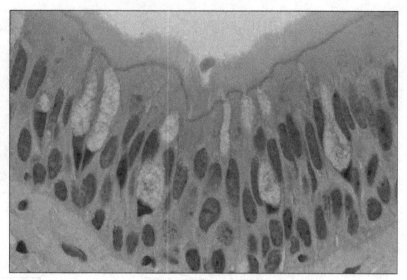

Figure 4-3
Pseudostratified epithelium is so termed because it appears to have more than one layer of cells. Actually, it is a variant of simple columnar epithelium with all cells resting on the basement membrane.

prepared? _____ How many cell layers thick is the epithelium? _____

2. *Transitional epithelium.* Transitional epithelium is a form of stratified epithelium confined to the urinary tract and bladder, where it is specialized for stretching (Figure 4-4B). When relaxed, the epithelium appears to be four or five cells thick; when stretched, it appears only two or three cells thick, with the surface cells flattened. Are all cells anchored to the basement membrane?

Connective Tissue

Connective tissues are tissues of mesodermal origin that provide structural and metabolic support for the body. They include **loose connective tissue** (areolar, reticular, and adipose), which serves as a sort of "fabric" that surrounds specialized cells, underlies epithelial tissues, and contributes in many ways to all other tissues and organs in the body, and **dense connective tissue** (sheaths, ligaments, tendons, cartilage, and bone), which performs major supportive functions. Connective tissue also includes vascular tissues, since blood cells are derived from a form of loose connective tissue.

Despite the diversity of connective tissues, all are composed of **cells** and **extracellular fibers** embedded in a structureless **ground substance** (also called **matrix**). Both fibers and ground substance are secreted by the cells.

What connective tissues do in the body depends in large measure on the properties of the fibers and ground substance. There are three kinds of fibers. **Collagenous**

fibers* appear as thick, wavy bundles of finer fibrils. They are very strong and resistant to stretching. **Elastic fibers** are thin, yellowish, branching threads that usually appear straight, although they may look wavy or curled in teased preparations. They may be stretched to 150% or more of their resting length but will spring back to their former length when released. **Reticular fibers**** are inelastic. Like collagenous fibers, they consist of bundles of small fibrils, but they are smaller and they branch and reunite to form a network.

The varying types, amounts, and arrangements of cells, ground substance, and fibers give rise to many forms of connective tissues. For example, adipose (fat) tissue is composed mainly of cells, tendons and ligaments are mostly fibers, and some cartilage is largely ground substance.

 Examine slides of the different types of connective tissue while reading the description of each that follows.

Areolar Connective Tissue. Areolar connective tissue (Figure 4-5) is a loose fibroelastic tissue, the most widespread of all connective tissues. It is found throughout the body, fastening down skin, membranes, vessels, and nerves and binding muscles and other parts together. In fresh tissue it appears whitish, translucent,

---

*Collagenous fibers are composed mainly of collagen (Gr. *kolla*, glue), the most abundant protein of vertebrate animals, making up nearly one-third the dry weight of the human body. Collagen is tough and inextensible and has great tensile strength. Among its many functions, collagen provides elasticity and strength to skin and its deterioration over time leads to the appearance of wrinkles that accompany aging.
**Reticular fibers characteristically form a delicate network, or reticulum (L. *reticulum*, small net).

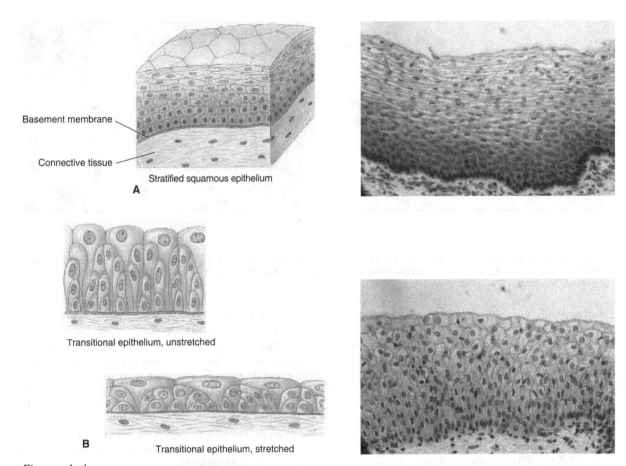

Basement membrane

Connective tissue

Stratified squamous epithelium

A

Transitional epithelium, unstretched

B   Transitional epithelium, stretched

Figure 4-4

Stratified epithelium. **A,** Stratified squamous epithelium consists of several layers of cells that are continually renewed from mitotic divisions from the basal layer of cells. **B,** Transitional epithelium is a type of stratified epithelium designed to accommodate great stretching.

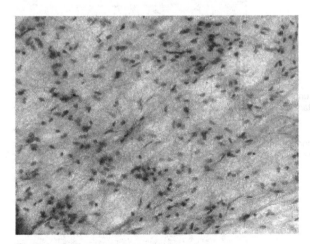

Figure 4-5

Areolar connective tissue. Note the spindle-shaped fibroblasts (the most common of cellular elements in connective tissue), collagenous fibers, and clear areas of matrix (ground substance). About ×500.

soft, and stretchy. It consists of clear, jellylike matrix; various cells; and all three types of fibers. The term "areolar," from the Latin *areola*, meaning small space, refers to the clear matrix (ground substance) that is usually removed in tissue preparation, leaving clear pockets between the fibers and cells.

Adipose (Fat) Connective Tissue. Living adipose tissue is specialized for storage of lipids. Each cell contains a single lipid droplet composed mostly of triglycerides. The cytoplasm and nucleus have been pushed to one side of the cell by the lipid droplet. Note the bubble-like appearance of the tissue (Figure 4-6A). From what tissue has your slide been prepared? _____ Are blood capillaries evident among the cells? _____ Would you expect adipose tissue to be well vascularized? _____ The scanning electron micrograph (Figure 4-6B) shows large and small fat-storing cells surrounded by supportive strands of extracellular fibers.

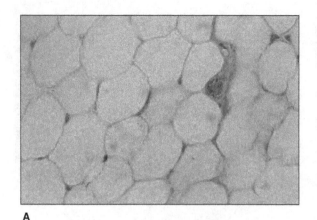

A

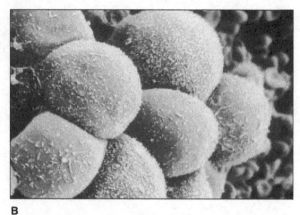

B

Figure 4-6

White adipose connective tissue. **A,** Each distended cell contains a single lipid droplet that pushes cytoplasm and nucleus to one side. Light micrograph, ×100. **B,** Scanning electron micrograph of aggregations of human fat cells surrounded by a thin supportive network of fibers. SEM, about ×175.

Cartilage. Cartilage is a type of dense connective tissue. Several forms of cartilage are recognized, distinguished mainly by differences in type and abundance of fibers incorporated within the matrix. The most common form of cartilage is **hyaline cartilage** (Figure 4-7). It is found on the ends of long bones and in the nose, trachea, and other places. Its ground substance is firm but flexible. Scattered through it are **lacunae,** little cavities, each containing at least one cell. The cells secrete ground substance and some collagen fibers. Can you see blood capillaries in the cartilage? _____
How do nutrients and gases reach the cells of cartilage?
_____

A description of the trachea with its cartilage and other tissues is found on p. 63.

Bone. Bone is the most specialized of supporting connective tissues. It not only supports but also protects vital organs by means of bony frameworks, and it forms red blood corpuscles and most white corpuscles. Bone also forms a complete system in its own right, the **skeleton.**

Bone matrix is heavily infiltrated with calcium and phosphate salts deposited by the action of bone-forming cells called **osteoblasts.**

A long bone, such as the femur or humerus, consists of a shaft of dense **compact bone** surrounding a

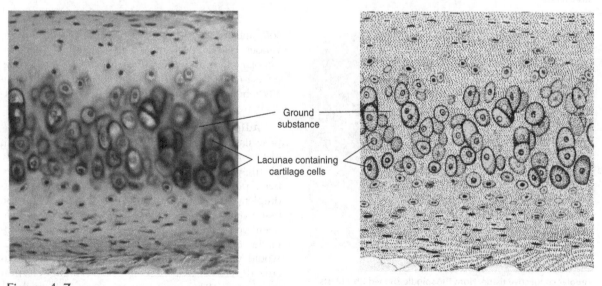

Ground substance

Lacunae containing cartilage cells

Figure 4-7

Photomicrograph *(left)* of hyaline cartilage, the most common type of cartilage, with interpretive drawing *(right)*. The cartilage cells secrete and maintain the ground substance of cartilage. Note the absence of blood vessels.

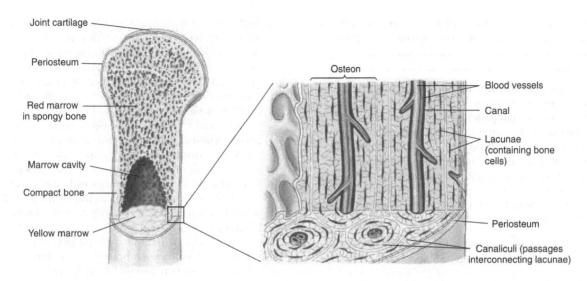

Figure 4-8

Structure of bone, showing appearance of spongy and compact bone. The enlarged section shows how bone cells and dense calcified matrix are arranged in units called osteons.

bone marrow cavity (Figure 4-8). The enlarged ends of the bone are made up of **spongy bone** consisting of an interlacing framework of bony tissue with spaces filled with bone marrow. The ends of the bone are padded with cartilage. The bone is covered with a thin layer of connective tissue called **periosteum.** Nerves and blood vessels penetrate and nourish the bone tissue.

Compact bone is made up of a series of **osteons** (Figures 4-8 and 4-9), each one built around a narrow canal containing blood vessels. In the formation of compact bone, the bone-forming cells, **osteoblasts,** become arranged in the matrix around blood vessels in layers (concentric rings) called **lamellae.** Each osteoblast occupies a space called a **lacuna.** The cells have branching processes that are continuous with the processes of adjacent cells, thus forming tiny channels, called **canaliculi,** through which nourishment can reach the cells from the blood supply. The activity of osteoblasts is responsible for deposition and maintenance of bone. Are all osteons running parallel to each other? _____

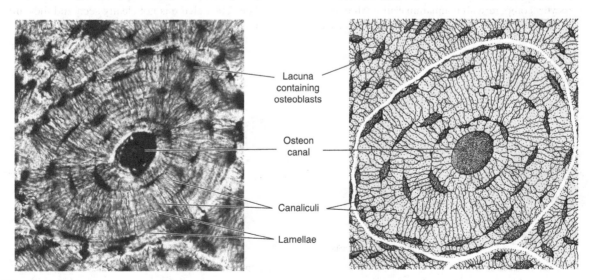

Figure 4-9

Section of compact bone, showing a single osteon. Bone cells (osteocytes) reside in the lacunae and are important in bone maintenance.

Do you see any incomplete osteons or lamellae? _____ Can you explain their presence? _____ _____

Vascular Tissue. Blood and **lymph** are often considered to be connective tissues having a variety of cell types **(corpuscles)** suspended in fluid matrix **(plasma)** and flowing within a system of blood vessels. Lymph and **tissue fluids** are filtered from the blood to bathe all body cells. Vascular tissue transports nutritive substances, oxygen, and hormones to the tissues and carries away wastes.

The cells in blood include erythrocytes, leukocytes, and blood platelets.

 Compare a stained slide of human blood with one of amphibian or reptile blood.

1. *Erythrocytes (red corpuscles) (Figures 4-10 and 4-11).* In humans and other mammals, erythrocytes are round, biconcave discs lacking nuclei. They average about 7μm in diameter but are very thin. Oval-shaped erythrocytes with large, granular nuclei are found in most other vertebrates. Vertebrate red corpuscles are packed with the respiratory pigment **hemoglobin,** which transports oxygen and carbon dioxide between the lungs and the body tissues. Erythrocytes are rare in invertebrates; instead, the respiratory pigments usually form giant molecules that circulate freely in the plasma.

From what vertebrate are the erythrocytes on your slide? _____ Are the cells biconcave or biconvex? _____ Do they contain nuclei? _____ How do mammalian erythrocytes compare with nonmammalian erythrocytes in size and shape? _____

2. *Leukocytes (white corpuscles) (Figure 4-10).* There are several types of leukocytes in vertebrate blood, all with large, darkly staining nuclei. In human blood they are larger than red cells; in other vertebrates they are smaller. By means of their ameboid movement they can pass through capillary walls and surround and ingest foreign particles and invading organisms (a process called **phagocytosis**). Monocytes and neutrophils are the most active phagocytes. Lymphocytes play a key role in all immune responses. Leukocytes perform their protective functions outside the blood vessels in connective tissue. Pus that forms in and around an infection consists largely of dead white blood cells.

Erythrocytes are usually stained red, and the nuclei of leukocytes appear blue. In what other ways can you distinguish erythrocytes from leukocytes? _____ Name the kinds of leukocytes that you can distinguish. _____

Most invertebrates have phagocytic blood cells, often termed *amebocytes,* that correspond to vertebrate leukocytes.

3. *Blood platelets (Figure 4-10).* Platelets are disc-shaped, tiny (2 to 3μm in diameter), very fragile, clot-promoting bodies found only in mammalian blood. Non-mammalian vertebrates have spindle-shaped cells called **thrombocytes,** which have a similar function. Plateletlike structures also have been identified in a very few invertebrates. You may not be able to distinguish platelets on your slide. Their shape is not clearly seen and they are often clumped together.

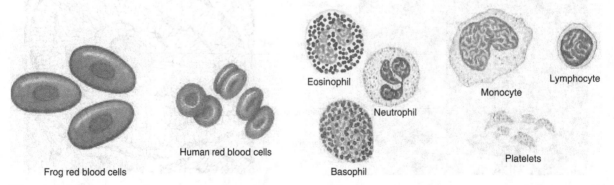

Figure 4-10

Some human blood cells. Neutrophils, basophils, and eosinophils are types of leukocytes called granulocytes. They have multilobed nuclei. Monocytes and lymphocytes lack clearly visible granules and lobed nuclei and are called agranulocytes.

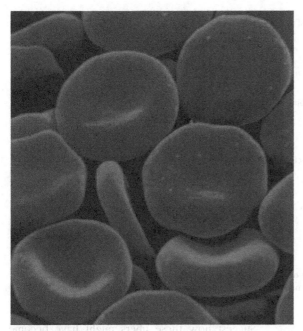

Figure 4-11

Human red blood cells (erythrocytes). Red blood cells are simple bags of hemoglobin without nuclei. The biconcave shape is an adaptation for maximizing surface for oxygen and carbon dioxide exchange. SEM ×12,000.

Muscle Tissue

Smooth Muscle. Smooth muscle, also called visceral muscle (Figure 4-12), is the simplest in structure of the three types of muscle. It is found where slow, sustained contractions are needed, such as digestive tract, uterus, and other visceral organs. It is entirely involuntary in its action; that is, it is under unconscious control of the autonomic nervous system.

Smooth muscle cells are long and spindle-shaped, though rarely longer than 0.5 mm. The nucleus is located in the middle, or thickest part, of the cell, and the ends of the fiber diminish gradually to a fine point. Muscle fibers are composed of bundles of slender myofibrils, which in smooth muscle do not have cross-striations, as in skeletal and cardiac muscle.

Smooth muscle will be studied on a cross section of amphibian small intestine (p. 61).

Skeletal Muscle. Skeletal muscle, also called striated muscle, is voluntary because it is under conscious cerebral control (Figure 4-13). It makes up the bulk of the muscular system. Skeletal muscle contracts more rapidly than smooth muscle, but it fatigues more easily and is not capable of sustained contraction.

Individual muscle cells, called fibers, are long (1 to 40 mm) and cylindric with blunt ends. Each fiber is comprised of many myofibrils, all enclosed in a tough membrane, the **sarcolemma.** Each fiber has a number of nuclei located just beneath the sarcolemma. Myofibrils bear alternate light and dark bands and are so arranged that the entire muscle fiber has a striated appearance. Muscle fibers are grouped into bundles, and the bundles are grouped into functional skeletal muscles. Fibers, bundles, and muscles are embedded in connective tissue fascia. The connective tissue of the muscle merges with the fibrous sheet, or tendon, that holds the muscle in place. Skeletal muscles are richly supplied with blood vessels and nerves.

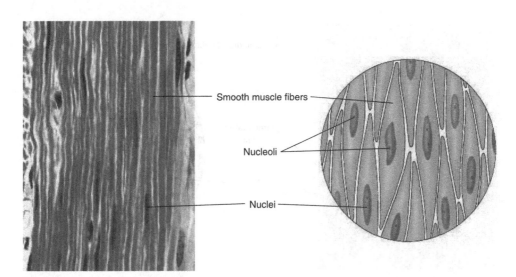

Smooth muscle fibers

Nucleoli

Nuclei

Figure 4-12

Smooth muscle. The spindle-shaped cells contain elongate nuclei. The cell boundaries are distinct. Smooth muscle is involuntary in action.

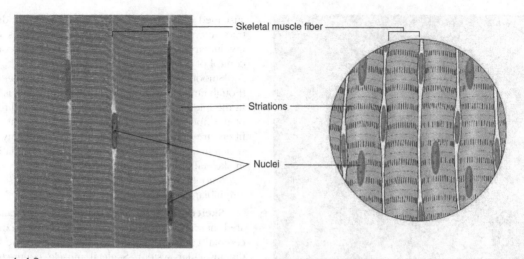

Figure 4-13

Skeletal muscle. The fibers are extremely long and unbranched, with numerous flattened nuclei located just beneath the sarcolemma. Regular cross-striations are characteristic of its appearance. Skeletal muscle is voluntary in action.

 Skeletal muscle slides are often made from sections of the tongue. Find an area where the fibers are lying parallel to each other. Using fine adjustment, observe the shape of the fibers, their cross-striations, the longitudinal striations that indicate the myofibrils, and the numerous nuclei. The slide may contain areas where the muscle fibers are cut across rather than lengthwise so that you are observing cut ends of fibers. Note how the fibers are arranged into bundles held together by fasciae. Is there more than one nucleus in each muscle fiber? _____

Suggest how these fibers might have become multinucleate._____
_____

Cardiac Muscle. Cardiac muscle (Figure 4-14) is striated much like skeletal muscle, but it functions more like smooth muscle. It is involuntary muscle, well adapted for rhythmic contractions. The fibers are arranged in branching columns interconnected in a fine meshwork.

 On a slide mount of heart muscle, note the branching nature of the striated fibers. Whereas

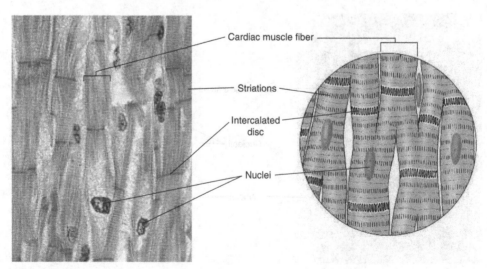

Figure 4-14

Cardiac muscle. The cells reveal cross-striations like skeletal muscle but, unlike the latter, are branched and joined end-to-end by intercalated discs. Cardiac muscle is involuntary in action.

the myofibrils are transversely striated, as in skeletal muscle, the nuclei are located centrally, as in smooth muscle. Nuclei lying between the fibers belong to connective tissue. Some preparations show dark bands called **intercalated discs,** junctional complexes that mark the boundaries between ends of cells. Do cardiac muscle cells have as many nuclei as skeletal muscle cells? _____ Would you expect cardiac muscle to have more or fewer blood capillaries than skeletal muscle? _____

Nervous Tissue

Nervous tissue is specialized for reception of stimuli (perception) and for conduction of nervous impulses to structures that are to act on the impulses. Nervous tissue is divided into central nervous system, consisting of brain and spinal cord, and peripheral nervous system, consisting of nerve cells and nerve cell processes that lie outside the central nervous system.

Nervous tissue consists of two distinct cell populations: nerve cells, called **neurons,** and supportive cells, called **neuroglia,** or **glial** cells. A neuron is made up of a nucleated **nerve cell body** from which extend one or more **dendrites** that carry impulses into the cell body, and a single **axon** that carries impulses away from the cell body. We often use the term **nerve cell** for the nucleated cell body and the term **nerve fibers** for the processes. In both central and peripheral nervous systems, glial cells surround many nerve fibers with a lipid wrapping called **myelin,** and this is enclosed by a thin outer boundary, the **neurilemma** (Figure 4-15A). In the peripheral nervous system, glial cells (called Schwann cells) that wrap around nerve processes develop with gaps, or nodes, between adjacent cells (Figure 4-15A). This arrangement greatly improves speed of impulse conduction, enabling the action potential to leap from node to node (saltatory conduction).

In the central nervous system, areas of **white** and **gray matter** can be distinguished (Figure 4-16). Gray matter contains nerve cell bodies, nerve processes, and glial cells. White matter consists mostly of axons wrapped in white myelin sheaths.

 Examine a cross section of a spinal cord. This should show the gray matter in an H-shaped, or butterfly-shaped, area surrounded by white matter (Figure 4-16). Nerve cell bodies are easily distinguished in gray matter. These are cell bodies of motor and association neurons. In white matter you will see axons and dendrites that connect various parts of the nerve cord with each other and with the brain. Nerve fibers in cross section

will appear as small, dark dots, each surrounded by a clean circle, the myelin sheath. The natural color may not be evident in the slides, which are usually stained during preparation.

EXERCISE 4A
Tissues Combined into Organs

 In addition to slides containing individual types of tissues that you have already seen, study the tissues in the following section, which contain sections through certain organs. These sections illustrate the manner in which tissues work together. While studying these slides, refer back to the descriptions and illustrations for help in identifying the various tissues.

Your instructor may wish to vary the following list of slides according to materials available in the laboratory.

Identification

Be prepared to recognize any of the various types of tissues that may later be set up by your instructor as "unknowns."

Section through Skin of a Frog. The outer layer of the skin, the epidermis, is made up of **stratified squamous epithelium** (Figure 4-17). Note the flat surface cells that give the epithelium its name. Columnar cells at the base divide to produce new cells that push out to the surface to replace surface cells as they are worn off.

Beneath the epidermis is a thick layer of dermis, which is made up of **connective tissue** and contains glands and pigment. Connective tissue nearer the surface (spongy layer) contains loosely arranged fibers, whereas that in the deeper layer (compact layer) is much denser. Can you identify **elastic** or **collagenous fibers** in the dermis? _____

In the spongy layer of the dermis you will find a number of mucous glands, each made up of a single layer of **epithelium.** Are the glands lined with squamous or cuboidal epithelium? _____ The section of skin may also contain some very large **poison glands.** What kind of epithelium lines poison glands? _____ The glands open to the outside by small ducts, but, because the ducts are narrower than the glands, not all of the cut sections will include ducts.

Scattered through the dermis are small blood vessels. These may be capillaries, made up of a single layer of **squamous epithelium,** or small arteries or veins,

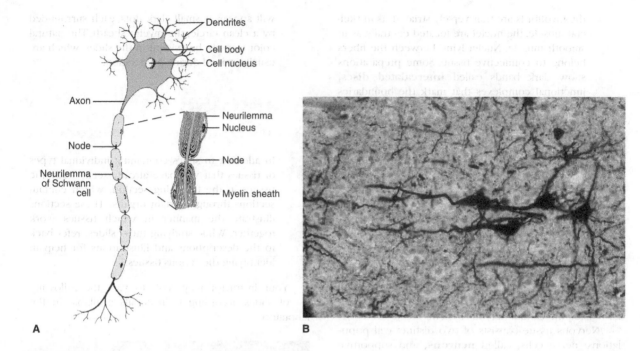

A

Dendrites
Cell body
Cell nucleus
Axon
Neurilemma
Nucleus
Node
Node
Neurilemma of Schwann cell
Myelin sheath

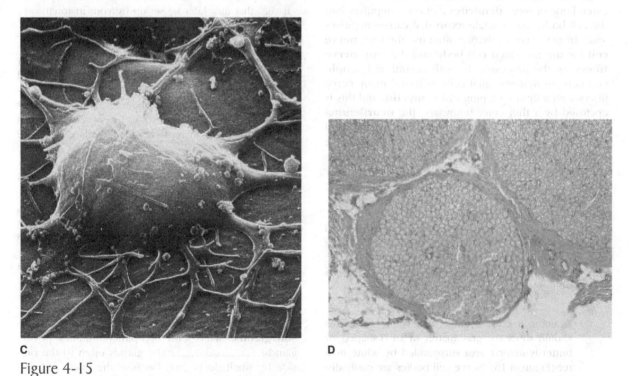

C

D

Figure 4-15

A, Diagram of a motor neuron with myelinated axon. The nodal area between insulating Schwann cells is shown enlarged. **B,** Neurons and fibers of the cerebrum, ×150. **C,** Scanning electron micrograph of a cell culture showing a large nerve cell surrounded by numerous nerve cell processes (dendrites and axons). **D,** Cross section of a nerve, showing the appearance of numerous nerve fibers (myelinated axons) in cut section, ×200.

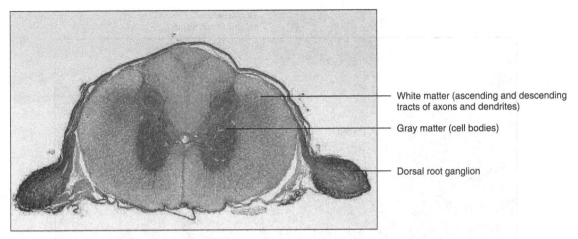

Figure 4-16
Cross section of the spinal cord of a cat.

White matter (ascending and descending tracts of axons and dendrites)

Gray matter (cell bodies)

Dorsal root ganglion

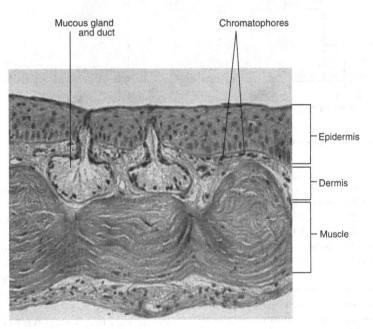

Mucous gland and duct

Chromatophores

Epidermis

Dermis

Muscle

Figure 4-17
Section through the skin of a frog.

containing layers of **smooth muscle.** Darkly stained, irregularly shaped bodies at the base of the epidermis and scattered through the dermis are pigment cells called **chromatophores.**

Cross Section of Amphibian Small Intestine (Preferably *Necturus* or *Amphiuma*). The intestine is a tube enclosing a cavity called the lumen. The lumen of the intestine is lined with a mucous membrane that lies in many folds (Figure 4-18). The mucous membrane is made up of **columnar epithelium** in which the nuclei are located near the base of the tall cells. Is the columnar epithelium simple or pseudostratified? _____ Two cell types can be identified: **columnar cells** and **goblet cells.** Columnar cells contain digestive enzymes that are added to the intestinal contents as the cells are continually

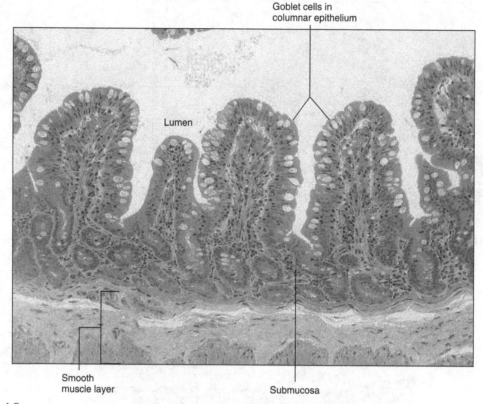

Goblet cells in
columnar epithelium

Lumen

Smooth
muscle layer

Submucosa

Figure 4-18

Cross section through the intestine of a monkey.

eroded away. New columnar cells are constantly being formed at the base of the mucosal folds by stem cell mitosis, then migrate upward to replace cells shed at the surface. Goblet cells, each shaped like a chalice permanently open to the lumen (see Figure 4-2B), continually eject protective mucus onto the intestinal surface.

Surrounding the mucous membrane and largely conforming to its contours is a submucosal layer of **areolar connective tissue,** containing mostly collagenous fibers. There are many blood vessels in this layer.

Outside the submucosa are layers of both circular and longitudinal **smooth muscle** responsible for the segmentation and peristaltic movements that mix the food and move it through the gut. In the circular layer, long, spindle-shaped cells can be seen fitting closely together. In the longitudinal layer, only cut ends of the fibers can be seen.

The outermost layer of the intestine is a thin layer of **squamous epithelium** that is a part of the peritoneum that covers all visceral organs. The cells you see are in cut section, so they appear very thin.

Section through Artery, Vein, and Nerve. Most blood vessels are muscular organs. An artery will have a smaller diameter and thicker walls than will the vein that accompanies it, but otherwise their structures are similar. On your slide the blood vessels are probably collapsed so that the artery may appear flattened or ovoid in shape (Figure 4-19), and the thinner walls of the vein may be thrown into folds. The innermost layer of an artery or a vein is a thin **endothelium.** Are the cells of the endothelium squamous or cuboidal? _____ Outside that is a layer of **smooth muscle** circularly arranged. Is smooth muscle voluntary or involuntary muscle? _____ There are often **elastic fibers** interspersed with the muscle. The outer layer is made up of elastic **fibrous connective tissue.**

Your slide may contain one or several sections through nerves. Each nerve trunk is made up of many

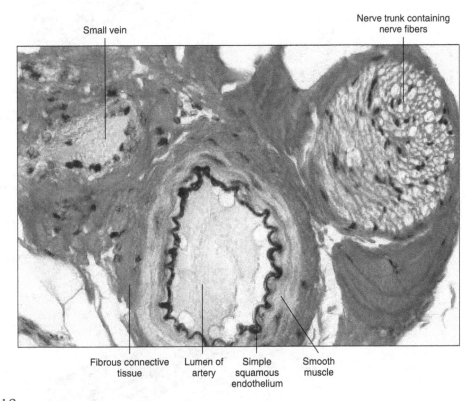

Small vein

Nerve trunk containing
nerve fibers

Fibrous connective
tissue

Lumen of
artery

Simple
squamous
endothelium

Smooth
muscle

Figure 4-19
Cross section through a large artery *(center)*, small vein *(left)*, and nerve *(right)* containing many nerve fibers.

nerve fibers, each enclosed in its myelin sheath (see Figure 4-15D). Some fibers may be cut transversely and so appear circular; others may be cut diagonally or longitudinally and so appear ovoid or long.

There will probably be some **adipose tissue** scattered through the connective tissue that holds the vessels and nerves in place. This tissue will contain large, clear cells, with the small nuclei pushed over to one side (see Figure 4-6A).

Cross Section through the Trachea. The trachea, or windpipe, is a tube that leads from the larynx to the lungs. It is supported and held open by c-shaped rings of **cartilage.** What type of cartilage do you see (refer to p. 54)? _____

The innermost layer of the trachea is a mucosal lining of ciliated **pseudostratified epithelium** containing many **goblet cells** (Figure 4-20), resting on a basement membrane of **connective tissue** containing a few fibers.

A submucosal layer contains many mucous glands composed of **cuboidal epithelium.**

Cartilage rings in the trachea do not completely surround the trachea but are open dorsally, thus providing limited expansion and constriction of tracheal diameter. **Cartilage** is easily recognizable by the large amount of clear ground substance interspersed with little lacunae (spaces), containing cartilage cells. In the space between the cartilage bands you may find some **smooth muscle** or **fibrous connective tissue.**

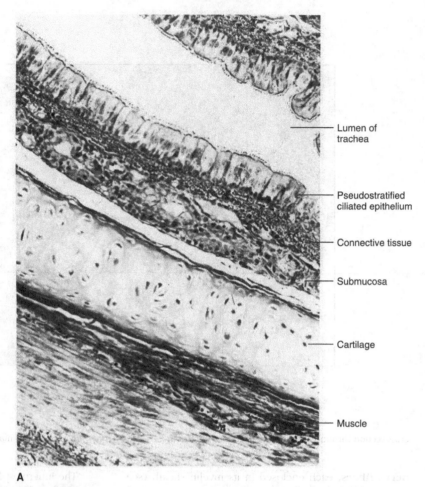

Lumen of trachea

Pseudostratified ciliated epithelium

Connective tissue

Submucosa

Cartilage

Muscle

A

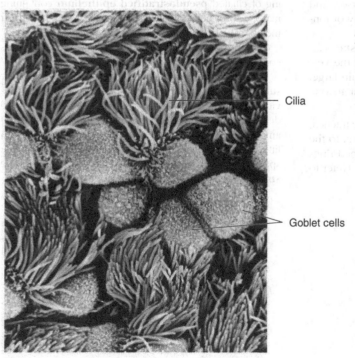

Cilia

Goblet cells

B

Figure 4-20

A, Photomicrograph through portion of the trachea, ×200. **B,** Scanning electron micrograph of pseudostratified epithelial surface of trachea, about ×3000. The goblet cells *(G)* are carpeted with short microvilli, whereas the rest of the tracheal cells are ciliated.

Tissues

Name _____

Date _____

Section _____

LAB REPORT

Simple squamous epithelium

From _____

Simple cuboidal epithelium

From _____

Simple columnar epithelium

From _____

Pseudostratified epithelium

From _____

Stratified epithelium

From _____

Loose connective tissue

From _____

Dense or fibrous connective tissue

From _____

LAB REPORT

Blood cells

From _____

Skeletal muscle

From _____

Smooth muscle

From _____

Cardiac muscle

From _____

Bone

From _____

Cartilage

From _____

EXERCISE

3

Gametogenesis and Embryology

EXERCISE 3A

Meiosis—Maturation Division of Germ Cells

EXERCISE 3A

Meiosis—Maturation Division of Germ Cells
Spermatogenesis
Oogenesis and fertilization in *Ascaris*

EXERCISE 3B

Cleavage Patterns—Spiral and Radial Cleavage
Spiral cleavage: early embryology of the ribbon worm, *Cerebratulus*
Radial cleavage: early embryology of the sea star, *Asterias*

EXERCISE 3C

Frog Development
Study of eggs in frog ovary

Mitosis (pp. 19–22) is a delivery system for distributing the chromosomes and the DNA they contain equally at cell division. Each daughter cell receives identical copies of the genetic information. A common feature of metazoan animals is that chromosomes occur in pairs. The members of a pair are called **homologous chromosomes,** and each individual member of a pair is called a **homolog** (Gr. *homologos,* agreeing). One homolog comes from the mother and the other from the father. Human cells, for example, have 46 chromosomes (called the **diploid** number) but only 23 *different kinds* of chromosomes, each with a unique linear sequence of genes.

Meiosis is a distinctive type of nuclear division in higher plants and animals that differs from mitosis in two important ways. First, meiosis gives rise to *gametes*—eggs and sperm cells—for sexual reproduction. Secondly, the key events in meiosis are that a *single* replication of chromosomes is followed by *two* cell divisions. These divisions result in four daughter cells (rather than two as in mitosis), each with only half as many chromosomes as the parent cell. Consequently, mature eggs and sperm have only one member of each pair of homologous chromosomes. The gametes are now **haploid** (Gr. *haploos,* single). When the haploid gametes fuse at fertilization to form a single zygote, the full diploid number of chromosomes is restored.

The process of forming mature gametes from primary germ cells is called **gametogenesis,** and it involves both mitosis and meiosis. Early in embryonic development of a sexually reproducing animal, certain cells called **primordial germ cells** are set aside. These predestined cells migrate to the developing gonads, which later become ovaries or testes. Primordial germ cells are larger than ordinary somatic cells and are the future stock of gametes for the animal. Once in the gonad, the primordial germ cells begin to multiply by ordinary mitosis.

Thus, both body cells and cells destined to become gametes contain an identical and complete, or diploid, set of chromosomes. The **maturation process** refers to the final divisions necessary to produce functional ova and spermatozoa. Gametogenesis, then, includes many divisions by mitosis during the early multiplication stages, followed finally by a reduction in number of chromosomes by meiosis.

When an animal approaches sexual maturity, its gonads begin to produce mature eggs or sperm by meiosis. As shown in Figure 3-1, meiosis involves two divisions, called **meiosis I** and **meiosis II.** In meiosis I homologous chromosomes, called **homologs,** pair lengthwise and exchange genetic material between them by a process called crossing over. The homologs then separate to opposite poles of the cell. Each of the two resulting cells has half the number of chromosomes present in the original diploid cell. However, because the DNA of each chromosome has replicated before onset of meiosis, each homolog actually consists of two sister chromatids joined at their centromeres.

In meiosis II, each haploid cell divides by a process similar to normal mitosis, except that the chromosomes do not replicate between meiosis I and II. The sister chromatids simply separate to opposite poles of the cell. The result is four cells, or gametes, each with a haploid number of chromosomes (Figure 3-1).

Exercise 3 Gametogenesis and Embryology 3-1

Gametogenesis in the testis is called **spermatogenesis,** and in the ovary it is called **oogenesis.** The same processes are involved in both, but there is an important difference in the end result. An oocyte undergoes meiosis to produce one large, functional egg (ovum) and three small polar bodies, whereas a spermatocyte produces four functional spermatozoa (Figure 3-3).

Spermatogenesis

Consider first the development of spermatozoa (spermatogenesis) (Figure 3-3). Early germ cells, which have migrated to the testis, are called primordial germ cells.

They become **spermatogonia** as they multiply rapidly by mitosis. These early germ cells, like ordinary somatic cells, have the diploid number of chromosomes and divide by ordinary mitosis. (For a review of mitosis see pp. 19–22.)

As an organism reaches sexual maturity, some spermatogonia cease to divide; instead, they enlarge, become **primary spermatocytes,** and begin meiotic divisions. The first stage in meiosis I, prophase, is more complex than mitotic prophase because the chromosomes become rearranged by genetic recombination.

When a primary spermatocyte begins prophase of meiosis I, each chromosome has *already doubled* during

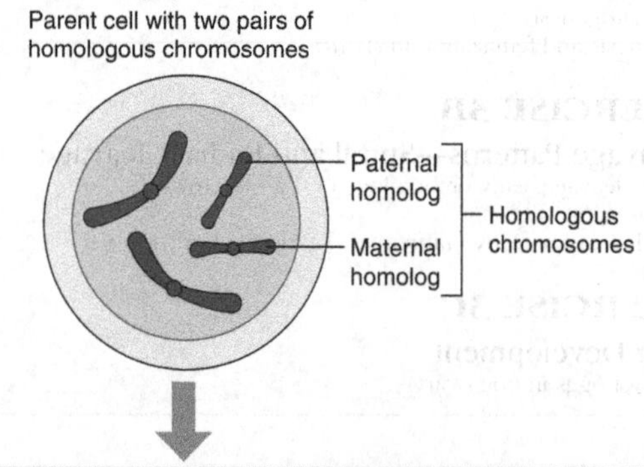

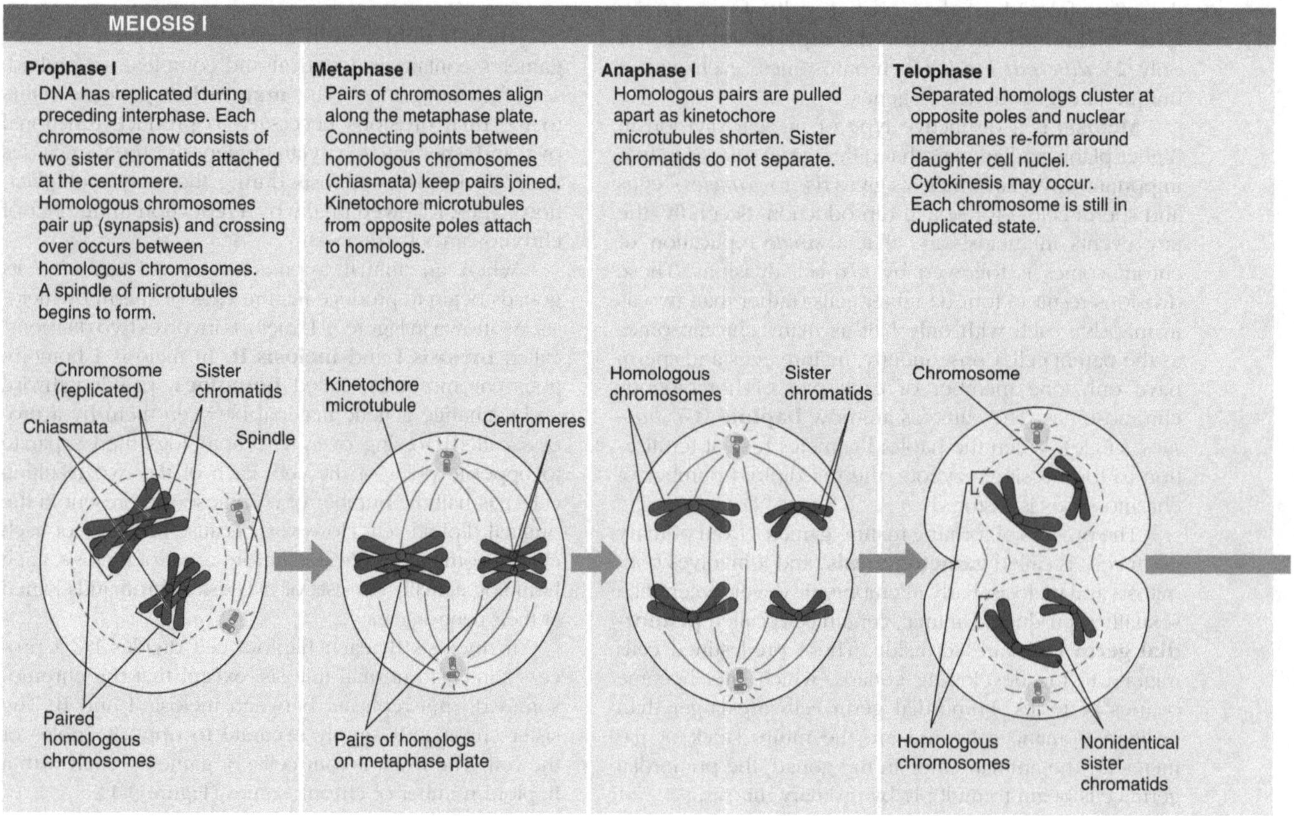

Parent cell (2n)

Parent cell with two pairs of homologous chromosomes

Paternal homolog

Maternal homolog

Homologous chromosomes

Figure 3-1

Stages of meiosis, showing division of cell with two pairs of chromosomes. At what stage does exchange of genetic material between homologous chromosomes occur? _____ When does doubling of DNA occur? _____ What is the haploid number in the example illustrated here? _____ At what stage are bivalents (tetrads) first evident? _____ What is the place called where sister chromatids are joined together? _____ Is the *chromosome* number halved at the end of meiosis I or II? _____ At the end of meiosis I, does each daughter cell contain 1N or 2N DNA? _____ Why? _____

MEIOSIS I

Prophase I

DNA has replicated during preceding interphase. Each chromosome now consists of two sister chromatids attached at the centromere. Homologous chromosomes pair up (synapsis) and crossing over occurs between homologous chromosomes. A spindle of microtubules begins to form.

Metaphase I

Pairs of chromosomes align along the metaphase plate. Connecting points between homologous chromosomes (chiasmata) keep pairs joined. Kinetochore microtubules from opposite poles attach to homologs.

Anaphase I

Homologous pairs are pulled apart as kinetochore microtubules shorten. Sister chromatids do not separate.

Telophase I

Separated homologs cluster at opposite poles and nuclear membranes re-form around daughter cell nuclei. Cytokinesis may occur. Each chromosome is still in duplicated state.

Chromosome (replicated)

Sister chromatids

Chiasmata

Spindle

Paired homologous chromosomes

Kinetochore microtubule

Centromeres

Pairs of homologs on metaphase plate

Homologous chromosomes

Sister chromatids

Chromosome

Homologous chromosomes

Nonidentical sister chromatids

the preceding interphase and consists of two chromatids so closely bound together that they cannot be distinguished with the light microscope. Next, the homologs, each consisting of two sister chromatids, line up with each other in **synapsis.** As prophase progresses, special points of contact appear, called **chiasmata** (Gr. *chiasma,* cross). At this time crossing over occurs (Figure 3-2). In this process, segments of genes are traded between homologous chromosomes. Crossing over is a profoundly important process because it results in the *recombination* of genes in chromosomes, leading to genetic variation in offspring of sexually reproducing organisms. Recombination is unique to meiosis. Neither synapsis nor recombination occurs in mitosis.

At the end of prophase I, a spindle forms and the centrioles complete their replication, as in mitosis. Metaphase begins. The homologous pairs separate and move to opposite poles (anaphase). Each chromosome is still double and is called a **dyad** (Gr. *dyas,* two) because it contains two sister chromatids. Two daughter cells **(secondary spermatocytes)** have been produced as a result of meiosis I, each containing one double chromosome from each homologous pair. Each secondary spermatocyte thus has half as many different chromosomes as any somatic cell.

The second meiotic division immediately follows. During meiosis II the sister chromatids of each chromosome separate into individual chromatids (Figure 3-1). One chromatid goes to one daughter cell and one to the other. Nuclear envelopes form around the chromatids, now full-fledged chromosomes. The daughter cells resulting from division of the secondary spermatocyte are called **spermatids** (Figure 3-3). Each spermatid has the **haploid** number of chromosomes, or just half as many as the spermatogonia or body cells. Without further division each of the four spermatids goes through an elaborate process of cytodifferentiation, producing spermatozoa. This is referred to as **spermiogenesis.**

Spermatogenesis in Grasshopper Testis

The maturation stages of sperm can be seen by studying cross sections of testes of many kinds of animals. Figure 3-4 shows a section through a lobe of the testis of the lubber grasshopper, *Romalea* (native to the southeastern United States). The testis consists of a number of lobes whose pointed ends empty into the vas deferens. Each lobe contains a number of compartments (cysts) separated by tissue septa, and each cyst contains a number of cells all in the same stage of development. These cysts were formed at the blunt, or apical, end of

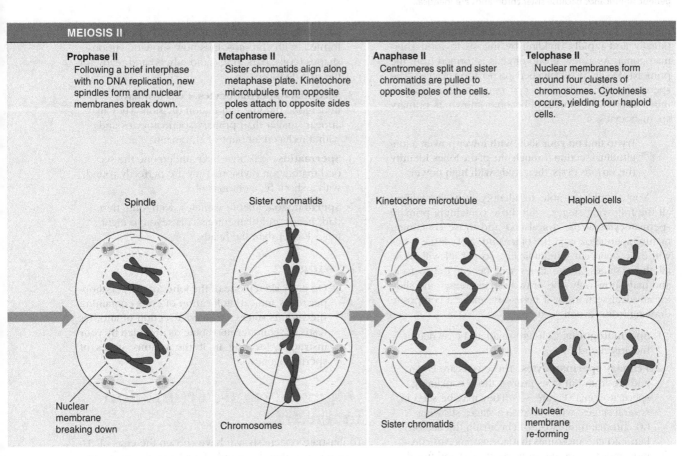

MEIOSIS II

Prophase II
Following a brief interphase with no DNA replication, new spindles form and nuclear membranes break down.

Metaphase II
Sister chromatids align along metaphase plate. Kinetochore microtubules from opposite poles attach to opposite sides of centromere.

Anaphase II
Centromeres split and sister chromatids are pulled to opposite poles of the cells.

Telophase II
Nuclear membranes form around four clusters of chromosomes. Cytokinesis occurs, yielding four haploid cells.

Spindle

Sister chromatids

Kinetochore microtubule

Haploid cells

Nuclear membrane breaking down

Chromosomes

Sister chromatids

Nuclear membrane re-forming

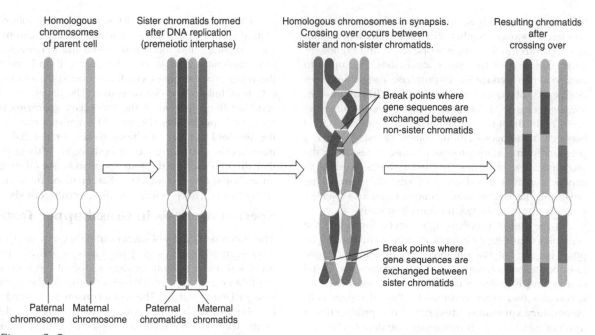

Homologous chromosomes of parent cell

Sister chromatids formed after DNA replication (premeiotic interphase)

Homologous chromosomes in synapsis. Crossing over occurs between sister and non-sister chromatids.

Resulting chromatids after crossing over

Break points where gene sequences are exchanged between non-sister chromatids

Break points where gene sequences are exchanged between sister chromatids

Paternal chromosome   Maternal chromosome   Paternal chromatids   Maternal chromatids

Figure 3-2

Crossing over during meiosis. Breaks and exchanges may occur on both non-sister and sister chromatids. Crossing over between non-sister chromatids results in genetic recombination of paternal and maternal genes. Crossing over between sister chromatids is without genetic significance because sister chromatids are identical.

the lobe. Here a group of primordial germ cells are continually and rapidly dividing by mitosis to form spermatogonia. As a new group of cells is formed from the primordial cells, it is pinched off to form a cyst. The spermatogonia in the new cyst begin to grow in volume, without dividing, and become known as primary spermatocytes.

 Try to find on your slide, with lower power, a longitudinal section through one of the lobes. Identify the various cysts; then study with high power.

You should be able to identify cysts containing all the following stages, with those containing primary spermatocytes at the apical end and those containing mature spermatozoa at the other end. Not all the lobes will have been cut longitudinally, so not all will show all these stages. Some lobes will be cut transversely and may show only one or two stages. Search the slide for an ideal section or, if necessary, make a composite drawing from several sections.

1. **Spermatogonia.** Cells are small and crowded at the apical end

2. **Primary spermatocytes.** These cells are larger and are found in cysts nearest those containing spermatogonia (Figure 3-4). They may be seen in several stages, with successive stages showing (a) chromatin threads, (b) chromatin threads broken into chromosomes that are pairing, (c) chromosomes thicker and in pairs (dyads) and fused

so that they seem to be haploid, and (d) split pairs formed, with chromosomes now showing curious shapes (coils, bars, rings, and others) and ready for the first division.

3. **Secondary spermatocytes.** Cells that have undergone the first maturation division. They may appear smaller than primary spermatocytes and with a reduced amount of chromatin.

4. **Spermatids.** Cells that have undergone the second maturation division. They are perfectly round, with a short, filamentous tail.

5. **Spermatozoa.** Mature gametes, with long, thin, dark heads and filamentous tails seven to eight times longer than the heads.

Drawings

 On p. 35, sketch one of the lobes of the grasshopper testis, indicating location of cysts containing the various stages. Or draw a section of another testis or seminiferous tubule, as provided by your instructor, locating in it the various stages of spermatogenesis.

Oogenesis and Fertilization in *Ascaris*

To illustrate oogenesis, we have chosen the eggs of *Ascaris* because they have only four large chromosomes.

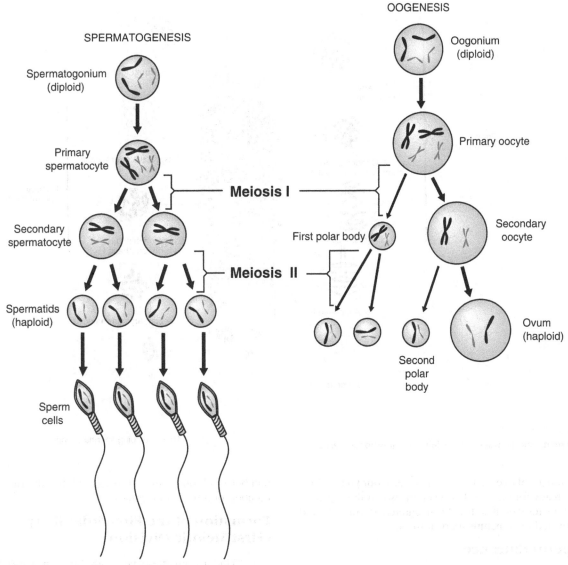

Figure 3-3

Spermatogenesis and oogenesis compared, showing division of a spermatogonium or oogonium with two pairs of chromosomes. What is the diploid number in the example illustrated here? _____ Haploid number? _____ How many chromosomes does each secondary spermatocyte contain? _____ How many chromatids? _____ If the diploid number of humans is 46, how many chromosomes are there in each spermatid? _____ In oogenesis are the polar bodies functional or nonfunctional? _____ What is the purpose of polar body formation?_____

Your slides are sections through the long, egg-filled uterus of a female *Ascaris* (intestinal roundworm found throughout the world). Copulation has already occurred because, in *Ascaris,* fertilization is necessary for completion of oogenesis.

If you have not already done so, read over the section "Spermatogenesis" and answer the questions in the legend of Figure 3-3. The process of meiosis is the same in spermatogenesis and oogenesis *except* that the meiotic divisions of an oocyte produce one large

ovum, whereas the meiotic divisions of a spermatocyte produce four spermatozoa.

Because these eggs have been sectioned at random, only a part of them will present the ideal views of division stages that are described here.

 Search through the sections for typical examples. Use high power and reduce the light, if necessary.

In females the primordial germ cells become oogonia, which increase in number by mitosis. Some of the

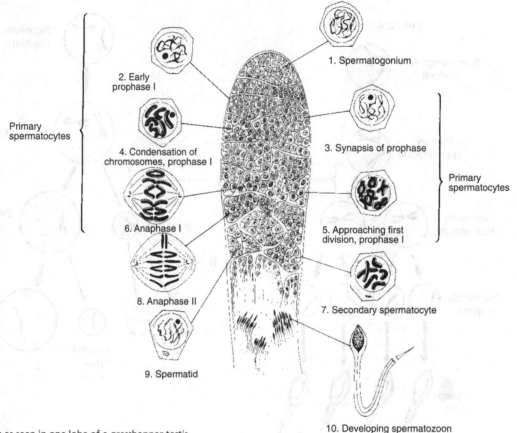

Figure 3-4
Spermatogenesis as seen in one lobe of a grasshopper testis.

oogonia enlarge to become **primary oocytes,** which are ready for meiosis. However, in *Ascaris* the egg does not mature until it has been entered (fertilized) and activated by a mature spermatozoon.

Sperm Entrance

 Locate unfertilized primary oocytes, which characteristically have thin cell membranes, inconspicuous nuclei, and vacuolated cytoplasm. Scattered between the oocytes, find the heads of spermatozoa, appearing as small, dark, triangular bodies with a centriole at the base of the triangle. Find a primary oocyte with a sperm just entering (Figure 3-5A).

After entrance the spermatozoon nucleus becomes more spherical, and the primary oocyte develops a shell that prevents penetration by other spermatozoa. While the egg is undergoing meiotic divisions, the spermatozoon nucleus (male pronucleus) will remain inactive at one side of the egg nucleus. It has already undergone meiosis in the male testis and now has the haploid

number of chromosomes. The egg still has the diploid number, or four chromosomes.

Formation of the First Polar Body (First Meiotic Division)

 Find a primary oocyte ready for its first meiotic division. It has a thick **shell,** with a **perivitelline space** between the shell and the cell membrane.

Synapsis has occurred, bringing the sister chromatids of each homologous chromosome together into a structure called a **bivalent.** The *Ascaris* egg in Figure 3-5B has two bivalents (one for each pair of homologous chromosomes) lined up on a spindle in the metaphase stage. Locate this stage on your slide. The male pronucleus is now spherical. In Figure 3-5C, the egg has reached telophase, and division is almost complete. One **dyad** from each bivalent will go to each daughter cell. However, one daughter cell **(secondary oocyte)** will retain all the cytoplasm, while the dyads of the other are pushed out into the perivitelline space and become the **first polar body.** Find a secondary oocyte with two dyads in the

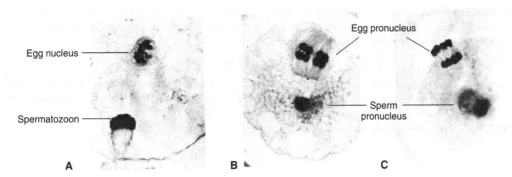

Figure 3-5

Maturation of fertilized *Ascaris* eggs. What is the diploid number of chromosomes in *Ascaris*? _____ **A,** Fertilization. A spermatozoon *(lower left)* has entered the egg. Is the spermatozoon haploid or diploid? _____ Is the egg nucleus at this stage haploid or diploid? _____ Is the spermatozoan nucleus visible? _____ Where? _____ **B,** Primary oocyte with two bivalents in metaphase stage of first meiotic division. How many chromatids are there in each bivalent? _____ **C,** Bivalents dividing (telophase stage) to form secondary oocyte and first polar body.

cytoplasm and a polar body appearing as a dark spot in the perivitelline space. The spermatozoan nucleus still waits to one side (Figure 3-6A).

Formation of Second Polar Body (Second Meiotic Division)

In the secondary oocyte the two dyads divide, throwing off two chromatids in the second polar body, which, like the first, has no cytoplasm and is nonfunctional. The other two chromatids, now individual chromosomes, remain in the egg, now a **mature ovum,** and take part in the formation of the **female pronucleus.** The first polar body may or may not divide, making two or three tiny, nonfunctional polar bodies in the perivitelline space, but only one functional mature ovum is

produced from each oogonium. How does this compare with spermatogenesis (refer to Figure 3-3)? Note that the nucleus of each mature ovum has now the haploid number of chromosomes, the same as the mature spermatozoon. Find an egg in which the second polar body is being formed.

Mature Ovum

Look now for eggs that have completed their meiotic divisions. Note that the egg nucleus, or **female pronucleus,** is a round ball with a nuclear membrane and granular chromatin material very much like the nucleus of an interphase stage (Figure 3-6B). Note that the **male pronucleus** looks much like the female pronucleus. They are called pronuclei because they help form the

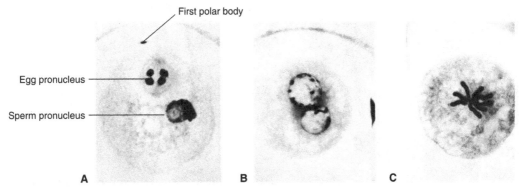

Figure 3-6

Maturation of fertilized *Ascaris* eggs. **A,** Dyads of secondary oocyte dividing to form a mature ovum and a second polar body. The first polar body is visible above as a small, dark spot in the perivitelline space. Note the male pronucleus *(center right).* How many chromatids have been disposed of in the first polar body? _____ In the second polar body? _____ **B,** Mature ovum with male and female pronuclei, each with haploid number of chromosomes. What is the haploid number? _____ **C,** Metaphase of the second meiotic division (polar view). The zygote nucleus is now diploid and preparing for the first cleavage division. This represents the genesis of a new embryo.

zygote nucleus. How many chromosomes does the zygote have now? _____ Although the two pronuclei come close to each other in the egg, only rarely do they fuse together in *Ascaris*. The nuclear membrane of each pronucleus disappears, and the two chromosomes from each nucleus move on to the spindle, which forms for the first cleavage division. Figure 3-6C shows the chromosomes, **two maternal** and **two paternal,** lined up in metaphase (polar view). This

will be the first of a series of mitotic (cleavage) divisions that will occur to produce the new embryo.

Drawings

 Prepare drawings on p. 36 as requested by the instructor. Or you may wish to make drawings for future reference.

Stages of Spermatogenesis in Grasshopper Testis

Name _____

Date _____

Section _____

Phylum _____

Genus _____

LAB REPORT

LAB REPORT

Name _____

Date _____

Section _____

Phylum _____

Genus _____

Stages of Oogenesis in *Ascaris*

EXERCISE 3B
Cleavage Patterns—
Spiral and Radial Cleavage

Cleavage, the earliest stage in embryonic development, consists of a succession of regular mitotic cell divisions that partition the egg into a multitude of small cells clustered together like a mass of soap bubbles. In lower animals, cleavage is so rapid that hundreds, sometimes thousands, of cells are produced in a matter of hours.

In animals such as sponges and cnidarians, cleavage is irregular and seemingly disorganized; egg cytoplasm is partitioned randomly into daughter cells of highly variable size and shape with no apparent relevance to future cell fates. As the metazoa evolved, however, cleavage began to follow precise patterns and rhythms. In virtually all animal groups above the cnidarians, cleavage is **regular;** the egg cytoplasm is segregated into specific cells called **blastomeres** (Gr. *blastos,* bud, + *meros,* part) occupying discrete positions and having specific developmental fates.

Patterns of regular cleavage depend greatly on amount and distribution of yolk in the egg. In eggs having a large amount of yolk, cleavage may be either **complete** (= holoblastic), as in amphibians, or **incomplete** (= meroblastic), as in birds and reptiles. In birds and reptiles with extreme **telolecithal** (Gr. *telos,* end, + *lekithos,* yolk) eggs, cleavage is restricted to a small disc of cytoplasm on the animal pole; this type of cleavage is called **discoidal.** The eggs of most insects follow another pattern of cleavage called **superficial.** In these, the nuclei divide mitotically into hundreds or thousands of "free" nuclei, which later migrate to the egg surface.

Only then do cleavage furrows form, rapidly partitioning the cytoplasm into a superficial layer of cells.

In most invertebrates, eggs have little yolk (= **isolecithal** ["equal-yolk"]), and cleavage is complete (holoblastic) and equal. Two major kinds of complete cleavage exist: **spiral** and **radial** (Figure 3-7). The first two cleavages are the same in both kinds of eggs: the cleavage planes are along the animal-vegetal axis, producing a quartet of cells. At the third cleavage, however, these two patterns—spiral and radial—can be distinguished from each other by the geometric positioning of the cells.

In radial cleavage, the third cleavage is perpendicular to the first two, yielding two quartets of cells, with the upper quartet lying directly on top of the lower. In spiral cleavage, the third cleavage planes are oblique to the polar axis and typically produce an upper quartet of smaller cells that come to lie between the furrows of the lower quartet of larger cells.

There are other important differences between these two cleavage patterns. Spiral cleavage is typically **mosaic,** meaning that the embryo is constructed as a mosaic, with each cell fitting into its predetermined location in the larval body. If cells of the embryo are experimentally separated at this early stage, each cell will develop into partial or defective larvae because the developmental fate of each cell has already been determined. Spiral cleavage is found in several phyla, including annelids, many molluscs, some flatworms, and ribbon worms (nemerteans). All groups showing spiral cleavage belong to the grouping of animal phyla called the **Protostomia,** in which the embryonic blastopore forms the mouth.

Radial cleavage is characteristically **regulative** because cell fate does not become fixed until after the

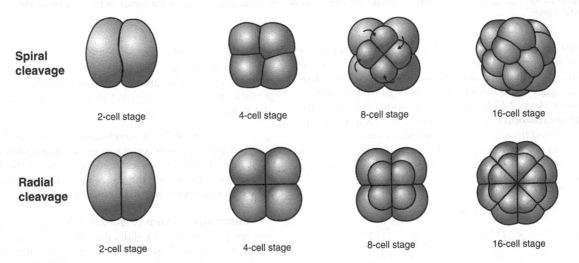

Spiral cleavage

2-cell stage   4-cell stage   8-cell stage   16-cell stage

Radial cleavage

2-cell stage   4-cell stage   8-cell stage   16-cell stage

Figure 3-7
Spiral and radial cleavage compared. Which kind of cleavage is mosaic? _____ Which kind is regulative? _____
Which kind of cleavage is typical of phyla belonging to the Deuterostomia division of the animal kingdom? _____ Which kind is typical of Protostomia? _____

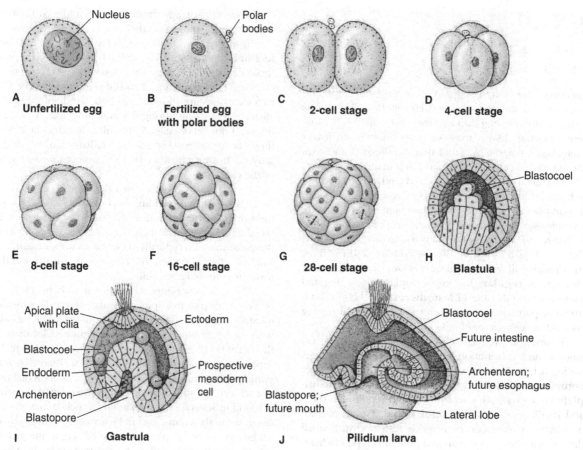

Figure 3-8

Early embryology of *Cerebratulus,* a nemertean worm. Are polar bodies formed and ejected before or after fertilization? _____ At what stage are micromeres and macromeres formed? _____ At what stage does the difference between spiral and radial cleavage become visually apparent? _____ What cavity is formed by gastrulation? _____ What is the significance of the 4d cell? _____ Is the mouth or the anus derived from the blastopore? _____

first few cleavages. Radial cleavage is found in eggs of echinoderms and many chordates, especially protochordates, amphibians, and mammals. (As mentioned earlier, eggs of birds and reptiles, as well as many fishes, show discoidal cleavage.) All of these belong to the **Deuterostomia,** a group of phyla in which the mouth is formed from a secondary embryonic opening.

In this exercise you will compare spiral cleavage in a ribbon worm (a protostome) with radial cleavage in a sea star (a deuterostome).

Spiral Cleavage: Early Embryology of the Ribbon Worm, *Cerebratulus*

Ribbon worms belong to the phylum **Nemertea** and often are called nemertean worms. You will study

eggs of *Cerebratulus* (ser'uh-brat'u-lus), a well-known genus with species distributed in seas around the world. *Cerebratulus* and other ribbon worms follow a highly regular form of spiral cleavage that is almost diagrammatic in pattern.

 On your slide of *Cerebratulus* early development,* you will see stages of development from the unfertilized or fertilized egg to about the 32-cell stage. Locate the stages with medium power and then switch to high power for study.

Unfertilized Ovum (Figure 3-8A). If unfertilized ova are present on your slide, they will be recognized by their irregular shape, with a conical protruberance on the vegetal pole. The nucleus is clearly visible.

*See Appendix A, p. 387 for sources of prepared slides of *Cerebratulus* development.

Fertilized Undivided Ovum (Figure 3-8B). After sperm penetration, the egg assumes a spherical shape. First and second polar bodies are formed and constricted off from the animal pole. Focus up and down through the egg to locate the polar bodies and the large asters surrounding the female pronucleus, which is lying near the center of the egg. What is the purpose of polar body formation? _____

After expulsion of polar bodies, the haploid female pronucleus fuses with the haploid male pronucleus near the center of the egg. Fertilization of the ovum is now complete and it is called a **zygote.**

Cleavage Stages. The zygote now divides along the egg axis into two equal-sized blastomeres (Figure 3-8C). The second cleavage plane forms at right angles to the first, producing four equal-sized blastomeres (Figure 3-8D). Locate these stages on your slide.

The third cleavage divides the zygote along the **equatorial** plane to produce eight blastomeres: four equal-sized "micromeres" in the animal hemisphere and four equal-sized "macromeres" in the vegetal hemisphere (Figure 3-8E). Locate an eight-cell embryo that is oriented so you are viewing it from above (i.e., looking down the polar axis). Note that the four micromeres are rotated to the right with respect to the four macromeres so that the two quartets of cells do not lie directly on top of each other in properly arranged tiers. This cleavage pattern, which strikingly distinguishes spiral cleavage from radial, occurs because the cleavage spindles that form just before the third cleavage are oriented obliquely with respect to the polar axis.

At the fourth cleavage, both quartets of cells divide, producing 16 cells in four layers (Figure 3-8F). Locate a 16-cell stage on your slide. Note how the quartets are stacked in an alternating spiral pattern. The orientation is now difficult to follow because the cells are compressed into a configuration with minimal surface area like a cluster of soap bubbles.

Morula Stage. With continued divisions, the embryo becomes a solid ball of cells too numerous to count with accuracy (Figure 3-8G). How does the size of the morula compare with that of the undivided egg? _____

 Examine the slide of *Cerebratulus* late development. On this slide you should find embryonic stages from blastula to young pilidium larvae.

Blastula Stage (Figure 3-8H). At the blastula stage, an off-center cavity, the **blastocoel,** appears. Although difficult to see, the surface of the blastula is covered with delicate cilia.

Gastrula Stage (Figure 3-8I). In the early gastrula stage, an indentation appears at the vegetal pole. These cells continue to migrate inward by a process called **invagination** to form an internal cavity, the **archenteron.** Look for lightly stained embryos at the stage shown in Figure 3-8I. The pouch-shaped archenteron opens to the outside through the blastopore, which will become the mouth of the worm. The embryo can now swim rapidly forward in a spiraling manner with the animal pole directed forward. With favorable specimens and reduced illumination, you may be able to see the long apical tuft of cilia on the animal pole.

The gastrula is now an embryo of two **germ layers.** The outer layer is the **ectoderm,** and the inner layer that lines the archenteron is the **endoderm.** The ectoderm will give rise to the epithelium, which covers the body surface, and the nervous system. The inner endoderm gives rise to the epithelial lining of the digestive tube. The cavity between these two layers is the old blastocoel.

Locate on your slide a late gastrula lying on its side and note the mass of cells arising in the blastocoel on either side of the blastopore. These cells are giving rise to the third germ layer, the **mesoderm,** which will form the muscles, blood vessels, and reproductive system of the future adult body. Meticulous cell-lineage studies by early embryologists established that, in many protostomes with spiral cleavage, the mesoderm arises from a special, large vegetal hemisphere blastomere of the 64-cell embryo called the 4d cell. This cell is also referred to as the **mesoderm mother cell.** But in *Cerebratulus,* the precise origin of the mesoderm has not been determined.

Pilidium Larva Stage (Helmet Larva) (Figure 3-8J). You will recognize this stage by its large size and by its remarkable resemblance, when viewed from the side, to a football helmet. (The name *pilidium* actually derives from a Greek word meaning felt nightcap; football helmets did not exist in Grecian times!) The blastopore has now sunk inward to open widely into the archenteron, which is bent over to form the gut. The large, innermost pouch will become the intestine of the worm; the tube connecting this pouch to the outside will become the esophagus of the adult body. There is no anus. Note that the pilidium is bilaterally symmetrical.

Summary

The development of *Cerebratulus* clearly shows the four features of development characteristic of many (though not all) protostomes. These are (1) _____ cleavage; (2) _____ development, with the developmental fate of the blastomeres fixed before the first cleavage division; (3) mouth derived from the _____; and (4) _____ derived from a particular blastomere (or blastomeres) located near the vegetal pole of the embryo.

Radial Cleavage: Early Embryology of the Sea Star, *Asterias*

Sea stars belong to phylum **Echinodermata,** which, like the chordates, are deuterostomes.

Development of the sea star *Asterias,* like that of *Cerebratulus,* is rather easy to study because the egg is of the **isolecithal** type, with yolk distributed evenly throughout. Cleavage is radial and complete (holoblastic).

 On your slide(s) of sea star development, you will find whole mounts of embryos at all stages of development, from unfertilized ovum to bipinnaria larva. With the help of Figure 3-9, locate the best representatives of each stage, using the low-power objective. Then switch to high power to study special features of each stage.

Unfertilized Ovum (Figure 3-9A). There should be several unfertilized ova scattered on your slide. Each can be identified by its very large, conspicuous nucleus. Note the small, dark nucleolus in the nucleus.

Fertilized Undivided Ovum (Zygote) (Figure 3-9B). Soon after the eggs are spawned and activated by sperm entry, the nuclear membrane breaks down and the nucleus disappears in preparation for fusion of the male and female pronuclei. You should be able to see a **fertilization membrane,** which may appear wrinkled in your prepared whole mounts; in life it is smooth and spherical. What is the function of this membrane? _____

Cleavage Stages (Figure 3-9C–E). Cleavage by mitosis begins immediately after fertilization.

 Identify two-cell, four-cell, and eight-cell stages on your slide.

Is the fertilization membrane still present? _____ As with *Cerebratulus,* cleavage planes for the first two cleavages run through the poles of the egg perpendicular to each other, and the third cleavage plane passes through the equator. Note that the blastomeres in the animal half of the eight-cell embryo lie squarely above the corresponding blastomeres of the vegetal half. Because any plane passing through the embryonic axis will divide the embryo into symmetrical halves, the embryo has radial symmetry. This type of cleavage accordingly is called **radial,** distinguishing it from the spiral pattern of cleavage seen in *Cerebratulus.*

Morula Stage (Figure 3-9F). A mass of 16 or more cells with no large cavity in its center is the **morula** (L. *morum,* mulberry) stage.

Blastula Stage (Figure 3-9G). As cleavage continues, the cells become smaller and arrange themselves in a single layer around a central cavity, the **blastocoel.** The embryo develops cilia toward the end of this stage, escapes from the fertilization membrane, and becomes free-swimming.

Gastrula Stage. The embryo is no longer a perfect sphere because the vegetal side of the blastula has begun to invaginate, or push inward, to begin the formation of the **archenteron** (Figure 3-9H). The opening to the archenteron is the **blastopore,** which will later form the anus (recall that in *Cerebratulus* the blastopore forms the mouth of the future adult). The cells streaming inward by invagination to form the archenteron will give rise to the **endoderm** and **mesoderm.** At the same time, **ectoderm** cells on the embryo's surface spread outward and downward toward the blastopore by a morphogenetic movement called **epiboly** (ee-pib'o-lee; Gr., putting on).

 Locate a midgastrula stage in which the innermost wall of the archenteron is greatly expanded into two pouchlike vesicles (Figure 3-9I).

These **coelomic vesicles** are the origin of the mesoderm that will give rise to the peritoneum (lining of the coelom), skeleton, and muscular system of the future adult. The vesicles will continue to enlarge and eventually separate from the archenteron to form left and right **coelomic pouches.** The mesoderm is now completely separated from the endoderm. The archenteron itself will give rise to the epithelial (endodermal) lining of the digestive tube. Note also at this stage the **mesenchyme** cells that have separated from the epithelium and migrated into the blastocoel. These cells will give rise to the larval skeleton.

Bipinnaria Larval Stage (Figure 3-9J).

 Locate a bipinnaria larva positioned so that it can be viewed laterally.

After gastrulation the endodermal archenteron bends to one side and meets an inpocketing of the ectoderm called the **stomodeum.** They fuse and perforate at this point of contact to form the **mouth.** Thus, the mouth forms from a *secondary* larval opening, the characteristic for which the deuterostomia ("secondary mouth") are named.

The basic organization of the digestive tube is now complete. Identify the **stomodeum** (mouth cavity with ectodermal lining), **esophagus** (thick-walled, muscular tube of endoderm), **stomach** (saclike enlargement of endoderm), and **intestine,** an endodermal tube curving ventrally to connect to the outside at the **anus.** The anus is derived from the embryonic blastopore. Note that the bipinnaria is bilaterally symmetrical. The bipinnaria

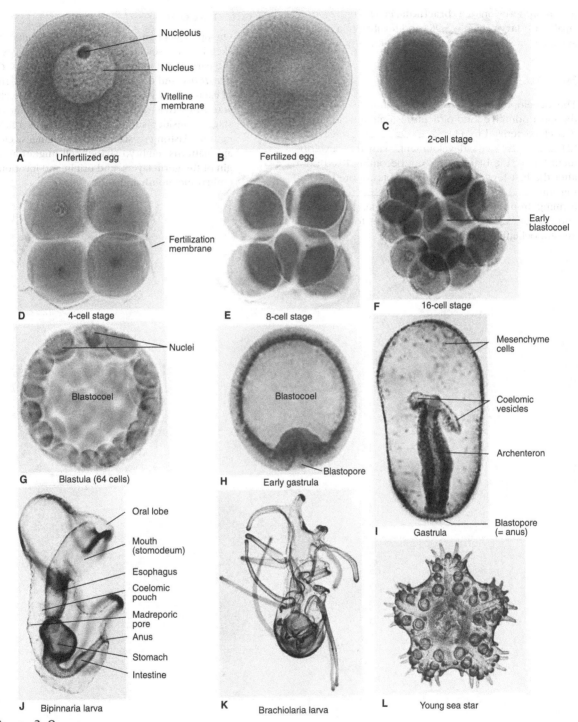

Figure 3-9

Embryology of a sea star, *Asterias* sp. With an unknown embryo, what is the earliest stage that would inform you that this is a radial cleaving and not a spiral cleaving embryo? _____ Is cleavage by mitosis or meiosis? _____ Is cleavage in sea stars regulative or mosaic? _____ How do these two forms of cleavage differ? _____ Into what cavity does the blastopore open? _____ What adult structure does the blastopore become? _____ Would knowing the fate of the blastopore be enough to assure you that this animal is a deuterostome? _____ What is the fate of mesenchyme cells? _____ How does the origin of mesoderm in sea stars differ from the origin of mesoderm in *Cerebratulus*? _____

metamorphoses into a **brachiolaria** (L. *brachiolum,* small arm) **larva** (Figure 3-9K) and finally into a radially symmetrical young sea star (Figure 3-9L).

Summary

The development of a sea star beautifully illustrates the most primitive kind of deuterostome development. It is characterized by (1) _____ cleavage; (2) _____ development, with the development fate of the blastomeres not becoming fixed until after the first few cleavages; (3)the blastopore becoming the _____, and the _____ forming from a secondary opening, the stomodeum; and (4) the _____ germ layer forming from an outpocketing of the primitive gut.

Written Report

On pp. 43–44 prepare a series of comparative sketches of selected representative stages in the early development of the ribbon worm, *Cerebratulus,* and the sea star, *Asterias.* To the right of each pair of sketches, comment on those characteristics that distinguish the embryos at that stage. Consider such characteristics as relative egg or blastomere size, nuclear changes, cleavage patterns, embryo shape, cell migration, origin of the germ layers, and origin and location of embryonic mouth and anus.

Comparison of Early Development of a Protostome and a Deuterostome

Name _____

Date _____

Section _____

Ribbon Worm *Cerebratulus*	Sea Star *Asterias*	Distinguishing Features
Unfertilized egg		
Fertilized undivided egg		
Eight-cell stage		
Morula		

LAB REPORT

Ribbon Worm *Cerebratulus*	Sea Star *Asterias*	Distinguishing Features
Gastrula		
Free-swimming larva		

EXERCISE 3C
Frog Development

Frog eggs are much larger than the marine invertebrate eggs studied in Exercise 3B. A frog egg is **mesolecithal**(Gr.*mesos,* middle, + *lekithos,* yolk), in which the yolk is more or less concentrated in one hemisphere (vegetal), and the cytoplasm and nucleus are found in the other hemisphere (animal). Such an egg shows definite **polarity.** The **animal pole** is the region of the egg just above the nucleus in the darkly pigmented hemisphere; the **vegetal pole** is a similar point on the light-colored yolk hemisphere diametrically opposite the animal pole.

Frog development shows a variant of radial cleavage called **bilateral** because the bilateral arrangement of the blastomeres in early cleavage is unmistakable. Cleavage is complete but unequal and begins at the animal pole. The nucleus divides by mitosis, but division of cytoplasm is retarded because of the concentration of yolk at the vegetal pole, with the result that cells of the vegetal hemisphere are larger and less numerous than those of the more rapidly dividing animal hemisphere.

You will study both preserved specimens and prepared slides of developing stages of a frog. Containers with various stages of frog egg development may be available. When you select a stage, be sure to keep it immersed in water while studying it; *do not allow it to dry.* Return your specimen to the proper container when you have finished your study of it. If the specimens have been mounted in deep-well slides, they are to be studied without removal from their containers.

Study of Eggs in Frog Ovary

 Obtain a stained slide showing a section through an ovary.

Note the **ova,** or eggs, of various sizes. Smaller ova contain little yolk and have conspicuous nuclei. Note the nature and position of the **chromatin granules** in these nuclei. Compare the location of nuclei in small and large ova. Early germ cells have distinct **cell membranes,** but older ova have **follicular cell layers** surrounding them. Find an ovum with such a follicular layer. The follicular cells support the maturation of the ovum.

Eggs in Cleavage Stages

 Use both whole developing eggs and stained slides showing cross sections of various stages of development.

One-Cell Stage. The one-cell stage may be represented by an unfertilized ovum or, as is more commonly

the case, by a fertilized egg (zygote) that has not yet started to develop. Note the thick, jellylike layer surrounding the egg. What do you think is the function of the jelly layer? _____ The black, or **animal, hemisphere,** which is not as heavy as the **vegetal hemisphere,** always floats uppermost in the water, where it can absorb the sun's warmth, which is necessary for development (Figure 3-10A).

Soon after fertilization, a **gray crescent** appears as a light, indistinct, crescent-shaped area on the margin of the pigmented zone (Figure 3-10B). It is formed on the side of the egg opposite that which the spermatozoon entered. It is produced by a migration of pigmented cytoplasm away from that region. Note that before fertilization the egg has radial symmetry; after fertilization it has bilateral symmetry.

Early Cleavage Stages. The frog egg divides repeatedly during cleavage. However, the presence of yolk slows down cell division so that cells in the animal hemisphere divide more rapidly than those in the vegetal hemisphere. Consequently cells of the two poles rapidly become unequal in size and number. Is cleavage by mitosis or meiosis? _____ Do the blastomeres contain the haploid or diploid number of chromosomes? _____

The first cleavage plane, which results in a **two-cell stage,** is vertical (meridional), beginning at the animal pole and passing through the vegetal pole. The second cleavage plane, resulting in a **four-cell stage,** is also vertical but at right angles to the first cleavage plane. The third cleavage plane is equatorial, or horizontal, but passes closer to the animal pole. The four blastomeres **(micromeres)** of the animal pole of this **eight-cell stage** are much smaller than the four **macromeres** at the vegetal pole (Figure 3-10C).

The **morula stage** contains 16 to 32 cells. There are two fourth-cleavage planes; both are vertical and appear simultaneously. Because of the greater concentration of yolk in the vegetal pole, the cells of the animal pole complete their division before those of the vegetal pole. The fifth cleavage, which results in 32 cells, is also made up of two furrows, both of which are horizontal (Figure 3-10D). Note that in these later stages the faster rate of cell division in the animal hemisphere results in a larger number of micromeres than macromeres. As cleavage continues, the cells and cleavage planes are difficult to recognize.

Blastula Stage. The blastula stage begins at about 32 cells. A **segmentation cavity,** or **blastocoel,** has begun near the animal pole. The blastula stage is not easily recognized in the unsectioned embryo; look for it in a cross-section slide (Figure 3-10E).

Gastrula Stage. The gastrula stage is recognized by the crescent-shaped slit at the margin of the pigmented animal hemisphere. Gastrulation in a frog is more complicated than in a sea star. In the sea star eggs studied earlier, you saw that the gastrula stage was brought about

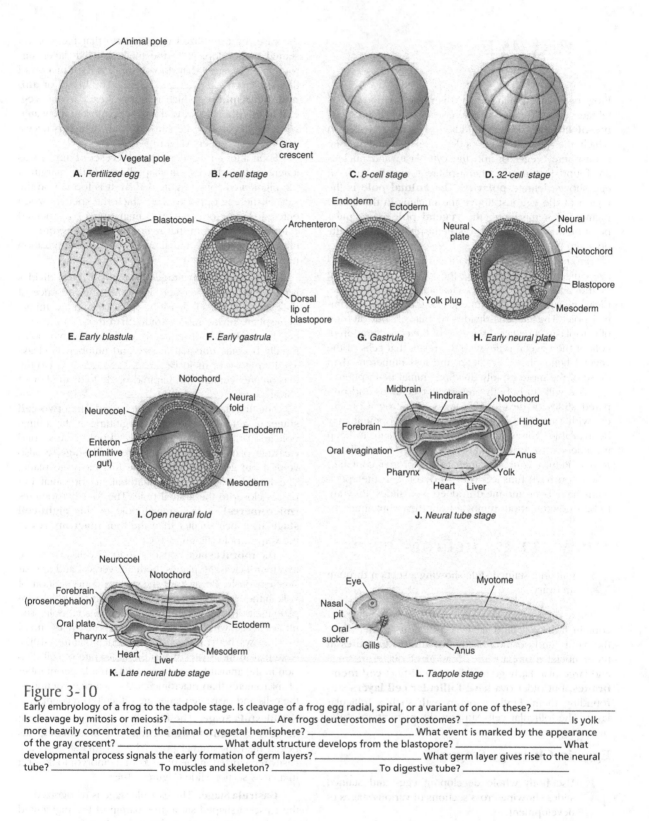

Figure 3-10

Early embryology of a frog to the tadpole stage. Is cleavage of a frog egg radial, spiral, or a variant of one of these? _____ Is cleavage by mitosis or meiosis? _____ Are frogs deuterostomes or protostomes? _____ Is yolk more heavily concentrated in the animal or vegetal hemisphere? _____ What event is marked by the appearance of the gray crescent? _____ What adult structure develops from the blastopore? _____ What developmental process signals the early formation of germ layers? _____ What germ layer gives rise to the neural tube? _____ To muscles and skeleton? _____ To digestive tube? _____

by a simple folding in of one side. In a frog embryo, the heavy yolk cells prevent such a simple movement. Instead, pigmented cells of the animal hemisphere begin growing down over the vegetal cells (a process called **epiboly**), folding in at the equator along a crescent-shaped line (Figure 3-10F). The opening thus formed is called the **blastopore.** As overgrowth continues, the lips of the blastopore draw closer together over the vegetal cells until only a small mass of vegetal cells is left showing, the **yolk plug.** On whole mounts this will appear as a light circle on one side of the gastrula (Figure 3-10G). Look at the cross section of this stage and identify the yolk plug and blastopore. The blastopore represents the future posterior end of the embryo.

As gastrulation progresses, the inturning (invaginating) cells form an inner layer, the **endoderm,** surrounded by an overgrowth of animal cells called the **ectoderm.** A third layer, the **mesoderm,** forms between these (Figure 3-10H). These three layers are the **germ layers,** and from them the various tissues and organs of the body will be formed. The new cavity formed by gastrulation, of which the blastopore is the opening, is called the **archenteron** (primitive gut). The blastocoel gradually becomes obliterated.

Neural Groove Stage.

 Examine preserved specimens and transverse sections (slide) of the neural groove stage (Figure 3-10I).

Note that in the preserved specimen the embryo has assumed an elongated form. The embryo, still in its jelly covering, has not yet hatched. The posterior end is more pointed than the anterior end. Find the **neural groove** along the dorsal side. Later this groove becomes a tube.

In the prepared slide of a transverse section, note the neural groove with a **neural fold** on each side of the groove. The neural groove develops in a thick ectodermal plate, the **neural plate.** Just ventral to the neural groove is the **notochord.** The mesodermal layer is now well defined. Do you notice any yolk material?

Neural Tube Stage. In a preserved specimen, note that the neural groove has now closed (Figure 3-10J). A **neural tube** has been formed by the meeting of the neural folds in the midline. Find on each side of the head two ventral ridges. **Eyes** will develop from the first of these ridges, **gills** from the second. Turn the specimen over and look for **ventral suckers** by which the tadpole may hold fast to an object. Look for the **oral plate** at the anterior end and the **anus** at the posterior end (Figure 3-10K).

Now examine a transverse section through the embryo at this stage. Note the neural tube, notochord, and gastrocoel (archenteron). Observe the condition of the mesoderm. Masses of epidermal mesoderm lateral to the notochord give rise to dermis, muscles, and skeleton; lateral to them is the intermediate mesoderm, which

forms most of the excretory system; and a thin hypomeric layer surrounds the yolk mass, which is destined to split and give rise to the coelomic cavity.

Tadpole Stages and Metamorphosis. Well before hatching, the embryo begins to move within its jelly layers by means of cilia on its epidermis. Such movements become more pronounced as hatching approaches. Hatching occurs when the embryo frees itself from its protective jelly membranes; the embryo is now termed a tadpole.

 Examine specimens of tadpoles at different stages of development, noting changes in external body form as development proceeds.

The rapid transformation from larva to adult frog is called **metamorphosis,** a process in which larval tissues are destroyed and replaced by cells destined to become adult tissues and organs. If living tadpoles are available, use a dissecting microscope to examine the thin and nearly transparent skin of the flattened tail to see the flow of blood through capillaries.

A few days after hatching, the oval **mouth** breaks through into the archenteron. The intestine develops rapidly into a coil visible through the ventral body wall, and the tadpole, which up to this time has been subsisting on yolk stores, begins feeding. Three pairs of fingerlike **external gills** grow rapidly after hatching (Figure 3-10L). **Gill slits** appear in the pharyngeal wall soon after the mouth forms. Somewhat later four pairs of **internal gills** replace the external gills. As the external gills disappear, folds of skin, the **opercula** (sing. **operculum**), arise on both sides of the head and grow posteriorly to cover the internal gills. Eventually the two opercula fuse ventrally and on the right to form a chamber for the gills. On the left side a small opening remains—the **spiracle.** The gills are now ventilated by water passing into the mouth, through the gill slits and over the gill filaments, and then out of the gill chamber through the spiracle.

As metamorphosis proceeds, the horseshoe-shaped ventral **sucker,** which the tadpole uses to adhere to vegetation, divides and degenerates. Hindlimbs appear as buds, become jointed, and develop toes. The forelimbs follow, the left forelimb passing out through the spiracle and the right forelimb pushing out through the wall of the operculum. The tail is resorbed, the intestine shortens, and other changes in the mouth and jaws follow as the herbivorous tadpole develops into a carnivorous frog. With the growth of lungs and disappearance of gills, metamorphosis is complete.

Drawings (Optional)

 On separate paper, sketch such stages of frog development as you may wish to have for future reference.

NOTES

EXERCISE 7

The Sponges
Phylum Porifera

Members of phylum Porifera are considered the simplest metazoans—little more than loose aggregations of cells, with little or no tissue organization. They are said to belong to the **cellular level of organization.** There is division of labor among their cells, but there are no organs, no systems, no mouth or digestive tract, and only very rudimentary nervous integration. Because adult sponges have no germ layers, sponges are neither diploblastic nor triploblastic. Adult sponges are all sessile in form. Some have no regular form or symmetry; others have a characteristic shape and radial symmetry. They may be either solitary or colonial.

Chief characteristics of sponges are their **pores** and **canal systems;** the flagellated sponge feeding cells, called **choanocytes,** which line their cavities and create currents of water; and their peculiar internal skeletons of **spicules** or organic fibers **(spongin).** They also have some form of internal cavity **(spongocoel)** that opens to the outside by an **osculum.** Most sponges are marine, but there are a few freshwater species. Freshwater forms are found in small, slimy masses attached to sticks, leaves, or other objects in quiet ponds and streams.

Classification

Phylum Porifera

Class Calcarea Cal-ca′re-a (Gr. *calcis,* limy). Sponges with spicules of calcium carbonate, needle-shaped or three-rayed or four-rayed; canal systems asconoid, syconoid, or leuconoid; all marine. Examples: *Sycon, Leucosolenia.*

Class Hexactinellida (hex-ak-tin-el′i-da) (Gr. *hex,* six, + *aktis,* ray). Sponges with three-dimensional, six-rayed siliceous spicules; spicules often united to form network; body often cylindrical or funnel-shaped; canal systems syconoid or leuconoid; all marine, mostly deep water. Examples: *Euplectella* (Venus' flower basket), *Hyalonema.*

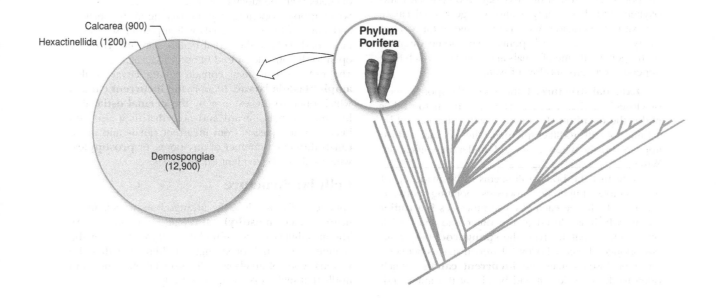

Class Demospongiae (de-mo-spun'je-e) (Gr. *demos*, people, + *spongos*, sponge). Sponges with siliceous spicules (not six-rayed), spongin, or both; canal systems leuconoid; one family freshwater, all others marine. Examples: *Spongilla* (freshwater sponge), *Spongia* (commercial bath sponge), *Cliona* (a boring sponge). Most sponges belong to this class.

EXERCISE 7A
Class Calcarea—*Sycon*

Sycon, a Syconoid Sponge

Phylum Porifera
　　Class Calcarea
　　　　Order Heterocoela
　　　　　　Genus *Sycon (=Scypha, Grantia)*

Where Found

Sycon is strictly a marine form, living in clusters in shallow water, usually attached to rocks, pilings, or shells. *Sycon* is chiefly a North Atlantic form. *Rhabdodermella* is a somewhat similar Pacific intertidal form, also belonging to class Calcarea.

Gross Structure

 Place a preserved specimen in a watch glass and cover with water. Examine with a hand lens or dissecting microscope.

Sycon (Gr., like a fig) is a **syconoid** type of sponge (Figure 7-1). What is the shape of the sponge? _____ The body wall is made up of a system of tiny, interconnected, dead-end canals whose flagellated cells draw in water from the outside through minute pores, take from it the necessary food particles and oxygen, and then empty it into a large central cavity for exit to the outside. What is the name of this central cavity? _____ All sponges have some variation of this general theme of canals and pores on which they depend for a constant flow of water.

External Structure. Is the base of the sponge open or closed? _____ The opening at the other end is the **osculum** (L., a little mouth), surrounded by a fringe of stiff, rodlike **spicules.** The external surface appears bristly when examined under magnification. Why? _____

Note that the body wall seems to be made up of innumerable, fingerlike processes pointing outward (Figure 7-1). Inside each of these processes is a **radial canal,** which is closed at the outer end but which opens into a central cavity, the **spongocoel** (Gr. *spongos,* sponge, +*koilos,* hollow). External spaces between these enclosed canals are **incurrent canals,** which open to the outside but end blindly at the inner end.

What is the name of the openings, or pores, to the outside of the sponge? _____

Water enters the incurrent canals and passes through minute openings called **prosopyles** (Gr. *prosō,* forward, + *pylē,* gate) into radial canals and then to the spongocoel and out through the osculum. There is no mouth, anus, or digestive system. What kind of symmetry does this sponge have? _____

Spongocoel. To study the spongocoel, do the following:

 Make a longitudinal cut through the midline of the body from osculum to base with a sharp razor blade. Place the two halves in a watch glass and cover with water.

Find the small pores, called **apopyles** (Gr. *apo,* away from, + *pylē,* gate), that open from the radial canals into the spongocoel (Figures 7-1 and 7-2). Can you distinguish the tiny canals in the cut edge of the sponge wall? _____ Which direction does the water move through these canals? _____

Study of Prepared Slide

Transverse sections of sponge are difficult to prepare for slides because the spicules prevent cutting sections thin enough for studying the cells. Therefore, the spicules have been dissolved away for slide preparation.

 On a prepared slide of a cross section of *Sycon,* examine the entire section with low power to get an idea of its general relations.

Note the **spongocoel** in the middle of the section (Figure 7-2). Study the canal system. Find the **radial canals,** which open into the spongocoel by way of the **apopyles.** Are apopyle openings smaller or larger in diameter than the radial canals? _____ Some apopyle openings will be lacking in this section, and some of the radial canals will appear closed at the inner end. Follow the radial canals outward. Do they open to the outside or end blindly? _____ The radial canals may contain young larvae, called **amphiblastula larvae.** Identify the **incurrent canals,** which open to the exterior by the **dermal ostia.** Follow these canals inward and note that they also end blindly. Water passes from incurrent canals into radial canals through a number of tiny pores, or **prosopyles,** which will not be evident on the slides.

Cellular Structure

Sponge cells are loosely arranged in a gelatinous matrix called **mesohyl** (also called mesenchyme). The mesohyl (Gr. *mesos,* middle, + *hyle,* wood) is the "connective tissue" of sponges, holding together the various types of ameboid cells, skeletal elements, and fibrils that make up the sponge body.

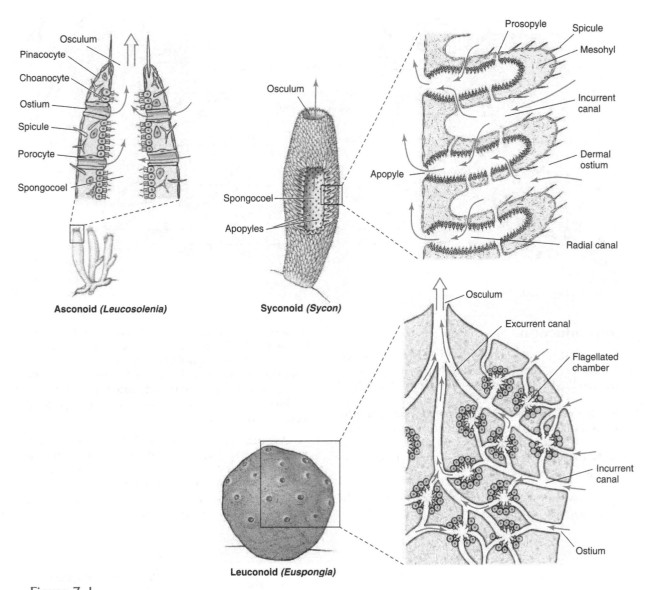

Figure 7-1

Three types of sponge structures. The degree of complexity from asconoid to complex leuconoid type involves mainly the water canal and skeletal systems, accompanied by outfolding and branching of the collar cell layer. The leuconoid type is considered the major body plan for sponges because it permits greater size and more efficient water circulation.

Choanocytes.

 With high power, observe the "collar cells," or choanocytes (Gr. *choanē*, funnel, + *kytos*, hollow vessel), that line the radial canals (Figure 7-3).

Although they are flagellated, you probably will not see the flagella. What is the function of the choanocytes? _____

Pinacocytes. Dermal pinacocytes (Gr. *pinax*, tablet, + *kytos*, hollow vessel) may be seen as extremely thin (squamous) cells lining the incurrent canals and spongocoel and covering the outer surface (Figure 7-3). What is their function? _____

Amebocytes. In the jellylike **mesohyl** that lies in the wall between the pinacocytes and choanocytes, look for large, wandering amebocytes of various functions (Figure 7-3). Some may differentiate into spicule-forming cells, some form sex cells, and some secrete spongin or spicules, serve as contractile cells, or aid in digestion.

 If living sponges are available, tease a bit of tissue on a slide with a drop of seawater and look for the various types of cells.

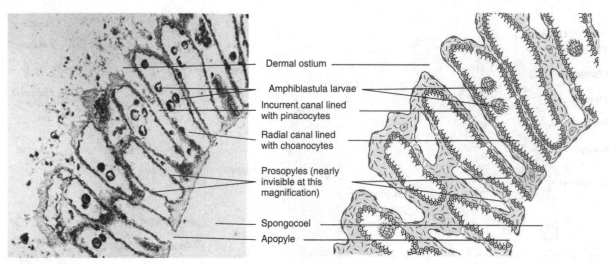

Figure 7-2
Section through wall of *Sycon*.

Reproduction

Sexual. *Sycon* sponges are monoecious, having both male and female sex cells in the same individual. Eggs and sperm are produced in the mesohyl. Fertilized eggs, after undergoing early cleavage in the mesohyl, develop into little blastula-like embryos, called **amphiblastula larvae.** These break through into the radial canals (Figure 7-2) and finally leave the parent by way of the osculum. They soon settle down on a substratum and grow into sessile adults.

 Look for the embryos in the radial canals of the cross-section slide.

What is the advantage to a sessile animal of producing free-swimming larvae? _____

Most sponges do not have amphiblastula larvae. In most Demospongiae and some calcareous sponges, the zygote develops into a **parenchymula** (pair-en-ki'mu-la) **larva** in which the flagellated cells invaginate to form a solid internal mass.

Asexual. Many sponges, including those of genus *Sycon,* also reproduce asexually by budding off new individuals from their base, thus forming sessile clusters. What would be the disadvantage if this were the sole means of reproduction?_____
Is there a bud on your specimen?_____

Figure 7-3
A, Small section through sponge wall, showing types of sponge cells and the water current created by choanocytes in flagellated chambers. **B,** Choanocyte as a food-catching cell. The "collar" is a series of cytoplasmic extensions that screen out larger food particles, letting them fall to the side of the cell for ameboid ingestion. Smaller particles flow through and are carried away in the current.

Freshwater sponges and some marine Demospongiae reproduce asexually by means of **gemmules,** made up of clusters of amebocytes. Gemmules (L. *gemma,* bud, + *ula,* dim.) of freshwater sponges are enclosed in hard shells (Figure 7-4) and can withstand adverse conditions that would kill an adult sponge. In spring, cells in gemmules escape through the micropyle and develop into young sponges. Marine gemmules give rise to flagellated larvae.

Skeleton

 Place a small bit of the sponge on a clean microscope slide; add a drop of commercial chlorine bleach, such as Clorox (sodium hypochlorite); and set aside for a few minutes to allow the cellular matter to dissolve. Break up the piece with dissecting needles, if necessary. Add a coverslip and examine under the microscope.

Look for **short monaxons** (short and pointed at both ends), **long monaxons** (long and pointed) (Figure 7-5), **triradiates** (Y-shaped with three prongs), and **polyaxons** (T-shaped). These spicules of crystalline calcium carbonate ($CaCO_3$) form a sort of network in the walls of the animal (Figure 7-3). What is the advantage of spicules to a loosely constructed animal such as *Sycon?*_____

Spicule types are used in the classification of sponges, along with the types of canal system. Demospongiae have siliceous (mainly $H_2Si_3O_7$) spicules, spongin fibers (composed of an insoluble scleroprotein that is resistant to protein-digesting enzymes) (Figure 7-6A), or a combination of both. Their spicules are either straight or curved monaxons or tetraxons, but never six-rayed. The glass sponges (Sclerospongiae) have siliceous triaxon (six-rayed) spicules.

Drawings

 On p. 119, draw the following:

1. External view of *Sycon*, gross structure

2. Longitudinal section showing spongocoel and internal ostia; use arrows to show direction of water flow

3. Types of spicules you have seen

On p. 120, draw a pie-shaped segment of a transverse section through *Sycon*, showing a few canals and some of the cellular details of their structure. On the same page, sketch any other sponges you have studied.
Label all drawings fully.

Other Types of Sponge Structure

Asconoid Type of Canal System
The asconoid canal system is best seen in *Leucosolenia,* another marine sponge of the class Calcarea.

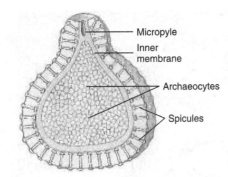

Figure 7-4
Gemmule of freshwater sponge.

Leucosolenia grows in a cluster, or colony (Figure 7-1), of tubular individuals in varying stages of growth. Large individuals may carry one or more buds.

 After observing the external structure of a submerged specimen, cut it in half longitudinally, place it on a slide with a little water, and cover. Study with low power or use a prepared slide.

The body wall is covered with pinacocytes on the outside and filled with mesohyl that contains amebocytes and spicules. Incurrent pores extend from the external surface directly to the spongocoel, which is lined with flagellated choanocytes. Choanocytes produce the water current and collect food. An osculum serves as an excurrent outlet of the spongocoel. On living specimens, you may be able to see some flagellar activity in the spongocoel.

Leuconoid Type of Canal System
Most sponges are of the leuconoid type and most leuconoids belong to the class Demospongiae (Figures 7-1 and 7-7). Leuconoid sponges have clusters of flagellated chambers lined with choanocytes, and water enters and

Figure 7-5
Skeletal spicules, mostly monaxons, from the cut and dehydrated surface of *Sycon*, SEM about ×480.

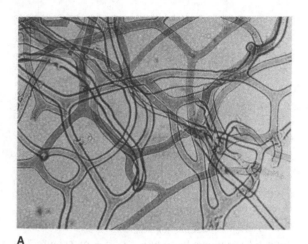
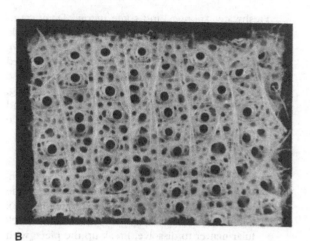

A

B

Figure 7-6

Skeletal elements. **A,** Spongin fibers found in Demospongiae (greatly enlarged). **B,** Portion of wall of sponge *Euplectella* (Hexactinellida), in which the spicules are arranged in a definite pattern (about natural size).

leaves the chambers by systems of incurrent and excurrent canals. Water from the excurrent canals is collected into spongocoels and emptied through the oscula. In large sponges, there may be many oscula. *Spongilla* and *Heteromeyenia,* which are freshwater sponges, and many marine sponges, such as *Halichondria, Microciona, Cliona,* and *Haliclona*—all belonging to Demospongiae—are of the leuconoid type.

 Examine any such sponges available, in both external view and cut sections, to see this type of canal system.

See Appendix A, p. 396, for projects on the preparation of spicule samples and a study of sponge gemmules, including the preparation of permanent mounts of gemmules.

A

B

Figure 7-7

Two leuconoid-type sponges of the class Demospongiae from the Caribbean. **A,** *Aplusina lacunosa,* a tube sponge. **B,** *Spinosella plicifera,* a barrel sponge.

Phylum _____

Subphylum _____

Genus _____

N a m e _____

D a t e _____

S e c t i o n _____

Sycon

External View

**Longitudinal Section
Internal View**

Calcareous Sponge Spicules

LAB REPORT

LAB REPORT

A Segment of a Transverse Section of *Sycon*

Sycon

1. Describe the pathway of water through *Sycon*, naming all canals and openings through which water passes from entrance to exit. _____

    _____

2. What drives the flow of water through the sponge? _____

    Explain how the two forms of reproduction in sponges, sexual and asexual, differ from each other. _____

    _____

3. In what way(s) does a sponge show evolutionary advancement, as compared with a colonial protozoan, such as *Volvox*? _____

    _____

    _____

Other Sponges

The Radiate Animals
Phylum Cnidaria

The two radiate phyla, Cnidaria (ny-dar′e-a) (= Coelenterata) and Ctenophora (te-nof′o-ra) are the most primitive of the eumetazoans—true multicellular animals. They are called radiates because all are radially (or biradially) symmetrical, a form of symmetry in which body parts are arranged concentrically around an oral-aboral axis. They are the simplest animals having a **tissue level of organization,** in which similar cells become aggregated into definite patterns or layers. With minor exceptions, however, tissues of radiates are not organized into organs having specialized functions and thus lack a feature characteristic of all the more complex metazoa.

Still, for all their structural simplicity, the radiates include several successful groups familiar to most people, such as sea anemones, jellyfish, and corals, as well as groups not so familiar, such as hydroids, zoanthids, and comb jellies. Many are brilliantly colored, and one group, the corals, form great tropical coral reefs that harbor a diversity of life rivaled only by tropical rain forests.

Classification
Phylum Cnidaria

EXERCISE 8A

Class Hydrozoa—*Hydra, Obelia,* and *Gonionemus*
Hydra, a solitary hydroid
Obelia, a colonial hydroid
Gonionemus, a hydromedusa
Projects and demonstrations

EXERCISE 8B

Class Scyphozoa—*Aurelia,* a "True" Jellyfish
Aurelia
Demonstrations

EXERCISE 8C

Class Anthozoa—*Metridium,* a Sea Anemone, and *Astrangia,* a Stony Coral
Metridium, a sea anemone
Astrangia, a stony coral
Projects and demonstrations

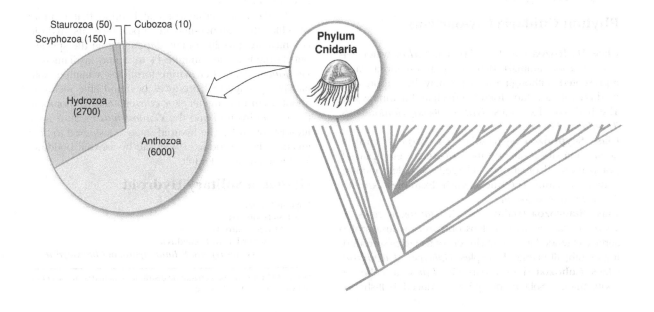

Two important metazoan features shared by all radiates are (1) two embryological primary **germ layers** (ectoderm and endoderm) that are homologous to those of more complex metazoa and (2) internal space for digestion, the **gastrovascular cavity,** which lies along the polar axis and opens to the outside by a mouth.

Some cnidarians have a skeleton (coral, for example), but in most radiates, fluid in the gastrovascular cavity serves as a simple form of **hydrostatic skeleton.**

Although both cnidarians and ctenophores are grouped together as radiate phyla, they differ in important ways. Cnidarians have characteristic stinging organelles (cnidocytes), usually absent in ctenophores. **Polymorphism**—the presence in a species of more than one morphological kind of individual—is common in cnidarians but absent in ctenophores. Ctenophores have distinctive adhesive cells, called **colloblasts,** on their tentacles and unique rows of ciliated comb plates not found in other phyla. However, because ctenophores are not readily available, that phylum will not be included in the laboratory exercises.

There are two main types of body form in cnidarians—**polyp** (hydroid) form, often sessile, and **medusa** (jellyfish) form, which is free-swimming. In some groups of cnidarians, both polyp and medusa stages are found in their life cycle; this is the polymorphic condition. In others, such as sea anemones and corals, there is no medusa; in still others, such as the scyphozoans, or "true" jellyfish, the polyp stage is reduced or absent. In life cycles having both polyps and medusae, the juvenile polyp stage gives rise asexually to a medusa, which reproduces sexually. Both polyp and medusa have the diploid number of chromosomes, but the gametes are haploid.

Classification

Phylum Cnidaria (ny-dar′e-a)

Class Hydrozoa (hy-dro-zo′a) (Gr. *hydra,* water serpent, + *zōon,* animal). Both polyp and medusa stages represented, although one type may be suppressed; medusa with a velum; found in fresh and marine water. The hydroids. Examples: *Hydra, Obelia, Gonionemus, Tubularia, Physalia.*
Class Scyphozoa (sy-fo-zo′a) (Gr. *skyphos,* cup, + *zōon,* animal). Solitary; medusa stage emphasized; polyp reduced or absent; enlarged mesoglea; medusa without a velum. The true jellyfish. Examples: *Aurelia, Rhizostoma, Cassiopeia.*
Class Staurozoa (sta′ro-zo′a) Gr. *stauros,* a cross, + *zōon,* animal). Solitary, polyps only, no medusa; polyp surface extended into eight clusters of tentacles surrounding mouth; all marine. Examples: *Haliclystis, Lucernaria.*
Class Cubozoa (ku′bo-zo′a) Gr. *kybos,* a cube, + *zōon,* animal). Solitary; polyp stage reduced; bell-shaped

medusae square in cross section, with a tentacle or group of tentacles at each corner; margin without velum but with velarium; all marine. Examples: *Carybdea, Chironex.*
Class Anthozoa (an-tho-zo′a) (Gr. *anthos,* flower, + *zōon,* animal). All polyps, no medusae; gastrovascular cavity subdivided by mesenteries (septa).
  Subclass Hexacorallia (hek-sa-ko-ral′e-a) (Gr. *hex,* six, + *korallion,* coral) **(Zoantharia).** Polyp with simple, unbranched tentacles; septal arrangement hexamerous; skeleton, when present, external. Sea anemones and stony corals. Examples: *Metridium, Tealia, Astrangia.*
  Subclass Ceriantipatharia (se-re-an-tip′a-tha′ri-a) (N. L. combination of Ceriantharia and Antipatharia, from type genera). With simple, unbranched tentacles; mesenteries unpaired. Tube anemones and black or thorny corals. Examples: *Cerianthus, Antipathes.*

  Subclass Octocorallia (ok′to-ko-ral′e-a) (L. *octo,* + Gr. *korallion,* coral) **(Alcyonaria).** Polyp with eight pinnate tentacles; septal arrangement octamerous. Soft and horny corals. Examples: *Gorgonia, Renilla, Alcyonium.*

EXERCISE 8A

Class Hydrozoa—*Hydra, Obelia, and Gonionemus*

Three hydrozoan forms are traditionally used as examples of class Hydrozoa. Freshwater hydras are easily available, are conveniently large (2 to 25 mm in length), and can be studied alive. Hydras are solitary polyp forms, but they are atypical of the class because they have no medusa stage.

Obelia is a marine colonial hydroid that is more plantlike than animal-like in appearance. Its hydroid colonies are 2 to 20 cm tall, depending on the species, but its medusae are minute (1 to 2 mm in diameter). *Gonionemus,* another marine form, has a minute, solitary polyp stage that produces beautiful little medusae about 2 cm in diameter. For convenience we combine the *Obelia* hydroid and the *Gonionemus* medusa for a life-history study. The hydroid stage, considered to be a juvenile stage, produces medusae by asexual budding. Medusae are sexual adults.

Hydra, a Solitary Hydroid

Phylum Cnidaria
  Class Hydrozoa
    Order Hydroida
      Suborder Anthomedusae
        Genus *Hydra, Pelmatohydra,* or *Chlorohydra**

*See p. 397 for notes on geographic distribution of hydra and selection of hydra species for class use.

Where Found

Hydra (Gr., a mythical nine-headed monster slain by Hercules) is the common name applied to any of about 16 species known to occur in North America. Species commonly provided for zoology classes are brown hydras, *Hydra littoralis* (eastern United States); false brown hydra, *Pelmatohydra pseudoligactis* (central North America); and green hydras, *Chlorohydra viridissima* (widely distributed in North America). Hydras are found in pools, quiet streams, and spring ponds, usually on the underside of leaves of aquatic vegetation, especially lily pads. To collect hydras, bring in some aquatic plants with plenty of pond water and place in a clean jar or an aquarium. In a day or so, hydras, if present, may be seen attached to the plants or to sides of the jar.

Behavior

 Place a live hydra in a drop of culture water on a depression slide or watch glass. Examine with a hand lens or dissecting microscope. Answer the questions in this section.

The hydra may be contracted at first. Watch it as it recovers from the shock of transfer. Does it have great powers of contraction and expansion? _____ How long is it when fully extended? _____ How many **tentacles** does it have? _____ Compare with other specimens at your table. Do the tentacles move about? _____ Touch one with the tip of a dissecting needle or fine artist's brush and watch its reaction. What parts of the animal are most sensitive to touch? _____ After a quiet period, when the animal is extended, tap the watch glass and note what happens. _____

The elevated area surrounded by tentacles is called the **hypostome** (Gr. *hypo,* under, + *stoma,* mouth) and bears the **mouth.** Does your hydra have any **buds** or **gonads?** _____ Does it attach itself to the glass by its **basal disc?** _____ Does it move about in the dish? _____ How?

_____

The warty appearance of the tentacles is caused by clusters of special cells, or **cnidocytes,** which contain the stinging organelles, called **nematocysts.**

Symbionts of Hydra. Small ciliated protozoans, such as *Kerona* or *Trichodina,* are sometimes seen gliding over the body and tentacles of the hydra, where they apparently do little harm.

Common green hydras *Chlorohydra viridissima* take their color from symbiotic algae, called zoochlorellae, that live in their cells.

Feeding and Digestion. To observe the feeding reaction of hydra, do the following:

 Add to the hydra culture on your slide a drop of water containing *Artemia* larvae (thoroughly washed to remove salt) or other suitable food organisms, such as *Daphnia* or enchytreid worms.

How does the hydra react to the presence of food? _____ How does it capture prey? _____ Does the prey struggle to escape? _____ When does the prey stop moving—before it is eaten or after? _____ What is the reaction of the hypostome? _____ How long does the feeding reaction take? _____ How does the hydra act when its appetite has been satisfied?

_____

If food is not available, or if the hydra will not eat, your instructor may want to demonstrate the feeding reaction by adding a little reduced **glutathione** (0.03 g/l) to a watch glass containing some hydras. Glutathione is found in living cells. It is released, in certain of the hydra's prey, from the wounds made by nematocysts. It stimulates the hydra to open its mouth and secrete mucus to aid in the swallowing process.

Some digestion occurs within the **gastrovascular** cavity, into which gland cells secrete digestive enzymes **(extracellular digestion).** Food particles are then engulfed by cells of the gastrodermis, in which digestion is completed **(intracellular digestion).** Indigestible materials must be regurgitated because there is no anus.

Written Report

 On separate paper record any feeding reactions you have observed, using notes and sketches.

External Structure

 Place a live hydra on a slide with some culture water, put short (1 cm) pieces of coarse thread on either side of it, and cover with a coverslip, or use a depression slide, if you prefer.

Note the cylindrical body. A conical **hypostome** is at the oral end and bears a **mouth** surrounded by 6 to 10 **tentacles** (Figure 8-1). The basal, or aboral, end secretes a sticky substance for attachment. Can you make out the outline of the **gastrovascular cavity** by focusing up and down? Is there an anal opening? _____ What kind of symmetry does the hydra have? _____ How does hydra's symmetry compare with that of a sponge?

_____

Cnidocytes. Examine the tentacles closely on the live specimen and note little, wartlike elevations. These are areas containing groups, or batteries, of specialized cells called **cnidocytes** (ni'dō-sīt; Gr. *knidē,* nettle, + *kytos,* hollow vessel), each of which encloses a stinging

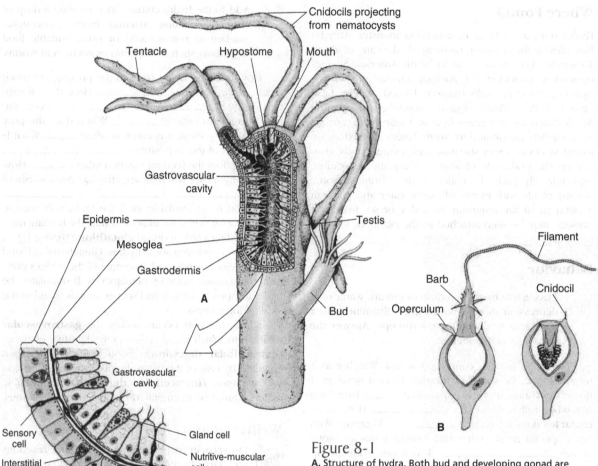

Figure 8-1

A, Structure of hydra. Both bud and developing gonad are shown, but in early life they rarely develop simultaneously. **B,** Cnidocytes with discharged *(left)* and undischarged *(right)* nematocysts. **C,** Diagrammatic cross section of a portion of the body wall.

organelle called a **nematocyst** (ne-mat′o-cyst). A nematocyst (Gr. *nēma,* thread, + *kystis,* bladder) is a tiny capsule containing a coiled, threadlike, tubular filament that can be everted. Focus on a battery of cnidocytes on the edge of a tentacle. Do you see tiny, projecting, hairlike "triggers" called **cnidocils?** A cnidocil (nī′dō-sil; Gr. *knidē,* nettle, + L. *cilium,* hair) is a modified cilium and seems to be involved in the discharge of the nematocyst. However, chemical stimulation (as from food) is necessary to lower the threshold before a cnidocil can be stimulated by contact. A hydra may discharge a quarter of its nematocysts during food capture but regenerates all within about 2 days.

Are there as many cnidocytes on the body as on the tentacles? _____ Why? _____ Are there any on the basal disc? _____

 Now add a drop of Bouin's fluid to the slide at the edge of the coverslip and draw it under by touching the water at the opposite side with a piece of filter paper. This will cause nematocysts to be discharged and will lightly stain the cells. Examine discharged nematocysts under high power with subdued light.

There are four kinds of nematocysts in hydras. The largest and most striking type is equipped with **barbs** near the base of a long, hollow **thread** (Figure 8-1B). **Hypnotoxin,** a poison that penetrates and paralyzes prey, is discharged through the hollow thread. The other kinds of nematocysts are smaller and are specialized for adhesion and entanglement.

Cross Section, Stained Slide

 Study a prepared stained slide of a cross section of the body. Examine under both low and high power.

Note that the body wall is made up of two layers of cells, an outer **epidermis** (derived from what germ layer? _____) and an inner **gastrodermis** (derived from what germ layer? _____), separated by a thin, noncellular layer, the **mesoglea** (mez'o-glee'a; Gr. *mesos*, middle, + *glia*, glue) (Figure 8-1C). Hydras are **diploblastic**, being derived from two germ layers, ectoderm and endoderm. How many germ layers do sponges have? _____

Epidermis. Most cells in the epidermal layer are **epitheliomuscular cells** (Figure 8-1C). These are medium-size cells with darkly stained nuclei that cover the body and are used for muscular contraction. Are these cuboidal or squamous cells? _____ Their inner ends are drawn out into slender, contractile fibers that run longitudinally in the mesoglea and make possible rapid contraction of the hydra's body and/or tentacles. Contractile fibers are closely associated with the **nerve net**, which also lies just beneath the epidermal layer. Now look for occasional cnidocytes containing spindle-like **nematocysts**. At the bases of the epitheliomuscular cells may be found some small, dark **interstitial cells**. These are embryonic cells that can transform into the other kinds of cells when needed. **Gland cells** secrete mucus onto the body surface, particularly around the mouth and basal disc.

Mesoglea. This noncellular layer, lying between epidermis and gastrodermis, extends over both body and tentacles of hydra as an elastic "skeleton," providing increased flexibility to the animal. It is very thin in hydroid polyps.

Gastrodermis. The **gastrodermis** layer is made up principally of ciliated columnar **nutritive-muscular cells** (Figure 8-1C). The cilia create currents in the gastrovascular cavity. Contractile fibers at the base of the cells form a muscle layer around the body. When these contract, the hydra becomes longer and thinner. The gastrodermis may give the appearance of two layers of cells because the outer part of the cells contain large, fluid-filled vacuoles, and the free ends of the cells contain food vacuoles formed by food engulfed by pseudopodia (phagocytosis). Intracellular digestion occurs in the nutritive-muscular cells. Gland cells discharge enzymes into the gastrovascular cavity, where extracellular digestion occurs. There are small interstitial cells at the bases of the other cells. What types of cells are common to both layers of the body wall? _____

How does digestion in the hydra compare with that in the sponge? _____
Does the sponge have intracellular or extracellular digestion? _____

Sensory cells are found in both epidermis and gastrodermis but would be difficult to identify.

Reproduction

Asexual. Budding is the asexual method of reproduction. A part of the body wall grows out as a hollow outgrowth, or bud, that lengthens and develops tentacles and a mouth at its distal end. Eventually the bud constricts at its basal end and breaks off from the parent. Buds may be found on live hydras.

 On a stained slide showing a budding hydra, study the relation of the bud to the parent. Note that the gastrovascular cavities of the two are continuous and that both layers of the parent wall extend into the bud.

Sexual. Some species are **monoecious** (mow-nee'shus; Gr. *monos*, single, + *oikos*, house), having both testes and ovaries; other species having separate male and female sexes are **dioecious** (di-ee'shus; Gr. *di*, two, + *oikos*, house). Sex organs develop in the epidermis (from the interstitial cells) of a localized region of the body column. Do sponges also have both asexual and sexual reproduction? _____

 Examine stained slides showing testes (spermaries) and ovaries.

Testes, small outgrowths containing many spermatozoa, are found toward the oral end; the single **ovary** is a large, rounded elevation nearer the basal end. The ovary produces a large ripe **egg** (Figure 8-2), which breaks out and lies free on the surface. **Spermatozoa** break out of the testis wall, pass to the egg, and fertilize it in position. The **zygote** so formed undergoes several stages of development before dropping off the parent.

Drawings

 On separate paper, sketch a budding hydra and specimens that show testes (spermaries) and ovaries.

Obelia, a Colonial Hydroid

Phylum Cnidaria
  Class Hydrozoa
    Order Hydroida
      Suborder Leptomedusae
        Genus *Obelia*

Where Found

Obelia (Gr. *obelias*, round cake) is one of many colonial hydroids found in marine waters and attached to seaweeds, rocks, shells, and other objects. Its minute medusae make up part of the marine plankton.

Life History

The life history of *Obelia* includes both polyp (hydroid) and medusa (jellyfish) stages (Figure 8-3). A hydroid colony arises from a free-swimming **planula** larva, which settles and attaches to a substratum. Then, by budding, a colony is formed. The colony includes two kinds of polyps (also called zooids): nutritive polyps called **hydranths** (Gr. *hydōr*, water, + *anthos*, flower)

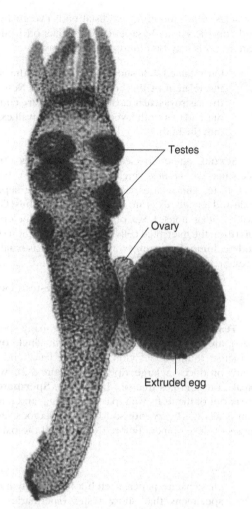

Testes

Ovary

Extruded egg

Figure 8-2

Hydra with five testes and large egg lying over the ovary from which it was recently extruded.

and reproductive polyps called **gonangia** (sing. **gonangium;** N.L. *gonas,* primary sex organ, + *angeion,* dim. of vessel). Medusa buds produced in gonangia break away to become free-swimming **medusae** (jellyfish). Medusae are dioecious. When each sex is mature, the medusa discharges its gametes into the surrounding water, where fertilization occurs. The zygote develops into a planula larva, which attaches to a substratum, and the cycle is repeated. Thus, medusae give rise sexually to asexual hydroid colonies, which in turn produce medusae.

Obelia has a macroscopic hydroid stage, but its medusa stage is microscopic. Another hydrozoan form, *Gonionemus,* has a similar life history, but its medusa is fairly large and its hydroid colony inconspicuous. To illustrate the life cycle, polyps of *Obelia* and medusae of *Gonionemus* are convenient.

The Hydroid Colony—Behavior

If living colonies of any hydroid species are available, examine them in fresh seawater under low power.

Allow time for some of the tentacled hydranths to extend their tentacles. Determine their reaction to gentle localized touch. They may be fed *Artemia* larvae and the feeding reaction observed, as in the hydra.

Written Report

Make notes or sketches on separate paper.

Study of a Preserved Colony

Place a small piece of marine algae with attached *Obelia* colonies in a watch glass of water and observe with dissecting microscope.

Colonies resemble tiny plants attached to the seaweed by rootlike **hydrorhiza** (Gr. *hydōr,* water, + *rhiza,* root). From the hydrorhiza arises the main stem, the **hydrocaulus** (Gr. *hydōr,* water, + L. *caulis,* stalk), which gives rise to many lateral branches (Figure 8-3). On these branches are found two kinds of polyps: nutritive **hydranths** and reproductive **gonangia.** Hydranths can be recognized by their vase shape and the tentacles at their free ends; gonangia by their elongated club shape and lack of tentacles. Are hydranths or gonangia more numerous? _____ Note where the different individuals occur on the hydrocaulus. Budding polyps may also be found on your specimen. Buds are usually small and lack tentacles. Note that the entire colony is encased in a thin, transparent, protective **perisarc,** secreted by the epidermis.

Study of a Stained Slide

Study a stained slide of *Obelia* and compare with the preserved colony and with any living colony you may have examined. Use low power of the compound microscope.

Examine the hydrocaulus. Its inner protoplasmic part is the **coenosarc** (sē'nō-sark; Gr. *koinos,* shared, + *sarx,* flesh), a hollow tube composed, like the hydra, of **epidermis, mesoglea,** and **gastrodermis.** It encloses a **gastrovascular cavity** that is continuous throughout the colony. Surrounding this living part is a transparent, nonliving perisarc (Figure 8-3).

Each nutritive polyp, or hydranth, is continuous with the coenosarc. A transparent extension of the perisarc, the **hydrotheca** (Gr. *hydōr,* water, + L. *theca,* encased), forms a protective cup around the hydranth.

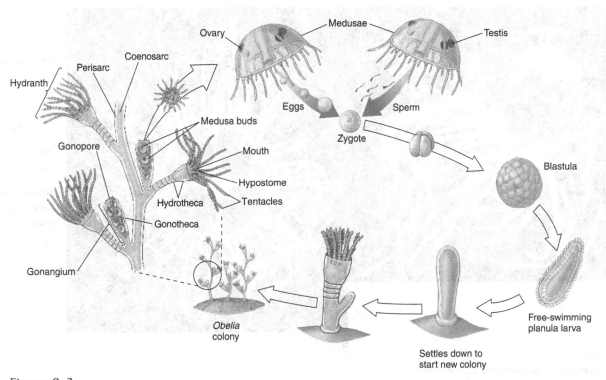

Figure 8-3

Obelia life cycle, showing alternation of polyp (asexual) and medusa (sexual) stages. In *Obelia* both its polyps and stems are protected by continuations of the perisarc. In some hydroids, only the stems are so protected.

Each hydranth has an elevated **hypostome** terminating in a **mouth** and bearing a circle of **tentacles** around the base. Each tentacle has in its epidermis rings of swellings caused by clusters of **cnidocytes,** which bear the **nematocysts.** Trace the continuous **gastrovascular cavity** from the hydranth through the branches and stem of the hydrocaulus. Food taken by the hydranths can thus pass to every part of the colony.

Reproductive **gonangia** are club-shaped and arise at the junction of the hydranth and coenosarc. Each gonangium is made up of a hollow continuation of the coenosarc called the **blastostyle** (Gr. *blastos,* bud, + *stylos,* pillar). A number of saucer-shaped **medusa buds** arise from the blastostyle by transverse budding and develop into mature **medusae.** Where are the most mature buds located? _____ The transparent **gonotheca** (Gr. *gonos,* progeny, birth, + *thēcē,* cup) around the blastostyle is a modification of the perisarc. Young medusae escape through the opening, or **gonopore,** at its distal end.

Gonionemus, a Hydromedusa

Phylum Cnidaria
   Class Hydrozoa
      Order Hydroida
         Suborder Limnomedusae
           Genus *Gonionemus*

Where Found

Gonionemus[*] is a marine medusoid species found mainly in shallow protected coastal and bay areas along both coasts of the United States. Hydrozoan medusae are often called **hydromedusae,** as distinguished from the usually larger **scyphomedusae,** or jellyfish of the class Scyphozoa. *Gonionemus* has a minute polyp stage in its life history.

Behavior

 If living hydromedusae (freshwater *Craspedacusta,* marine *Gonionemus,* or others) are available, watch their movements.

Note the pulsating contractions that force water from the underside of the umbrella (subumbrella) and so propel the animal by a feeble "jet propulsion" (Figure 8-4A). Can they change direction? _____ How? _____ Does the animal swim continuously, or does it float sometimes? _____ What happens if a tentacle is touched? _____ Feeding reactions differ with different species. Some

_____

[*]The name *Gonionemus,* meaning "angled thread," refers to the tentacles that appear to bend as though jointed when the animal swims with its pulsed contractions (see Figure 8-4A).

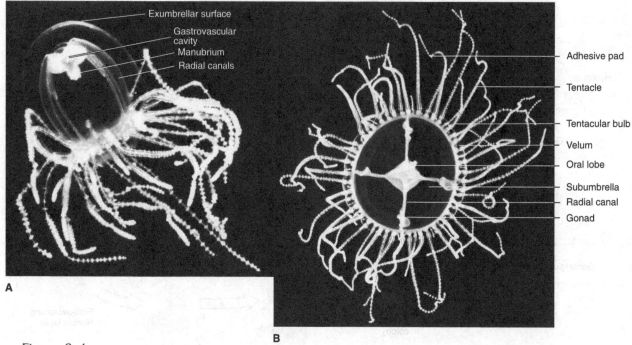

Figure 8-4
Gonionemus. **A,** Swimming. **B,** Oral view.

apparently depend on chance contact with food; others, such as *Gonionemus,* swim to the surface and then turn over and float downward with tentacles spread in search of food. *Gonionemus* is often found moving slowly about among marine algae and sea grass. If algae is present in the aquarium with *Gonionemus,* note how it uses its tentacles to move about. How does it use the adhesive pads on the tentacles? _____
_____

Written Report

 Record your observations on separate paper.

General Structure

 Place a preserved *Gonionemus* in a small dish filled with water. Examine with a hand lens. It is fragile, so do not grasp with forceps. Orient it by lifting or pushing with a blunt instrument.

The convex outer (aboral) surface is called the **exumbrella;** the concave (oral) surface is the **subumbrella.** Each of the **tentacles** around the margin of the bell bears rings of **cnidocytes,** an **adhesive pad** near its distal end, and a pigmented **tentacular bulb** at its base (Figure 8-4B). Tentacular bulbs make and store

nematocysts, help in intracellular digestion, and act as sensory organs. Between the bases of the tentacles are tiny **statocysts** (Gr. *statos,* stationary, + *kystis,* bladder), considered to be organs of equilibrium. They are little sacs containing calcareous concretions. You will need low power of a compound microscope to see them.

Now look at the subumbrellar surface. Around the margin, find a circular, shelflike membrane, the **velum** (L., veil, covering). The velum is characteristic of hydromedusae and is absent in "true" jellyfish of class Scyphozoa. Medusae move by a form of jet propulsion, forcing water out of the subumbrellar cavity by muscular contractions, thus propelling the animals in the opposite direction.

Note the **manubrium** (L., handle) suspended from the central surface of the subumbrellar cavity. At its distal end is the **mouth,** with four liplike **oral lobes** around it.

The **gastrovascular cavity** includes the **gullet,** the **stomach** at the base of the manubrium, four **radial canals** extending to the margin, and a **ring canal** around the margin.

Note the convoluted **gonads** suspended under each of the radial canals. The sexes look alike and can be determined only by microscopic inspection of the gonadal contents.

The medusa has the same cell layers as the hydroid or polyp form. All surface areas are covered with **epidermis,** the **gastrodermis** lines the entire gastrovascular cavity, and between these two layers is the jellylike **mesoglea,** which is much thicker in the medusa than in the hydroid form.

Drawings

 On p. 131, label the diagrammatic drawing of an oral-aboral section through *Gonionemus.*

Projects and Demonstrations

1. *Portuguese man-of-war (Physalia pelagica).* The Portuguese man-of-war illustrates the highest degree of **polymorphism** among cnidarians, for several types of individuals are found in the same colony.

Study a preserved specimen. Note the **pneumatophore** (Gr. *pneuma,* air, + *pherein,* to bear), or bladder. What is its function? _____
Suspended from the pneumatophore are many zooids (polyps) that have budded from it. Two kinds of polyp individuals are the feeding polyps (gastrozooids) and fishing polyps (dactylozooids), which are equipped with long, stinging tentacles. Male and female gonophores are modified medusoid individuals that remain attached as buds, producing eggs and sperm.

2. *Obelia.* Examine some medusae of *Obelia.*

3. *Various colonial hydroids.* Examine forms of colonial hydroids, such as *Eudendrium, Tubularia, Pennaria, Sertularia,* or *Bougainvillia,* either preserved or on slides.

NOTES

Phylum _____

Subphylum _____

Genus _____

N a m e _____

D a t e _____

S e c t i o n _____

Hydra

1. What is meant by the term "polymorphism"? _____
   Is hydra polymorphic? _____

2. Describe feeding and digestion in hydras, explaining how extracellular digestion differs from intracellular.
   _____
   _____
   What is the function of nutritive-muscular cells? _____

3. How does hydra respire? _____
   How does hydra excrete nitrogenous wastes? _____

4. Cnidarians are "diploblastic." What does this term mean? _____

5. Describe and contrast sexual and asexual reproduction in hydra. _____
   _____
   Is the species of hydra you used for behavioral observations monoecious or dioecious? _____

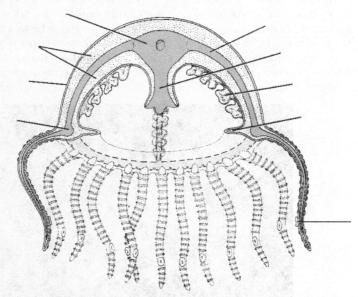

Gonionemus. Diagrammatic oral-aboral section—to be labeled.

EXERCISE 8B

Class Scyphozoa—*Aurelia,* a "True" Jellyfish

Aurelia

Phylum Cnidaria
   Class Scyphozoa
      Order Semaeostomeae
         Family Ulmaridae
            Species *Aurelia aurita*

Where Found

Aurelia aurita, the "moon jelly," is common along both coasts of North America. It is a cosmopolitan species distributed from temperate and tropical to subpolar latitudes.

Aurelia (L. *aurum,* gold) is a scyphozoan (sy-fo-zo'an) medusa (often referred to as a scyphomedusa). Scyphomedusae are generally larger than hydrozoan medusae (hydromedusae); most of them range from 2 to 40 cm, but some reach as much as 2 m or more in diameter. The jelly layers (mesoglea) are thicker and contain cellular materials, giving scyphomedusae a firmer consistency than hydromedusae. Nevertheless, all jellyfish are largely water (94% to 96% water in marine species, such as *Aurelia,* and up to 99% water in some freshwater hydromedusae) and active tissues are mostly epithelial.

Scyphozoans are often called "true" jellyfish. Scyphomedusae are constructed along a plan similar to that of hydromedusae, but they lack a velum. Their parts are arranged symmetrically around the oral-aboral axis, usually in fours or multiples of four, so they are said to have **tetramerous** radial symmetry. Their gastrovascular systems have more canals and more modifications than those of hydrozoans.

The large size and fiery nematocysts of many jellyfish make them disagreeable and sometimes dangerous to swimmers. One of these is *Cyanea capillata,* the "lion's mane jellyfish" of the North Atlantic. Even more dangerous is the cubomedusan *Chironex fleckeri,* sea wasp of the Australian region. This jellyfish has caused numerous fatalities in Australia; deaths occur rapidly from anaphylactic shock.

Behavior

If living *Aurelia* or other scyphozoan genera are available, observe their swimming movements (Figure 8-5).

How is movement achieved? _____ Are they strong swimmers? _____ How many times per minute does the medusa pulsate? _____ Does it swim horizontally or vertically? _____ Use a gentle touch with a small artist's brush to test reaction to touch. To test response to food chemicals, dip the brush into glucose solution, clam or oyster juice, or other food substances; small crustaceans or other small food organisms may be placed near their tentacles.

Written Report

Record your observations on separate paper.

General Structure

Using a ladle (the medusa is too fragile to be handled with a forceps), transfer a preserved specimen of *Aurelia* to a finger bowl of water and spread out flat.

Note that *Aurelia* is more discoidal and less cup-shaped than *Gonionemus.* When spread flat, the jellyfish shows a circular shape broken at eight regular intervals by marginal notches (Figure 8-5). Each marginal notch contains a **rhopalium** (ro-pay'li-um; N.L. from Gr. *rhopalon,* a club), a sense organ consisting of a statocyst

Figure 8-5
Swimming *Aurelia aurita.*

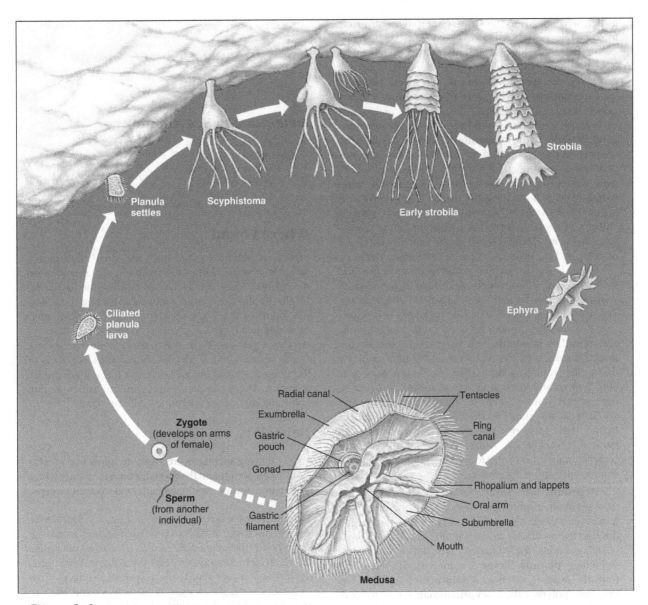

Figure 8-6
Life cycle of *Aurelia*, a marine scyphozoan medusa.

and an ocellus. This is flanked on each side by a marginal extension, the **lappet** (Figures 8-5 and 8-6). What is the function of a statocyst? _____ An ocellus? _____

Snip out a rhopalium* with scissors and examine under the higher power of a dissecting microscope.

In living medusae, the excision of all rhopalia would interfere with swimming, either slowing down the contractions or stopping them altogether.

Note the short **tentacles** that form a fringe around the animal's margin. Compare these tentacles with those of *Gonionemus* medusae. How do they differ?

_____

Gastrovascular System. In the center of the oral side are four long, troughlike **oral arms.** These are modifications of the manubrium. Note that the oral arms converge toward the center of the animal, where the square **mouth** is located. The mouth opens into a short

---

*The specific epithet *aurita* of the species *Aurelia aurita* means "eared," probably in reference to the lobelike rhopalia.

gullet, which leads to the **stomach.** From the stomach, four **gastric pouches** extend. They can be identified by the horseshoe-shaped **gonads** that lie within them. Near the inner edges of the gonads are numerous thin processes, the **gastric filaments,** which are provided with **nematocysts.** What would be the use of stinging cells here? _____ On the oral side of each gastric pouch is a round aperture that leads into a blind depression, the **subgenital** pit. These pits have no connection with the gonads or gastric pouches and may be respiratory in function. A complicated system of radiating canals runs from the gastric pouches to the **ring canal,** which follows the outer margin (Figure 8-6). This system of stomach and canals, resembling hub, spokes, and rim of a wheel, forms the medusoid gut, or gastrovascular cavity. Contrast this with the simple, saclike gut of polyp individuals such as hydra or *Obelia* polyps.

Jellyfish are carnivorous, most feeding on fish and a variety of marine invertebrates. *Aurelia,* however, is a suspension feeder that feeds largely on zooplankton. The tentacles are not used in food capture. Food organisms are caught in mucus secreted on the subumbrella and moved by cilia to the bell margin. Food is collected from the margin by the oral arms and is transferred by cilia to the stomach. Gastric filaments with nematocysts help pull in and subdue larger organisms and secrete digestive enzymes. Partially digested food and seawater are then circulated by cilia through the system of canals. In this way, nutrients and oxygen are carried to all parts of the body. The canals are lined with cells that complete digestion of the food. Thus, digestion is both extracellular and intracellular.

Reproduction. Sexes are separate in *Aurelia,* as they are in all scyphozoans. Sex cells are shed from the gonads into the gastrovascular cavity and are discharged through the mouth for external fertilization. Within folds of the oral arms, the young embryos develop into free-swimming **planula larvae** (Figure 8-6). These escape from the parent, attach to a substratum, and develop into tiny polyps called **scyphistomae** (sy-fis'to-mee; Gr. *skyphos,* cup, + *stoma,* mouth). The scyphistoma later becomes a **strobila,** which begins to bud off young medusae (**ephyrae** [Gr. *Ephyra,* Greek city, in reference to castlelike appearance]) in layers resembling a stack of saucers (Figure 8-6). This budding process is called **strobilation** (Gr. *strobilos,* pinecone).

Demonstrations

1. *Slides.* Examine slides showing stages in the life cycle of *Aurelia*—scyphistoma, strobila, and ephyra.

2. *Scyphozoan jellyfish.* Examine various species of preserved scyphozoans or, if available, living specimens of the "upside-down" jellyfish *Cassiopeia* (see p. 398 for additional information).

EXERCISE 8C

Class Anthozoa—*Metridium,* a Sea Anemone, and *Astrangia,* a Stony Coral

Metridium, a Sea Anemone

Phylum Cnidaria
  Class Anthozoa
    Subclass Hexacorallia
      Order Actiniaria
        Genus *Metridium*
          Species *Metridium senile*

Where Found

Metridium senile, a name from the Greek that means "ancient womb," is the most common sea anemone on the Atlantic Coast from Delaware north to the Arctic and on the Pacific Coast from Santa Catalina Island, California, north to the polar seas. It occurs from low intertidal, where it is commonly seen on rocks and pilings, to depths of perhaps 75 m. Most sea anemones are solitary sessile animals and do not live in colonies. Members of the class Anthozoa are all polyps in form; there are no medusae. There is a great variety in size, structure, and color among the sea anemones. All are marine.

Behavior

 If living anemones are available, allow one to relax completely and then touch a tentacle lightly with a new (untouched) coverslip held in clean forceps.

Do the nematocysts discharge? _____ Will nematocysts discharge if the coverslip is touched more vigorously to the tentacle? _____ Now put some saliva (which contains protein) on a dry coverslip and again touch a tentacle. Is the response stronger? Why? _____ Discharged nematocysts should stick to the glass and may be examined under the microscope.

Using another relaxed anemone, drop bits of clean filter paper on the tentacles and time the type and speed of the response. Now test with bits of filter paper soaked in shrimp, clam, or mussel juice and compare the reactions. Test again with bits of clam or other sea food. What conclusions can you draw from this simple experiment? _____

Is response to food similar to response to touch? _____ Is the reaction of these animals a part of the normal feeding reaction? _____ If live sea stars are available, try touching an anemone with the arm of a star. What happens? Is this a feeding response or a defense reaction? _____ Some anemones react to certain predatory stars by detaching their pedal discs and moving away from the star.

Use a glass rod to probe the pedal disc. What happens? _____ If you prod the animal vigorously, it will shoot out white, threadlike **acontia** (a-con′she-a; Gr. *akontion*, dart), which are filled with nematocysts used for defense.

Place an acontium thread on a slide, cover with a coverslip, and examine with a microscope. Do the acontia move? _____ Examine the edge of an acontium with high power. What do you see that might explain acontia movement? _____

For a dramatic demonstration of nematocysts in action, draw some methyl green under the coverslip using a piece of filter paper touched to the opposite edge of the coverslip. Viewed at high power, the undischarged nematocysts in the acontia look like grains of long rice. What happens when they discharge?

Written Report

Record your observations on separate paper.

External Structure

Place a preserved specimen in a dissecting pan. Note the sturdy nature of its body structures compared with those of other cnidarians you have studied.

The **body** is cylindrical (Figure 8-7), but in preserved specimens it may be somewhat wrinkled. Note that the body of the animal can be divided into three main regions: (1) **oral disc,** or free end, with numerous conical **tentacles** and **mouth;** (2) cylindrical **column,** forming the main body of the organism; and (3) **basal disc** (aboral end), by which during life the animal attaches itself to a solid object by means of its glandular secretions. Although it is called a sessile animal, a sea anemone can glide slowly on its basal disc.

Is there more than one row of tentacles? _____ Note that the inner surface of the mouth is lined with ridges and that a smooth-surfaced, ciliated groove, the **siphonoglyph** (sy-fun′o-glif; Gr. *siphōn*, tube, siphon, + *glyphē*, carving), is found at one side of the mouth. (In some specimens, there are two of these grooves.) Siphonoglyphs, aided by cilia, circulate water throughout the gastrovascular cavity. The mouth is separated from the nearest tentacles by a smooth space, the **peristome** (Gr. *peri*, around, + *stoma*, mouth).

Note the tough outer covering **(epidermis)** of the specimen. Small pores on tiny papillae are scattered over the epidermis, but they are hard to find.

Internal Structure

Study of internal anatomy is best made by comparing two sections, one cut longitudinally through the animal and a second cut transversely. Study first one and then the other of these two sections

Figure 8-7
Structure of a sea anemone. The free edges of the septa and the acontia threads are equipped with nematocysts to complete the paralysis begun by the tentacles.

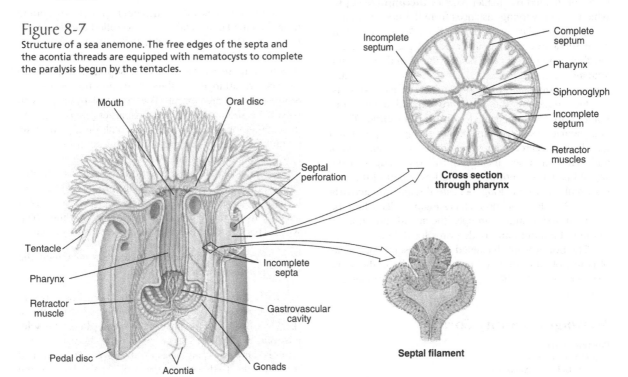

to understand the general relations of the animal. Determine through what part of the animal the transverse section was made.

Look at the longitudinal sections and note that the **mouth** opens into a **pharynx** (fair′inks; Gr. *pharynx,* gullet) (Figure 8-7), which extends down only part way in the body to where it opens into the large **gastrovascular cavity.** Thus, the upper half of the body appears as a tube within a tube; the outer tube is the **body wall,** and the inner tube is the pharynx. Look at the cross section and determine these relations. Notice that not only is the gastrovascular cavity the space aboral to the pharynx, but it also extends upward to surround the pharynx.

The gastrovascular cavity is subdivided into six **radial chambers** by six pairs of **primary** (complete) **septa,** which run from the oral to the aboral end. In the gullet region, these primary septa extend from the body wall to the pharynx; aboral to the pharynx, their inner degree are free in the gastrovascular cavity (Figure 8-7). Are they the same width throughout their length? _____ Examine transverse sections to determine this. Note that chambers formed by primary septa in the pharynx region communicate with each other through **septal perforations.** Find these perforations next to the pharynx near the oral end. Note the longitudinal retractor muscles on the complete septa, which, together with muscles in the body wall, enable the anemone to contract when disturbed.

Now notice that these six larger chambers are partially subdivided by smaller pairs of **incomplete septa,** which extend varying distances from the body wall into the gastrovascular cavity (Figure 8-7). Are these incomplete septa free at their inner edges? _____ Do they extend from the oral to the aboral end of the animal? _____ Each septum is composed of a double sheet of gastrodermis.

Free edges of the septa are expanded into convoluted thickenings called **septal filaments.** These bear nematocysts (to help subdue struggling prey) and glands that secrete digestive enzymes. In *Metridium* and many other sea anemones, the lower edges of the septal filaments continue into the lower part of the gastrovascular cavity as long, delicate threads, the **acontia** (Figure 8-7). Each acontium has stinging cells; when the sea anemone contracts strongly, the acontia are shot out through the mouth and body pores for defense.

The **gonads** are thickened bands resembling stacks of coins, often orange-red in color, that lie in the septa just peripheral to the septal filaments. Anemones are dioecious.

Astrangia, a Stony Coral

Phylum Cnidaria
 Class Anthozoa
  Subclass Hexacorallia
   Order Scleractinia
    Genus *Astrangia*
     Species *Astrangia danae*

Stony corals resemble small anemones but are usually colonial. Each polyp secretes a protective calcareous cup, into which the polyp partly withdraws when disturbed. Some corals form colonies consisting of millions of individuals, each new individual building its skeleton upon the skeletons of dead ones, thus forming, over many years, great coral reefs. Reef-building corals build only in tropical or subtropical waters, where the water temperature stays at or above 21° C.

Astrangia (Gr. *astron,* star, + *angeion,* vessel), known as the star coral, is our only shallow-water northern coral. It occurs on the Atlantic and Gulf coasts locally from Florida north to Cape Cod. It does not build reefs but forms small colonies of 5 to 30 individuals encrusted on rocks and shells. Its food consists of small organisms, such as protozoans, hydroids, worms, crustaceans, and various larval forms.

Behavior

The same sort of touching and feeding experiments as suggested for *Metridium* are applicable to corals, making allowance for the smaller size.

Structure

 Examine living or preserved coral polyps.

Note the delicate, transparent polyps extending from the circular skeletal cups, also called corallites (Figure 8-8A). The polyps resemble those of anemones, with a column, an oral disc, and a crown of tentacles. Two dozen or more simple tentacles, supplied with nematocysts, are arranged in three rings around the mouth. Siphonoglyphs are absent. The edges of the septa can usually be seen through the transparent polyp walls. As in sea anemones, stony corals are built on a plan of six or multiples of six (hexamerous). Digestion in the gastrovascular cavity is similar to that of anemones.

Colonies usually arise by budding or division from a single polyp that has been sexually produced. The surface of the colony between skeletal cups is covered by a sheet of living tissue, which is an extension of the polyp walls. This tissue connects all members of the colony.

 Now study a piece of skeleton from which the polyps have been removed.

Each cup (Figure 8-8B) was the home of a polyp, which secreted it. The rim of the cup is called the **theca** (L. *theca,* box), and the base is the **basal plate.** The **sclerosepta,** or radial partitions within the theca, form the same hexamerous pattern as do the septa. They are laid down by the folds of the epidermis at the base of the

A

Figure 8-8
Stony corals. **A,** Living polyps of *Astrangia danae.* **B,** Structure of a coral polyp, diagrammatic.

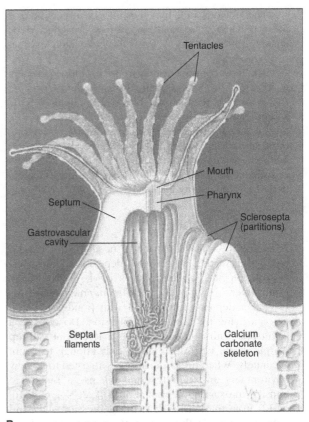

B

polyp. The theca is secreted by the epidermis of the lower part of the column. As the coral polyp grows, the cup tends to fill up with calcium carbonate, so that the theca and sclerosepta are continually extended upward. The entire skeleton is outside the body of the polyp.

Projects and Demonstrations

1. *Various hard coral skeletons.* Examine such skeletons as white corals; red coral, *Corallium;* staghorn coral, *Acropora;* organpipe coral, *Tubipora;* or brain coral, *Meandrina.*

2. *Nematocysts.* Nematocysts may be collected from various live cnidarians. Zoantharian corals (soft corals) usually have fairly large nematocysts, and the little red colonial anemone *Corynactis* is good

for this purpose. Wiping a clean coverslip across the oral disc is likely to attract both discharged and undischarged nematocysts, which can be studied by inverting the coverslip over a drop of seawater on a slide. A good-quality microscope is necessary.

Collect and compare the nematocysts of various hydrozoans, scyphozoans, and anthozoans.

EXPERIMENTING IN ZOOLOGY[1,2]
Predator Functional Response: Feeding Rate in *Hydra*

An important property of the predator-prey relationship is that the behavior of predators often changes as the availability of prey in the environment changes. One aspect of such behavior is known as the **functional response,** in which a predator changes its feeding rate as prey density changes (Hurd and Rathet, 1986). This measure of predation efficiency is important not only to understanding the behavioral ecology of predators but also to evaluating the ability of predators to control pest

populations in biological control programs. The cnidarian, *Hydra,* is unlikely to be a satisfactory candidate for pest control, but it is a good model predator with which to measure functional response.

[1]Materials and method for implementing this exercise are found in Appendix A, p. 399.

[2]This exercise was contributed by Lawrence Hurd, Washington & Lee University.

The obvious null hypothesis to be tested here is the following: Functional response is not affected by changing prey density. What is the most likely alternative hypothesis?

The most convenient prey to use for this experiment is *Artemia,* the brine shrimp. Brown hydra *(Hydra littoralis)* readily feed on the first stage nauplii of brine shrimp but may have trouble capturing later developmental stages as the shrimp increase in size. Therefore, brine shrimp should be hatched no earlier than 1–2 days before they are needed. Functional response rate will be recorded as the number of prey eaten during a 10-minute period as prey density increases.

How to Proceed

Assemble the materials you will need for this experiment: a dissecting microscope, depression slides, disposable pipettes, a Petri dish, a clock or stopwatch, pond water, brown hydra, and *Artemia* nauplii.

Fill a depression slide 2/3 with pond water and place a living hydra in the depression. Do not use a coverslip. With a pipette, place a few brine shrimp nauplii in the Petri dish. Put in only enough to count accurately. When the hydra appears adjusted to its new environment and is fully extended, use a pipette to transfer an exact number of shrimp (1, 2, 3, 4, 6, 8, 10, or 12) from the Petri dish to the depression slide and note the time. At the end of 10 minutes, record the number of shrimp that have been killed by the hydra. Begin with one shrimp for the first trial. Then, with a new hydra, repeat the procedure with two shrimp, then with three, and so on through the series of prey densities, ending with 12 shrimp. *Use a new hydra with each trial.* Add your data to a master sheet for the whole class.

Results and Discussion

The class data represent replicates, so you can calculate the mean and standard deviation for each prey density. Plot x = prey density and y = mean predation rate. How does the functional response of hydra change with increasing prey density? Does the curve level off or continue increasing for each successive prey density? Does the functional response variability, as reflected in the standard deviation, change with changing prey density? Why would results be variable among replicates (different students, different hydra, etc.)? What is the value of replication in such experiments?

Extending the Experiment (Optional)

Other experimental variables to consider might be increased volume of water, which might be expected to slow predation rate by reducing spatial density of brine shrimp and making it easier for the shrimp to avoid being stung. Another variable is the size of the hydra. If budding hydra are available, test them against non-budding specimens to see if feeding rate is influenced by asexual reproduction. Why might you expect this to affect the results? What if the temperature at which you ran the experiment had been higher or lower? Can you design an experiment to test this? Can you think of other variables that might be worth testing?

Written Report

Summarize your findings in a written report organized into introduction, results, and discussion. The introduction should explain the purpose of the study and state the null hypothesis. The results should summarize the data and tell the reader what the data show. Include a table with the class data and a graph showing prey density plotted against mean predation rate. Note that tables and graphs have legends and each table and graph is placed on a separate sheet of paper. In the discussion consider the following: Was your null hypothesis rejected? What does rejection of (or failure to reject) a null hypothesis mean biologically? How does your finding add to what was known?

Reference

Hurd, L. E. and I. H. Rathet. 1986. Functional response and success in juvenile mantids. *Ecology* **7:**163–167.

EXERCISE 9

The Flatworms
Phylum Platyhelminthes

The flatworms are members of the phylum Platyhelminthes (Gr. *platys,* flat, + *helmins,* worm). This large and economically important group contains both free-living forms, such as the common planarians, and parasitic forms, such as tapeworms and flukes. They are more complex in organization than the radiate animals in several ways: (1) They exhibit **bilateral symmetry,** with distinct head and associated sense organs, which allows forward, directed movement. (2) They have a **third germ layer—mesoderm**—that arises between the ectoderm and endoderm. This creates the triploblastic condition as distinguished from the two-germ layer, or diploblastic, condition of the radiate animals. The mesoderm serves as a source for many tissues, organs, and systems. (3) Their **excretory system** is made up of specialized flame cells and tubules for the removal of nitrogenous wastes. (4) They possess a highly organized nervous system and concentration of nervous tissue and sense organs in the anterior end (cephalization).

The flatworms are **acoelomate** (Gr. *a,* not, + *koilōma,* cavity) animals that have no coelom. A coelom is a cavity lying within the mesoderm. In flatworms

---

Acoelomate Phyla
Classification
Phylum Platyhelminthes

EXERCISE 9A

Class Turbellaria—Planarians
Dugesia
Projects and demonstrations

EXERCISE 9B

Class Trematoda—Digenetic Flukes
Clonorchis, liver fluke of humans
Schistosoma, human blood fluke
Projects and demonstrations

EXERCISE 9C

Class Cestoda—Tapeworms
Taenia or *Dipylidium*
Projects and demonstrations

EXPERIMENTING IN ZOOLOGY
Planaria regeneration experiment

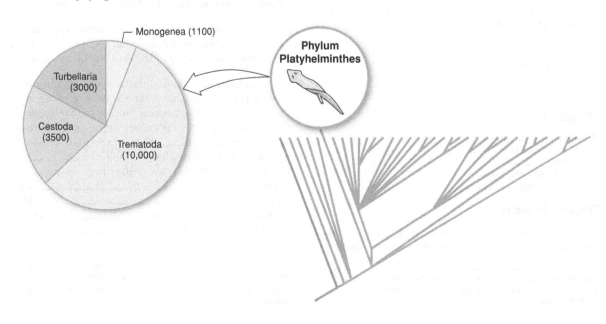

the mesodermal space is filled with muscle fibers and a loose tissue called parenchyma, rather than a cavity. The radiate animals, considered in the previous exercise, also lack a coelom but are not considered acoelomate because they do not possess mesoderm.

Classification

Phylum Platyhelminthes

Class Turbellaria (tur'bel-lar'e-a) (L. *turbellae* [pl.], stir, bustle, + *aria,* like or connected with). Turbellarians. Mostly free-living, with a ciliated epidermis. A paraphyletic grouping. Example: *Dugesia tigrina.*

Class Monogenea (mon'o-gen'e-a) (Gr. *mono,* single, + *gene,* origin, birth). Monogenetic flukes. Adult body covered with syncytial tegument without cilia; leaflike to cylindrical in shape; posterior attachment organ with hooks, suckers, or clamps, usually in combination; all parasitic, mostly on skin or gills of fishes; single host; monoecious; usually free-swimming ciliated larva. Examples: *Polystoma, Gyrodactylus.*

Class Trematoda (trem'a-to'da) (Gr. *trematodes,* with holes, + *eidos,* form). Digenetic flukes. Adult body covered with nonciliated syncytial tegument; leaflike or cylindrical in shape; usually with oral and ventral suckers, no hooks; development indirect, first host a mollusc, final host usually a vertebrate; parasitic in all classes of vertebrates. Examples: *Fasciola, Clonorchis, Schistosoma.*

Class Cestoda (ses-to'da) (Gr. *kestos,* girdle, + *eidos,* form). Tapeworms. Adult body covered with nonciliated, syncytial tegument; scolex with suckers or hooks, sometimes both, for attachment; long, ribbonlike body, usually divided into series of proglottids; no digestive organs; parasitic in digestive tract of all classes of vertebrates; first host may be invertebrate or vertebrate. Examples: *Taenia, Diphyllobothrium.*

EXERCISE 9A

Class Turbellaria—Planarians

Dugesia

Phylum Platyhelminthes
   Class Turbellaria
      Order Tricladida
         Family Planariidae
            Genus *Dugesia*

Where Found

Freshwater triclads,* or planarians, are found on the underside of stones or submerged leaves or sticks in

---

*Triclads, members of the order Tricladida (Gr. *treis,* three, + *klados,* branched), are so named for the three-branched intestine characteristic of all planarians.

freshwater springs, ponds, and streams. They are often confused with leeches, which they resemble in color and somewhat in shape. There are 9 genera and more than 30 species of planarians in North America. Common and widely distributed species are the brown planarians, *Dugesia** tigrina* and *Dugesia dorotocephala,* adapted to warm and standing (or slowly moving) water. Black planarians, *Dendrocoelopsis*** vaginata,* are found west of the Continental Divide.

Observation of Live Planarians

 Using a small artist's brush, place a live planarian on a ringed slide, depression slide, or Syracuse watch glass in a drop of culture water. Replace water as it evaporates. Keep the surrounding glass dry to prevent the animal from wandering out of range. By holding the slide above a mirror, you can also observe its ventral side.

External Structure.

 Observe the animal's **anterior, posterior, dorsal,** and **ventral** aspects.

Note the triangular **head.** Its earlike **auricles** (Figure 9-1A) bear many sensory cells, but they are tactile and olfactory, not auditory, in function. Are the **eyes** movable? _____ Do they have lenses? _____ Note the pigmented **skin.** Is it the same color on the underside? _____ Is its coloring protective? _____ Are the length and breadth of the worm constant? _____ Holding the slide for a moment over a bright light, can you locate the muscular **pharynx** along the midline? When the animal feeds, the pharynx can be protruded through a ventral **mouth** opening. Can you verify this by use of the mirror?

 Use a hand lens, a dissecting microscope, or the low power of a compound microscope for further examination of the eyes and body surface.

Locomotion. Observe the animal's gliding movement. Glands in its ciliated epidermis secrete a path of mucus on which the planarian propels itself by means of its cilia. Do you think cilia alone are responsible for its movement? _____ What do you think causes the waves of contractions along its body? _____ Does the animal ever leave the drop of water and travel on the dry glass? _____ Why? _____ How does it use the head and auricles? _____ Does it ever move backwards? _____

---

*The genus *Dugesia* was named to honor Antoine-Louis Dugès, a nineteenth-century French zoologist and physician.

**Dendrocoelopsis* derives from the Greek *dendron,* stick, + *koilos,* hollow.

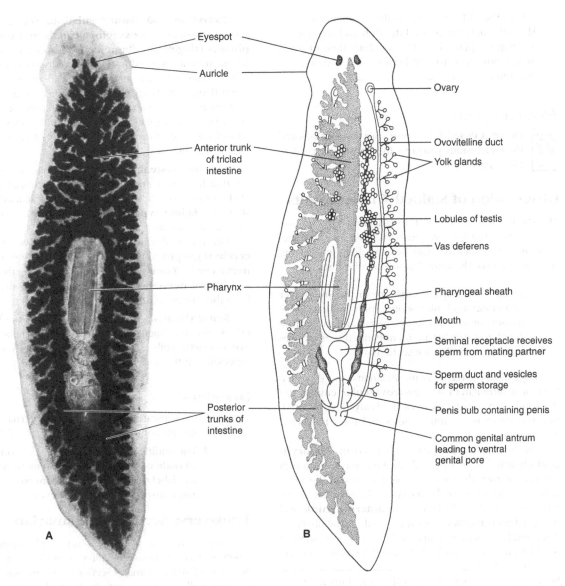

Figure 9-1

Planaria, a freshwater turbellarian. **A,** Stained whole mount. **B,** Internal anatomy; half the anterior trunk of the intestine is removed to reveal the testes.

Reactions to Stimuli.

 Observe the responses of planarians to touch **(thigmotaxis),** food **(chemotaxis),** and light **(phototaxis)** by doing some of the following simple experiments.

1. *Response to touch. Very gently* touch the outer edges of the worm with a piece of lens paper or a soft brush. What parts of its body are most sensitive to touch? Are its reactions more localized or less localized than those of the hydra?

2. *Response to food.* To observe the pharynx, stick a *very small* bit of fresh beef liver (or cut-up meal-worms) on the center of a coverslip. Invert the coverslip over a deep depression slide containing one or two planaria in pond water. Examine under a dissecting microscope. If the planarians have not been fed for several days, they will soon find the meat by gliding upside down across the coverslip; you will then be able to watch them extend the pharynx to feed.

3. *Response to directional illumination.* Direct a strong beam of light at the planarians from one

side of the dish and observe their movements. Move the light 90° around the dish and direct it again at the planarians. Do you think their movements indicate a "trial and error" response or a directed response? _____

Written Report

On pp. 145 and 146, report your observations and the conclusions you drew from observing the live planarians.

Observation of Stained Whole Mounts

The stained whole mount of a planarian shows an animal that was fed food mixed with India ink, carmine, or some other suitable stain before killing and fixing, resulting in a darkly stained gastrovascular tract.

Using a dissecting microscope or the low power of a compound microscope, study stained whole mounts of a freshwater planarian and the marine *Bdelloura* (de-lur′a), identifying the structures listed in the following sections.

Digestive System. As in cnidarians, the digestive tract of a turbellarian is a **gastrovascular cavity,** the branches of which fill most of the body (Figure 9-1B). Because there is no anus, undigested food is ejected through the mouth.

The muscular **pharynx** is enclosed in a **pharyngeal sheath,** but its free end can be extended through the ventral **mouth.** Ingestion occurs through the muscular sucking action of the pharynx. The pharynx opens into the intestine, which has one **anterior trunk** and two **posterior trunks,** one on each side of the pharynx. What might be an advantage to the digestive process of the branching diverticula that extend laterally from the intestinal trunks? _____
Some digestion may occur within the lumen of the digestive cavity by means of enzymes secreted by intestinal gland cells **(extracellular digestion).** As in the cnidarians, digestion is completed within phagocytic cells of the gastrodermis **(intracellular digestion).**

Reproduction. Flatworms are monoecious, and their reproductive system is complex (Figure 9-1B). Because of the large digestive tract, most reproductive organs of turbellarians are obscured on stained whole mounts. However, the penis and genital pore may be seen on the *Bdelloura* slides. See your text for further description of the reproductive system. The reproductive system will be more easily studied in liver flukes and tapeworms.

Planarians and other freshwater turbellarians also reproduce asexually by transverse fission; in some species, chains of zooids are formed asexually.

Excretion and Osmoregulation. The excretory system, consisting of **excretory canals** and **protonephridia (flagellated flame cells),** cannot be seen in whole mounts; see your text for a discussion of this system. The instructor may prepare a demonstration of living flame cells from planaria (see Projects and Demonstrations). The main function of the protonephridial system may be regulation of internal fluid content of the animal (osmoregulation). The system is often absent in marine turbellarians.

Nervous System. *Bdelloura* is a marine turbellarian that lives as a commensal on the external surface of the horseshoe crab, *Limulus.* Properly stained slides show the **ladder type of nervous system,** as well as the triclad digestive tract.

On a stained whole mount of *Bdelloura,* find the **cerebral ganglia** at the anterior ends of the two lateral **nerve cords. Transverse nerves** connecting the cords and **lateral nerves** extending outward from the cords form the "rungs" of the ladder.

Sense Organs. A pair of **eyespots,** or **ocelli,** are light-sensitive pigment cups (Figure 9-1A). Chemoreceptive and tactile cells are abundant over the body surface, especially on the auricles.

Drawings

1. On separate paper, sketch the external morphology of a planarian and label fully.
2. The outline of *Bdelloura* on p. 146 contains an outline of the digestive system. Draw in and label the cerebral ganglia, nerve cords, and transverse and lateral nerves.

Transverse Sections of Planarian

The appearance of a cross section will depend on whether it is cut from the anterior, middle, or posterior part of the planarian. Sections cut anterior to the pharynx will contain a centrally located section of the anterior trunk of the intestine; those cut posterior to the pharynx will contain laterally located sections of the two posterior trunks of the intestine; those cut through the pharynx will show the conspicuous round, muscular pharynx, with branches of intestine on each side (Figure 9-2).

The **epidermis** of cuboidal epithelial cells (derived from ectoderm) contains many dark, rodlike **rhabdites** (Gr. *rhabdos,* rod), which, when discharged in water, swell and form a protective mucous sheath around the body. Epithelial cells are ciliated only on the animal's ventral surface. What function do they serve? _____
Inside the epidermis is a layer of **circular muscles** and then a layer of **longitudinal muscles** (cut transversely and appearing as dark dots). **Dorsoventral muscle fibers** are also visible, particularly at the sides of

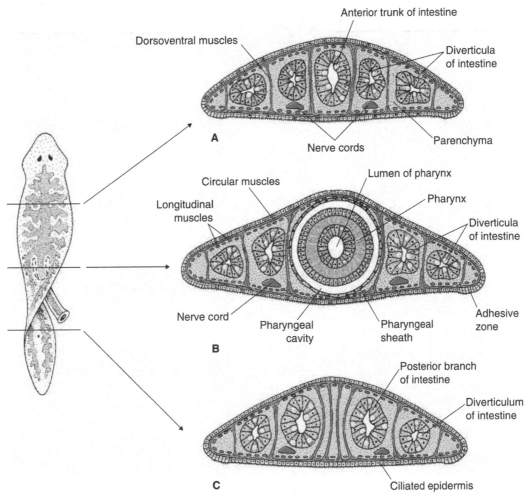

Figure 9-2
Cross section of a planarian (diagrammatic). **A,** Anterior section. **B,** Section through the region of the pharynx. **C,** Posterior section.

the animal. Do these muscles explain the waves of contractions you saw in the living animal? _____ Note that there is *no body cavity*. Flatworms are called **acoelomate** animals. **Parenchyma** (pair-en′ka-ma; Gr., anything poured in beside), largely of mesodermal origin, is the loose tissue filling up space between the organs.

Several hollow sections of the intestine and its diverticula (derived from endoderm) may be seen, depending on the location of the section. What kind of epithelial cells make up the intestinal walls? _____ In a middle section, note the thick, circular **pharynx,** covered and lined with epithelium and containing layers of circular and longitudinal muscle similar to those in the body wall. The **pharyngeal chamber** is also lined with epithelium.

Nerve cords, reproductive and excretory ducts, testes, and ovaries are found in the parenchyma of adult animals, but they are difficult to identify.

Drawings

 Make a drawing on p. 146 of such section(s) as your instructor directs. Label completely.

Projects and Demonstrations

Observing flame cells. Flame cells of the excretory system are difficult to see in living planarians because they are usually obscured by pigment in the integument. To demonstrate flame cells, compress the body (or sectioned portion of the body) of a planarian between a slide and coverslip to crush and partially disperse the tissues. Search the tissue debris with high power of a compound microscope. Flame cells appear as a rapidly flickering movement of the ciliated tuft, resembling a wavering current of water. Once located (often several flame cells are found close together), switch to oil immersion for closer study.

NOTES

Planarian Behavior

Name _____

Date _____

Section _____

Locomotion

Response to Touch (Thigmotaxis)

Response to Food (Chemotaxis)

LAB REPORT

Response to Directional Illumination

Turbellarian Structure

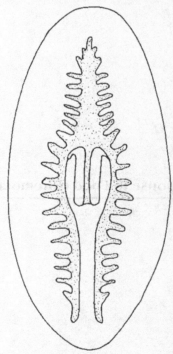

Nervous system of *Bdelloura* (digestive system is already shown).

EXERCISE 9B

Class Trematoda— Digenetic Flukes

Clonorchis, Liver Fluke of Humans

Phylum Platyhelminthes
　Class Trematoda
　　Subclass Digenea
　　　Order Opisthorchiformis
　　　　Species *Clonorchis sinensis* (human liver fluke)

Where Found

All trematodes are parasitic, harbored in or on a great variety of animals. Many of them have three different hosts in their life cycle.

The adult, or sexual, stage of *Clonorchis* lives in the human bile duct. It is widely distributed in Japan, Korea, China, Taiwan, and Vietnam, where it causes widespread suffering and economic loss. Prevalence ranges from 14% in cities such as Hong Kong to 80% in some rural areas. The asexual, or larval, stages are found in aquatic snails and fishes.

Study of a Stained Whole Mount

 Study a stained slide of an adult fluke—first with a hand lens, then with the low power of the microscope.

How long is the specimen? _____ Compare it with the planarian studied in Exercise 9A in size and shape. Note the **oral sucker** at the anterior end and the **ventral sucker (acetabulum)** on the ventral surface (Figure 9-3). What is their function? _____

Body Wall. The body covering of both flukes and tapeworms was formerly believed to be a nonliving cuticle, but the electron microscope reveals it to be a living syncytial **tegument** (L. *tegumentum,* to cover) consisting of cytoplasmic processes of cells that dip down into **parenchyma,** a meshwork of cells derived from mesoderm.

Circular and longitudinal **muscle layers** of the body wall are similar to those of turbellarians, and body spaces are filled with parenchyma.

Digestive System. The **mouth** of *Clonorchis* lies anteriorly in the oral sucker. It leads to a muscular **pharynx** and short **esophagus** that divides into two lateral branches of the digestive tract. The sucker serves for attachment and for the abrasion of the bile duct in which the fluke lives. Food—blood cells and lacerated cells from the inflamed bile duct—is aspirated by the muscular pharynx. There is no anus.

Protonephridial System. An **excretory pore** at the posterior end is the outlet of the **bladder.** Follow the bladder forward to see where it divides into two long tubules. The tubules collect from flame cells, which you will not be able to see.

Reproduction and Life Cycle. Flukes are monoecious; each animal has both male and female reproductive systems (Figure 9-3). The **testes** are conspicuous, branched organs located one in front of the other in the posterior half of the body. From each testis, a slender duct **(vas efferens)** extends forward and unites with the duct on the other side to form a single sperm duct **(vas deferens).** This duct enlarges anteriorly to form a swollen **seminal vesicle** that empties through a small **genital pore** just anterior to the ventral sucker. A penis and cirrus sac are found in many trematodes but not in this species.

After cross-fertilization with another fluke, sperm pass through the uterus to the **seminal receptacle,** where they are stored, probably for the life of the fluke, which may be several years. Both seminal receptacle and a trilobed **ovary** are connected to an oviduct, which gives off a tube (Laurer canal, probably a vestigial vagina) that curves posteriad around the seminal receptacle and opens by a tiny pore to the dorsal surface. The oviduct also receives two **yolk ducts** from **yolk glands** located laterally in the fluke's body. The oviduct connects to an **ootype** surrounded by a loosely organized **Mehlis gland** (both ootype and Mehlis gland may be difficult to see). In this region, eggs are combined with yolk and enclosed in a shell. Shelled eggs then pass to a conspicuous **uterus,** usually filled with eggs, and finally to the outside through the genital pore.

Eggs containing ciliated larvae are shed into the bile, carried to the host's intestine, and voided with feces. If feces pass into water, the larvae hatch and are eaten by snails, in which they multiply asexually through additional larval stages before leaving the snails as tadpolelike **cercariae.** If successful in finding a fish host, the cercariae bore into the muscle where they encyst. Humans (and other mammals) are infected when they eat raw or undercooked fish bearing the cysts. Young flukes then emerge, travel to the bile ducts, and mature into adults. Consult your textbook for details of this animal's life cycle. Why do you think this parasite is prevalent in Southeast Asia?

Schistosoma, Human Blood Fluke

Phylum Platyhelminthes
　Class Trematoda
　　Subclass Digenea
　　　Order Strigeiformes
　　　　Family Schistosomatidae
　　　　　Genus *Schistosoma*
　　　　　　Species *Schistosoma mansoni* (or *Schistosoma haematobium*)

Where Found

Schistosomes of the genus *Schistosoma* are blood flukes of humans that affect an estimated 200 million people in Asia, Africa, the Caribbean (including Puerto Rico), and

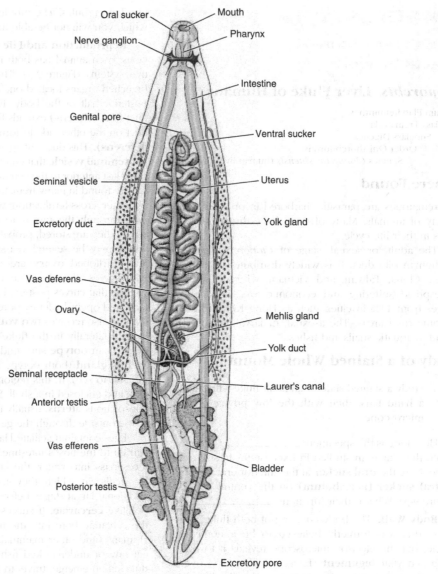

Figure 9-3

Clonorchis, the liver fluke of humans. Is this species monoecious or dioecious? _____ By what pathway do sperm from the testes reach the genital pore? _____ After cross-fertilization, how do sperm reach the seminal receptacle? _____ What is the function of the seminal receptacle? _____

northeastern South America. As a major global health problem, **schistosomiasis** is exceeded only by malaria. In many areas, the disease is commonly known as "bilharzia" rather than the more correct schistosomiasis.

Three species of schistosomes are of enormous medical significance. *Schistosoma mansoni* lives primarily in venules draining the large intestine; *S. haematobium* lives in venules of the urinary bladder; *S. japonicum* inhabits venules of the small intestine. All three species cling to venule walls with their suckers and feed on blood.

The life cycle of *Schistosoma* is similar in all species (Figure 9-4). If discharged eggs from human feces

or urine reach fresh water, they hatch as ciliated **miracidia.** If these find a host snail, within a few hours they burrow in and transform into a saclike form, the **sporocyst.** These multiply asexually to produce another generation of sporocysts, within each of which develop numerous **cercariae.** Successive sexual generations of sporocysts and the cercariae they contain over a period of several months ensure an enormous increase in numbers: each miracidium may give rise to more than 200,000 cercariae.

Cercariae escape from the snail and swim about until they contact bare skin of a human. They penetrate the skin, enter the circulatory system, and make

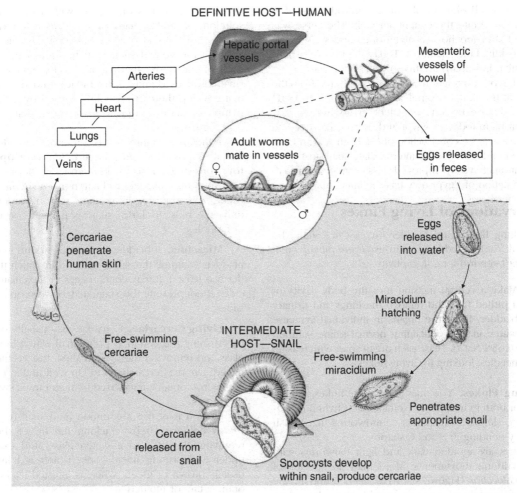

DEFINITIVE HOST—HUMAN

Figure 9-4
Life cycle of *Schistosoma mansoni.*

their way to the hepatic portal system, where they develop before migrating to their characteristic sites. Here they mate with another fluke and the female begins producing eggs.*

Study of Prepared Slides

 Examine a slide of *Schistosoma mansoni* adults in copula.

Schistosomes are an exception to the rule that flatworms are monoecious. In fact, an odd feature of this genus is the strong sexual dimorphism (Figure 9-4). Males are stouter than females and have a ventral longitudinal groove, the **gynecophoric canal** (gi′ne-ka-fore′ik; Gr. *gyne,* woman, + *pherein,* to carry). (The

name *Schistosoma,* meaning "split body," refers to this canal.) Even more oddly, the thinner female normally resides there, permanently embraced by the male. Note the strong oral sucker and a secondary sucker near the anterior end called the **acetabulum.**

 Examine a slide of schistosome eggs.

Note the elliptical shape of the eggs, each of which bears a sharp spine (the spine is terminal in *S. haematobium* eggs and lateral in *S. mansoni* eggs; the eggs of *S. japonicum* lack a spine). The main ill effects of schistosomiasis result from the eggs, which, as they work their way out of the venules where the adults live, cause ulceration, abscesses, bloody diarrhea, and abdominal pain.

Calcified eggs of *S. haematobium* have been found in Egyptian mummies dating from 1200 B.C. There is a well-reasoned hypothesis that the curse Joshua placed on Jericho (after destroying the city and killing all of

*Although the life cycle is similar in all species of *Schistosoma,* it differs from that of other digeneans in that the cercariae penetrate the definitive host directly. There is no second intermediate host (unlike *Clonorchis,* for example, in which there are two intermediate hosts, a snail and a fish).

its inhabitants [Joshua 6:26]) was the introduction of *S. haematobium* into the communal well. The curse was removed after Jericho was abandoned and subsequent droughts killed the snail host. Today the people of Jericho (Ariha, in Jordan) are free of schistosomiasis.

Of Egypt's population, 30% to 40% suffered from the disease at the time of Napolean's invasion (1799–1801) and the disease became prevalent in his troops. It is still a problem today in Egypt and, in fact, has become much worse since construction of the High Aswan Dam because conditions for the intermediate snail host were unintentionally vastly improved. It is estimated that half the population of Egypt now has the infection.

Observations of Living Flukes

Living lung flukes and bladder flukes can usually be obtained from pithed leopard frogs *(Rana pipiens)* that have not been too long in captivity.

 Make a ventral incision into the body cavity of a pithed frog and remove the lungs and urinary bladder. Place the organs in individual Syracuse watch glasses containing normal saline solution (0.65% NaCl). Tease each organ apart with teasing needles, looking for living flukes.

Lung Flukes. You may find lung flukes, nematodes, or both in frog lungs. Nematodes (phylum Nematoda) are slender, transparent roundworms that thrash about by bending in S and C shapes.

Flukes are mottled dark and light flatworms with slow, writhing movements. More than 40 species of *Haematoloechus* (Figure 9-5) have been found in the lungs of amphibians over the world. How does their movement compare with that of planarians? Do they have eyes? _____ The uterus of *Haematoloechus* is probably so filled with thousands of eggs that most internal organs are obscured.

 Place a specimen on a slide with some tap water and a cover glass.

The tap water and pressure of the glass may cause the animal to discharge most of its small brown eggs and thus leave the animal transparent enough to study.

You may now be able to see the intestinal tract filled with ingested blood and the uterus with its remaining eggs. The eggs of *Haematoloechus* are ingested by a certain aquatic snail in which the cercariae develop. Free-swimming cercariae encyst in the gills of the aquatic nymph of a dragonfly. Frogs become infected by ingesting either the nymph or the adult dragonfly.

Bladder Flukes. In the urinary bladder, look for small flukes with large suckers, or acetabula. Study

details of the flukes on a slide with a drop of saline solution. Several species of *Gorgodera* and *Gorgoderina* occur in the bladder (Figure 9-5). These have a very large ventral sucker at the end of the anterior third of the body. In their life cycle, miracidia enter small bivalves (family Sphaeriidae), and the cercariae that develop there are usually ingested by a damselfly nymph or another aquatic insect larva that serves as food for frogs.

Polystoma (Figure 9-5) is a monogenetic fluke that has at its posterior end a large holdfast, or **opisthaptor,** consisting of six suckers and two hooks located on a muscular disc. Reproduction in *Polystoma* is associated with the frog's breeding season, and there is only one host. Its larval stage is parasitic on the gills of tadpoles.

Miracidia. If bladder flukes were found in the frog bladder, examine the saline solution in which the bladder was teased. It may contain eggs or the ciliated miracidia. If not present, this stage may be seen on prepared slides.

Living Cercariae. Cercariae may usually be found by crushing the common pond snail *Physa* in a watch glass and removing the broken shell. Just visible to the naked eye, the cercariae show up well under a dissecting microscope, characterized by their erratic swimming movements.

Or you may use a common mud snail (e.g., *Cerithidea californica*) by cracking the tip of the shell, removing the liver to a watch glass, and examining under a dissecting microscope. Uninfested livers are usually brown or green, whereas infested livers appear orange, tan, or mottled.

 Place some of the cercariae on a microscope slide, cover, and examine with a compound microscope.

Drawings

 On separate paper, sketch any living flukes, miracidia, or cercariae you found. Did you find any nematodes?

Projects and Demonstrations

Making semi-permanent mounts of frog parasites. Remove parasites from lungs or bladder to a dish of 15% alcohol. When they have ceased moving, place one in the center of a clean glass slide, blot with a bit of paper towel, and cover with three or four drops of stain mountant. Drop a coverslip onto the preparation (straight down, not obliquely), allowing the medium to flow out to the edge of the slip. Keep level until firm.

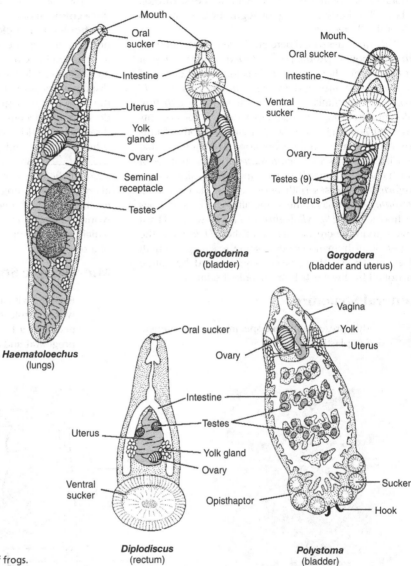

Figure 9-5
Some common trematode parasites of frogs.

EXERCISE 9C
Class Cestoda—Tapeworms

Taenia or *Dipylidium*

Phylum Platyhelminthes
   Class Cestoda
      Order Cyclophyllidea
         Species *Taenia pisiformis* (dog tapeworm) or
         Dipylidium caninum (small dog tapeworm)

Tapeworms are all endoparasitic and show remarkable adaptations for their parasitic existence. For example, they lack a digestive system and there is great emphasis

on reproduction. Most require two hosts of different species, with the adult tapeworm characteristically living in the digestive tract of a vertebrate.

As their name implies, tapeworms are ribbonlike, and their long bodies (the **strobila**) are usually made up of units called **proglottids** (Gr. *proglottis,* tongue tip). (Proglottids are not to be confused with segmentation in higher forms; proglottids are formed by a continuous process of **budding** from the anterior end, or *scolex* [Gr. *skōlēx,* worm, grub].) As new proglottids are formed anteriorly, the older ones are pushed backward, so that the oldest, or most mature, proglottids are always at the posterior end. The scolex, which serves as a holdfast, is usually equipped with **suckers, hooks,** or both. The body covering, or **tegument,** is similar to that of the flukes.

The forms described here are *Taenia pisiformis* (Gr. *tainia,* ribbon; L. *pisum,* pea, + *forma,* shape), a dog or cat tapeworm whose larval stage is found in the liver of rabbits (Figure 9-6), and *Dipylidium caninum* (Gr. *di,* two, + *pyle,* entrance, + *idion,* dim. suffix; L. *caninus,* belonging to a dog), a small tapeworm of dogs or cats (Figure 9-7), with fleas as the alternate host. Other forms may be substituted in the laboratory. Among those that parasitize humans are *Taenia solium,* the larval stage of which encysts in muscle of pigs and which, like *Taenia pisiformis,* possesses both hooks and suckers; *Taenia saginata,* which has cattle as the alternate host and has no hooks; and *Diphyllobothrium latum,* whose larval stage is found in crustaceans and fishes. *D. latum* is the largest of all human cestodes, some reaching a length of 20 m (65 ft). Humans become infected by eating uncooked freshwater fish or uncooked salmon.

General Structure

 Study a preserved whole specimen or one embedded in plastic.

How long is the specimen? _____ Examine the **scolex** under a dissecting microscope and identify **hooks** and **suckers.** Note the **neck,** from which new proglottids are budded off. As older proglottids are pushed back by addition of new ones, they mature and become filled with reproductive organs. Can you distinguish maturing from very young proglottids by the presence of a **genital pore** at one side? As eggs develop and become fertilized, the proglottid becomes distended (gravid), with the uterus filled with embryos. Where do you find **gravid proglottids** (Figure 9-7)? _____ Such proglottids soon break off and are shed in the feces of the host. Ingested by a suitable alternate host, young embryos of *T. pisiformis* migrate to the liver and encyst there as cysticerci (bladder worms). Eggs of *D. caninum* are eaten by larval fleas, which, when mature, are nipped or licked out of the fur of a dog or cat.

Microscopic Study

 Examine with low power a prepared slide of a tapeworm whole mount containing (1) scolex with neck and a few immature proglottids, (2) mature proglottid, and (3) a gravid proglottid.

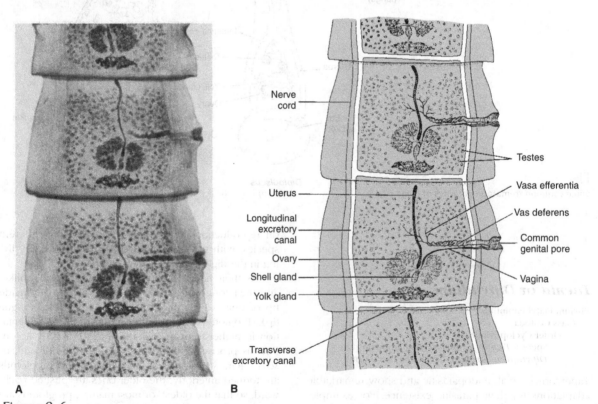

A   **B**

Figure 9-6

Photomicrograph and interpretive drawing of *Taenia pisiformis,* the dog tapeworm. Genital pores may be oriented toward either right or left side.

Labels: Nerve cord, Uterus, Longitudinal excretory canal, Ovary, Shell gland, Yolk gland, Transverse excretory canal, Testes, Vasa efferentia, Vas deferens, Common genital pore, Vagina

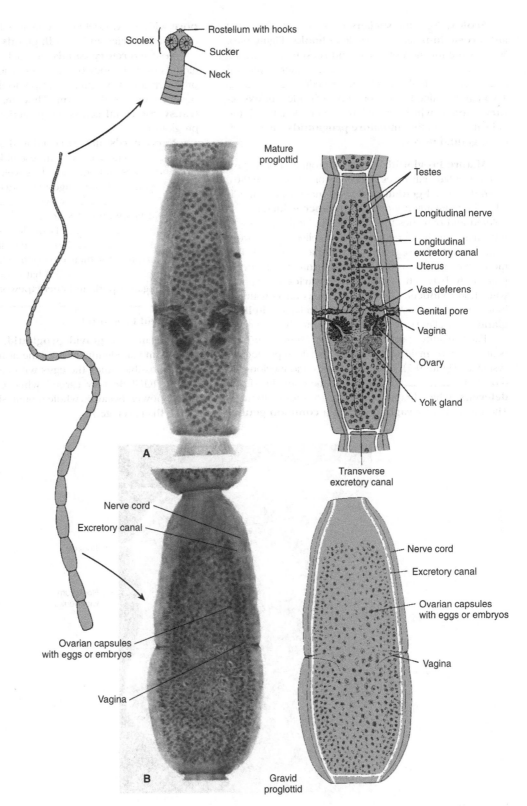

Figure 9-7
Dipylidium caninum, the small tapeworm of dogs and cats.

Scolex. Note the **suckers** (how many? _____) and a **rostellum** bearing a circle of **hooks** (Figure 9-8). What is the function of hooks and suckers? _____ _____ Is there a mouth? _____ Is the **neck** segmented? _____ Two lightly stained tubes, one on each side, are **excretory canals,** which extend the entire length of the animal. Some of the **immature proglottids** have developed **genital pores.**

Mature Proglottid. A mature proglottid of *T. pisiformis* is a little narrower at its anterior end (Figure 9-6). From the lateral **genital pore,** two tubes extend medially. The more anterior of these, the **sperm duct,** is convoluted and branches from the middle of the proglottid into many small efferent ducts that collect sperm from many small **testes** scattered through the proglottid. The more posterior duct is the slender **vagina,** which curves posteriorly between the branched **ovaries** to connect with short **oviducts.** The oviducts also connect with the long central **uterus.** A **shell gland** and a larger **vitelline gland** (yolk gland) are found posterior to the uterus.

Each mature proglottid of *Dipylidium caninum* bears a set of male and a set of female reproductive systems (Figure 9-7). Are tapeworms monoecious or dioecious? _____ Locate the convoluted **vas deferens,** which branches to numerous testes lobules. The more slender **vagina,** sharing a **common genital pore** with the vas deferens, connects by an **oviduct** to branched **ovaries** and to **yolk glands** and the **uterus.**

Note **excretory canals** on each side of the proglottids of both tapeworm species. They are part of the protonephridial system and empty to the outside at the posterior end of the worm. They are connected by a **transverse canal** across the posterior margin of each proglottid.

Nerve cords run just lateral to the excretory ducts. The tapeworm nervous system resembles that of planarians and flukes, although it is less well developed.

Do you find any digestive organs in the tapeworm? _____ Why? _____ What is a tapeworm's food? _____ Where is it digested? _____ How does the worm obtain it? _____ How is the structure of tapeworms adaptive for their environment? _____ _____ What control methods can be used against pork and beef tapeworms? _____ _____

Gravid Proglottid.

 Examine a **gravid proglottid.** What structures can you identify besides the distended **uterus?** If possible, study the **eggs** with high power. (CAUTION! Be very careful when changing to high power because whole-mount slides are thicker than average.)

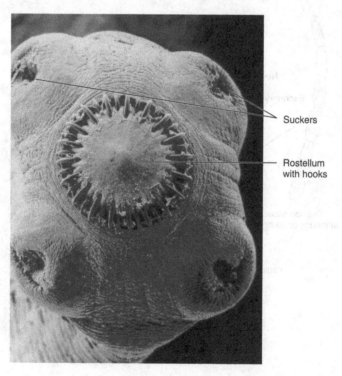

Figure 9-8
Scolex of *Taenia* sp., showing four suckers and a circlet of hooks on the rostellum. SEM × 125.

Suckers

Rostellum
with hooks

Can you distinguish in any eggs a six-hooked larval form called an **onchosphere** (Gr. *onkinos*, hook, + *sphaira*, globe)? _____

Drawings

 On separate paper, draw and label the scolex and neck, a mature proglottid, and a gravid proglottid. Include the scale of the drawings, and be sure to identify the species you are drawing.

Projects and Demonstrations

1. *Slides of cross sections of tapeworm*. Identify the tegument, parenchyma, excretory ducts, nerve cords, uterus, and other reproductive organs that appear in section.

2. *Preserved specimens or prepared slides*. Examine (a) preserved specimens or prepared slides of various species of tapeworms and (b) prepared slides of ova and cysts.

EXPERIMENTING IN ZOOLOGY
Planaria Regeneration Experiment

Planarians are easy to work with and have remarkable powers of regeneration.

 Before starting, assemble your materials: sharp razor blade or scalpel blade, snap-cap vial or screw-cap specimen jar for *each* planarian, clean culture water (pond water or dechlorinated tap water), pipette, small artist's brush, lens paper, and ice cube. Decide how you want to cut the worms (Figure 9-9).

Fold a lens tissue over an ice cube and, with a camel's hair brush, transfer a planarian to the top surface of the ice cube; it will become quiescent almost immediately. Using a dissecting microscope, make the desired cut or cuts with the razor blade. If the worm is being partially split longitudinally, make certain the cut is clean and has completely separated the cut surfaces. Make a sketch in your notebook or on p. 157. With the pipette, rinse the pieces off the lens paper into the vial (previously half-filled with culture water). Label each vial with your name and the date, and prepare a sketch of the cut made. Put in a cool place.

Culture water *must* be changed every 3 or 4 days to keep the planaria healthy. *Do not* feed the animals. Remove any dead pieces, which will appear grayish or fuzzy. Additional tips for this experiment are found in Appendix A, p. 400.

Examine the worms about every 3 days for 2 weeks. To obtain two-headed or two-tailed planarians from the partial cuts shown in the second, third, and fifth sketches in Figure 9-9, you will need to recut them after 12 to 18 hours and probably again at 2 days to prevent the parts from fusing back together. Soon a blastema will form on the cut edge. Is the growth faster at the posterior end of a cephalic piece or the anterior end of a caudal piece? _____ On decapitated pieces, when do new eyes appear? _____ When can you distinguish new auricles? _____ Which is regenerated first, eyes or pharynx? _____ Do you find any evidence of polarity in the manner of growth of these pieces? _____

Drawings

 On the record sheet, p. 157, make a sketch of the shape of each piece. Examine the specimens twice a week if possible, each time recording the date and sketching each regenerating piece. Summarize the results on p. 158. In your report, describe (1) your technique, (2) any problems you encountered, (3) potential or real sources of error in the experimental approach, and (4) your results. If you were to repeat the experiment, what would you do differently?

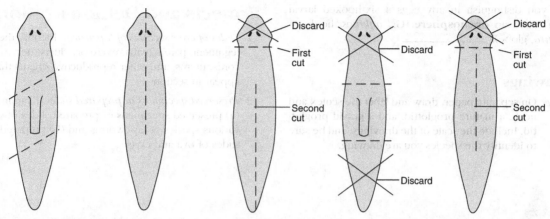

Figure 9-9
Some suggestions for regeneration experiments.

Regeneration Experiment with *Dugesia*

Name _____

Date _____

Section _____

Sketches of original cuts of specimens:

Dates	1	2	3	4	Control

Record of growth:

Dates	1	2	3	4	Control

LAB REPORT

Methods Used

Observations and Conclusions

The Annelids
Phylum Annelida

The annelids include a variety of earthworms, leeches, and marine polychaetes. Their various adaptations allow for freshwater, marine, terrestrial, and parasitic living. They are typically elongate, wormlike animals; are circular in cross section; and have muscular body walls. The most distinguishing characteristic that sets them apart from other wormlike creatures is their **segmentation.** They are often referred to collectively as the "segmented worms." This repetition of body parts, also called **metamerism** (meta′me-ri′sum; Gr. *meta,* between, + *meros,* part), not only is external but also is seen internally in the serial repetition of body organs. Development of segmentation is of significance, because along with segmentation comes the opportunity for segments to become specialized for certain functions. Such specialization is not as noticeable in annelids as in arthropods, but the introduction of metamerism coincided with the rapid evolution seen in arthropods and chordates, the only other phyla emphasizing segmentation.

Classification
Phylum Annelida

EXERCISE 12A
Class Polychaeta—Clamworm
Nereis
Projects and demonstrations

EXERCISE 12B
Class Oligochaeta—Earthworm
Lumbricus, common earthworm

EXERCISE 12C
Class Hirudinida—Leech
Hirudo, medicinal leech

EXPERIMENTING IN ZOOLOGY
Behavior of Medicinal Leeches, *Hirudo medicinalis*

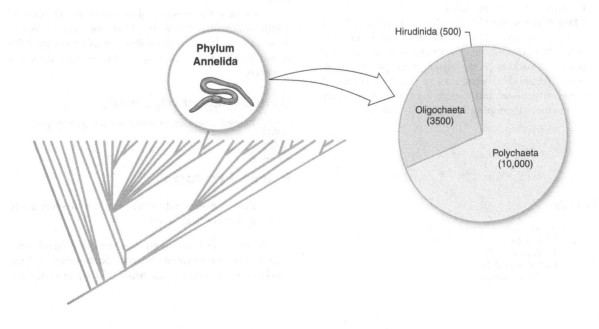

Division of the coelomic cavity into fluid-filled compartments also has increased the usefulness of hydrostatic pressure in the locomotion of annelids. The coordination between their well-developed neuromuscular system and more efficient hydrostatic skeleton makes annelids proficient in swimming, creeping, and burrowing.

Annelids have a complete mouth-to-anus digestive tract with muscular walls, so that digestive tract movements are independent of body movements. There is a well-developed closed circulatory system with pumping vessels, a high degree of cephalization, and an excretory system of nephridia. Some annelids have respiratory organs.

Classification

The three groups of annelids are classified chiefly on the basis of presence or absence of clitellum, parapodia, setae, annuli, and other features.

Phylum Annelida

Class Polychaeta (pol'e-ke'ta) (Gr. *polys,* many, + *chaitē,* long hair). Segmented inside and out; parapodia with many setae; distinct head with eyes, palps, and tentacles; no clitellum; separate sexes, trochophore larva usually present; mostly marine. Examples: *Nereis, Chaetopterus.*

Class Oligochaeta (ol'i-go-ke'ta) (Gr. *oligos,* few, + *chaitē,* long hair). Body segmented inside and out; number of segments variable; clitellum present; few setae; no parapodia, head poorly developed; coelom spacious and usually divided by intersegmental septa; direct development; chiefly terrestrial and freshwater. Examples: *Lumbricus,Tubifex.*

Class Hirudinida (hir'u-din'i-da) (L. *hirudo,* leech, + *ea,* characterized by). Segments 33 or 34 in number, with many annuli; clitellum present; anterior and posterior suckers; setae absent (except *Acanthobdella*); parapodia absent; coelom closely packed with connective tissue and muscle; terrestrial, freshwater, and marine. Examples: *Hirudo, Placobdella.*

EXERCISE 12A
Class Polychaeta—Clamworm

Nereis

Phylum Annelida
   Class Polychaeta
      Order Phyllodocida
         Family Nereididae
            Genus *Nereis*

Where Found

Clamworms (also called sandworms or ragworms) are strictly marine. They live in the mud and debris of shallow coastal waters, often in burrows lined with mucus. Largely nocturnal, they usually are concealed by day under stones, in coral crevices, or in their burrows. The common clamworm *Nereis virens* (Gr. *Nereis,* a sea nymph) may reach a length of 0.5 m.

Behavior

If living nereid worms are available, study their patterns of locomotion.

When the animal is quiescent or moving slowly, note that the **parapodia** (Gr. *para,* beside, + *pous, podos,* foot) (lateral appendages) undergo a circular motion that involves an effective stroke and a recovery stroke, each parapodium tracking an ellipse during each two-stroke cycle. In the effective stroke, the parapodium makes contact with the substratum, lifting the body slightly off the ground. The two parapodia of each segment act alternately, and successive waves of parapodial activity pass along the worm.

For more rapid locomotion, the worm uses undulatory movements of the body produced by muscular contraction and relaxation in addition to parapodial action. As the parapodia on one side move forward in the recovery stroke, longitudinal muscles on that side contract; as the parapodia sweep backward in their effective stroke, the muscles relax. Watch a worm in action and note these waves of undulatory movements. Can the worm move swiftly? Does it seek cover? Does it maintain contact with substratum, or does it swim freely?

Place near the worm a glass tube with an opening a little wider than the worm. Does the worm enter it? Why? Place a bit of fresh mollusc or fish meat near the entrance of the tube. You may be able to observe feeding reactions.

Written Report (Optional)

Record your observations on separate paper.

External Features

Place a preserved clamworm in a dissecting pan and cover with water.

Observe the body, with its specialized **head,** variable number of segments bearing **parapodia,** and the caudal segment bearing the **anus** and a pair of feelers, or **cirri** (sing. **cirrus;** sir′us; L., curl). Compare the length and number of segments of your specimen with those of other specimens at your table. Do they vary? The posterior segments are the smallest because they are the youngest. As the animal grows, new segments are added just anterior to the caudal segment.

Examine the **head.** It comprises a **prostomium** (Gr. *pro,* before, + *stoma,* mouth)—which is a small protuberance with two small median **tentacles,** a pair of fleshy **palps,** and four small, dark **eyes**—as well as a **peristomium** (Gr. *peri,* around, + *stoma,* mouth), or first segment, bearing four pairs of **peristomial tentacles** (Figure 12-1). The palps and tentacles are sensory organs of touch and taste, and the eyes are photoreceptors. The **mouth** is a slit on the ventral side of the peristomium, through which the **pharynx** can be protruded. If the pharynx is everted on your specimen, do not confuse it with head structures. The pharynx is large and muscular, bearing a number of small, horny teeth and a pair of dark, pincerlike, chitinous **jaws.** If the pharynx is fully everted, the jaws will be exposed. If not, you may be able to probe into the pharynx to find them.

 Cut off, close to the body, a parapodium from the posterior third of the body. Mount it in water on a slide, cover with a coverslip, and examine with a hand lens or dissecting microscope.

Parapodia are used for respiration as well as locomotion. Are they all identical? _____ Each parapodium has a dorsal lobe called the **notopodium** (Gr. *nōtos,* back, + *pous, podos,* foot) and a ventral lobe called the **neuropodium** (Gr. *neuron,* nerve, + *pous, podos,* foot) (Figure 12-1). Each lobe has a bundle of bristles called **setae** (see′tee; sing. **seta;** L., bristle). A small process called the **dorsal cirrus** projects from the dorsal base of the notopodium, and a **ventral cirrus** projects from the neuropodium. Each lobe has a long, chitinous, deeply embedded spine called an **aciculum** (L. *acicula,* dim. of *acus,* a point). The acicula are the supporting structures of the parapodium (they are more conspicuous in the posterior parapodia). Each aciculum is attached by muscles that can protrude it as the parapodium goes into its effective stroke and retract it during the recovery stroke. How might the spines help in locomotion? _____

 Peel off a piece of the thin cuticle that covers the animal and study it in a wet mount under a microscope.

The cuticle is fibrous, and its iridescence is caused by its cross-striations. It is full of small pores, through which the gland cells of the underlying epidermis discharge their products.

Internal Structure

Because the internal structure of polychaetes is similar to that of oligochaetes, study of the internal anatomy will be limited to that of earthworms.

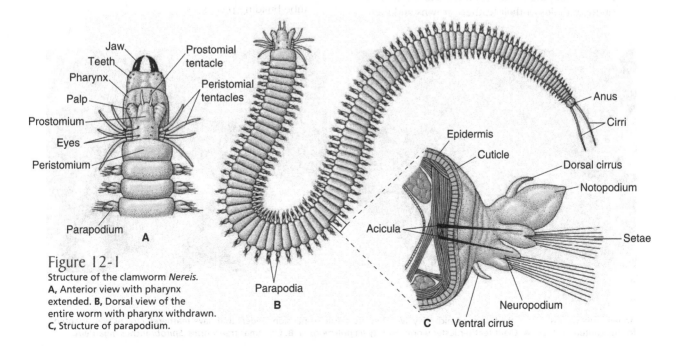

Figure 12-1
Structure of the clamworm *Nereis.*
A, Anterior view with pharynx extended. **B,** Dorsal view of the entire worm with pharynx withdrawn. **C,** Structure of parapodium.

Projects and Demonstrations

There are over 10,000 species of polychaetes, most of them marine. They include some unusual and fascinating animals. Besides the errant, or free-moving, worms, such as *Nereis* and its relatives, there are many sedentary species, including the burrowing and tube-building forms (Figure 12-2).

 Examine the marine aquarium for living polychaetes and examine the preserved material on the demonstration table.

1. *Chaetopterus* (Gr. *chaitē,* bristle, + *pteron,* wing) *variopedatus* is a suspension feeder often found on mudflats. This species secretes a U-shaped parchment tube, through which it pumps and filters a continuous stream of water with its fanlike parapodia. The animal is profoundly adapted to its permanent tube environment and completely helpless if removed from it. Feeding currents generated by three pairs of modified parapodia are filtered through a mucous bag held open by another highly modified pair of parapodia. Plankton trapped in the mucus is gathered into a food-laden mucous pellet, which is passed forward by cilia to the mouth.

2. *Diopatra* is an errant tubeworm that camouflages the exposed portion of its tube with bits of shell, seaweed, and sand. Note its gills and long, sensitive antennae. Fanworms (Figure 12-2) are ciliary feeders, trapping minute food particles on mucus on the radioles of their feathery crowns and then moving the particles down toward their mouth in ciliated grooves.

3. *Amphitrite* (Gr., a mythical sea nymph) is a deposit feeder. It runs long, extensible tentacles over the mud or sand, picking up food particles. These are carried along each tentacle in a ciliated groove to the mouth. Note the cluster of gills just below the tentacles.

4. *Examine tubes of various worms.* What kinds of materials do you find? Examine an old seashell or a rock bearing calcareous worm tubes. The variety of secreted tubes and materials used to supplement them seems endless.

5. *Constructing an observation chamber.* If living, burrowing polychaetes are available, an observation chamber can be constructed of two pieces of glass, clear plastic, or Lucite (each about 30 to 40 cm square), a length of plastic or rubber tubing 10 to 15 mm in diameter, and some large rubber bands or small clamps (not metal). Arrange the tubing in a U shape on one glass, cover with the other glass, and hold in place with clamps or rubber bands. Fill the U space nearly full with mud or sand. Stand the tubing in an aquarium and place one or more burrowing polychaetes on the mud surface. The lugworm *Arenicola* will burrow into sand, then form a tube with mucous lining. You might try *Clymenella,* which needs sand for its tube; *Amphitrite;* or other burrowing species. You should be able to observe the burrowing and tube-building processes.

A

B

Figure 12-2

Annelid tubeworms secrete the tubes in which they live. They are sessile suspension feeders that have feathered crowns well adapted for the capture of food. **A,** Giant featherduster worm, *Eudistyllia polymorpha.* **B,** Christmas tree worms, *Spirobranchus giganteus.*

Chaetopterus variopedatus is an especially fascinating filter feeder that may be displayed in a U-shaped glass or plastic tube. If living worms can be collected, cut off the narrow end of parchmentlike tube and slit along the side of the tube with scissors, being careful not to damage the worm. Prepare a U-shaped glass or plastic tube of approximately the same diameter and length as the original tube. Submerge the tube, open ends up, in a marine aquarium. You may then witness the rhythmic parapodial movements as the animal pumps water through the surrogate tube. Try placing some fine carbon particles at the incurrent end of the tube; then see if they become trapped in the mucous bag that *Chaetopterus* forms for filtering food particles from the water.

Check the tube at intervals to see the secretion of a new mucous lining for the tube.

EXERCISE 12B
Class Oligochaeta—Earthworm

Lumbricus, Common Earthworm

Phylum Annelida
    Class Oligochaeta
        Order Haplotaxina
            Family Lumbricidae
                Genus *Lumbricus*
                    Species *Lumbricus terrestris*

Where Found

Earthworms prefer moist, rich soil that is not too dry or sandy. They are found all over the earth. They are chiefly nocturnal and come out of their burrows at night to forage. A good way to find them is to search with a flashlight around the rich soil of lawn shrubbery. Large "night crawlers" are easily found this way, especially during warm, moist nights of spring and early summer. *Lumbricus terrestris* (L. *lumbricum*, earthworm), named by Linnaeus, is one of the most common earthworms in Europe, Asia, and North America and has been introduced all over the world.

Behavior

 Wet the center of a paper towel with pond or dechlorinated water, leaving the rest of the paper dry. Place a live earthworm on the moist area. Using the following suggestions, observe its behavior.

Is the skin of the worm dry or moist? _____
Do you find any obvious respiratory organs? _____ Where do you think exchange of gases occurs? _____ Would this necessitate a dry or damp environment? _____ _____ Does the worm respond positively or negatively to moisture? _____ _____

Notice the mechanics of crawling. The earthworm's body wall contains well-developed layers of circular and longitudinal muscles. As it crawls, notice the progressing peristaltic waves of contraction. These are produced by alternate contraction and relaxation of longitudinal and circular muscles in the body wall acting against noncompressible coelomic fluid. An earthworm's body is divided internally into segments by septa. When longitudinal muscles of a segment contract, the segment becomes shorter and thicker because the volume within each body segment remains constant. Conversely, when circular muscles contract, the segment elongates. Do the waves of circular muscle contraction move anteriorly or posteriorly when the worm as a whole is moving forward? _____ How far apart (what proportion of total body length) are the waves of contraction? _____ Watch the anterior end as the worm advances. Do short and thick or long and thin regions advance the head end forward? _____

Run a finger along the side of the worm. Do you detect the presence of small setae (bristles)? How might these setae be used? _____

How does the animal respond when you gently touch its anterior end? _____ Its posterior end? _____ Draw the towel to the edge of the desk and see what happens when the worm's head projects over the edge of the table. Is it positively or negatively thigmotactic (responsive to touch)? _____ Turn the worm over and see if it can right itself, and how.

Can you devise a means of determining whether an earthworm is positively or negatively geotactic (responsive to gravity)?

 Place the earthworm on a large plate of wet glass. Does this difference in substratum affect its locomotion? Is friction important in earthworm locomotion?

Does the earthworm have eyes or other obvious sensory organs? _____ Can you devise a means of determining whether it responds positively or negatively to light?

Written Report

 On p. 200, record the responses of the earthworm. Comment on hydrotaxis, locomotion, thigmotaxis, phototaxis, and the importance of friction.

External Structure

Anesthetize an earthworm by immersing it for 30 to 40 minutes in 7% ethanol.* When the worm is completely limp, transfer it to a dissecting tray that has been dampened with water. Examine the worm with a dissecting microscope or hand lens as necessary.

What are the most obvious differences between the earthworm and the clamworm? List two or three here.

_____

_____

The first four segments make up the head region. The first segment is the **peristomium.** It bears the **mouth,** which is overhung by a lobe, the **prostomium.** The earthworm's head, lacking specialized sense organs, is not a truly typical annelid head.

Find the **anus** in the last segment. Observe the saddlelike **clitellum** (L. *clitellae*, packsaddle), which in mature worms secretes egg capsules, into which eggs are laid. In what segments does it occur? _____

How many pairs of setae are on each segment, and where are they located? _____ Use a hand lens or dissecting microscope to determine this. What does the name "Oligochaeta" mean? _____ "Polychaeta"? _____ Are these names well chosen?

There are many external openings other than mouth and anus. Earthworms are monoecious. Note **male pores** on the ventral surface of segment 15. These are conspicuous openings of sperm ducts, from which spermatozoa are discharged. Note two long **seminal grooves** extending between the male pores and the clitellum. These guide the flow of spermatozoa during copulation. Use a small hand lens to look for small **female pores** on the ventral side of segment 14. Here the oviducts discharge eggs. You may not be able to see the openings of 2 pairs of **seminal receptacles** in grooves between segments 9 and 10 and between 10 and 11 or paired excretory openings, **nephridiopores,** located on the lateroventral surface of each segment (except the first 3 and the last).

A **dorsal pore** from the coelomic cavity is located at the anterior edge of the middorsal line on each segment from 8 or 9 to the last. Many earthworms eject a malodorous coelomic fluid through the dorsal pores in response to mechanical or chemical irritation or when subjected to extremes of heat or cold. Dorsal pores may also help regulate the turgidity of the animal. How would loss of coelomic fluid affect the animal's escape mechanism (quick withdrawal into its burrow)? _____ How does lack of dorsal pores in its anterior segments protect its burrowing ability? _____

_____

*Prepared by diluting 74 ml of 95% ethanol with 1 L of water.

Drawings

Complete the external ventral view of the earthworm on p. 199. Draw in and label prostomium, peristomium, mouth, setae, male pores, female pores, seminal grooves, clitellum, and anus.

Internal Structure and Function

Reanesthetize the earthworm in 7% ethanol, if necessary. Place the anesthetized worm dorsal side up in a dissecting pan and straighten it by passing one pin through the fourth or fifth segment (just behind the peristomium) and another pin through any segment near the posterior end of the worm. With a razor blade or new scalpel blade, and beginning at about the fortieth segment (just behind the clitellum), cut through the body wall at a point just to one side of the dark middorsal line (the **dorsal blood vessel**). Use fine-tipped scissors to complete the middorsal cut all the way to the head, pulling up on the scissors as you proceed to avoid damaging internal organs. Keep your incision slightly to one side of the dorsal blood vessel. With a pipette, squirt some isotonic salt solution on the internal organs to keep them moist. Now, starting at the posterior end of the incision, pin the animal open. You will need to break the septa (partitions between the metameres) with a needle as you proceed anteriorly. When you have finished, remove all the pins except those anchoring the worm at the anterior end. Stretch out the worm by pulling gently on the posterior end and repin, placing the pins at an oblique angle. If you are using a dissecting microscope rather than a hand lens, you may need to position the worm to one side of the dissecting tray for viewing. Now flood the tray with enough isotonic saline (0.6% NaCl) to cover the earthworm completely.

Note peristaltic movements of the **digestive tract,** which propel food posteriorly. Find 3 pairs of cream-colored **seminal vesicles** in segments 9 to 12 (Figure 12-3), 2 pairs of glistening white **seminal receptacles** in segments 9 and 10, and a pair of delicate, almost transparent, tubular **nephridia** in the coelomic cavity of each segment. Note the **dorsal vessel** riding on the digestive tract. In which direction is blood flowing in this vessel? _____ A total of 5 pairs of pulsating **aortic arches,** sometimes called "hearts," surround the **esophagus** in segments 7 to 11 (some of these arches are covered by the seminal vesicles).

Digestive System. Identify the **mouth;** the muscular **pharynx** attached to the body by **dilator muscles** for sucking action (the muscles, torn by the dissection, give the pharynx a hairy appearance); the slender

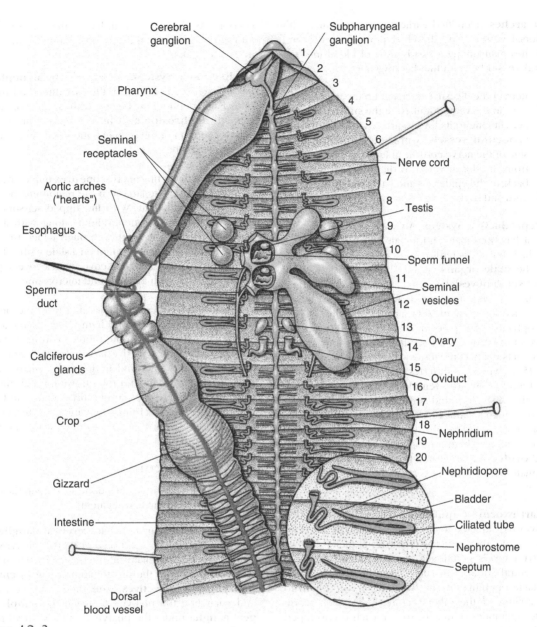

Figure 12-3

Internal structure of *Lumbricus,* dorsal view.

esophagus in segments 6 to 13, which is hidden by the aortic arches and seminal vesicles; the large, thin-walled **crop** (15, 16) for food storage; the muscular **gizzard** (17, 18) for food grinding; the **intestine** for digestion and absorption; and the **anus.** Two or three pairs of yellowish to brownish **calciferous glands** lie on both sides of the esophagus (usually partly concealed by the seminal vesicles). They are believed to remove excess calcium and carbonates taken in with the soil; these ions are accumulated as calcite crystals and passed out with the feces. Bright yellow or green **chloragogue** cells often cover the intestine and much of the dorsal vessel. They are known to store glycogen and lipids but probably have other functions as well, similar to those of the vertebrate liver. Make an off-center longitudinal cut into the intestine in the region of the clitellum to expose the **typhlosole** (Gr. *typlos,* blind, + *sōlēn,* channel), a ridgelike structure projecting into the lumen of the intestine. The typhlosole increases the surface available for digestive enzyme production and absorption.

Circulatory System. An earthworm has a **closed** circulatory system. Note that both **dorsal vessel** and

aortic arches (identified earlier) are contractile, with the dorsal vessel being the chief pumping organ and the arches maintaining a steady flow of blood into the **ventral vessel** beneath the digestive tract.

 Retract the digestive tract. Lift up the white nerve cord in the ventral wall. Note the **subneural vessel** clinging to its lower surface and a pair of **lateroneural vessels,** with one located on each side of the nerve cord. Be able to trace blood flow from the dorsal vessel to the intestinal wall and back, to the epidermis and back, and to the nerve cord and back.

Reproductive System. An earthworm is monoecious; it has both male and female organs in the same individual, but cross-fertilization occurs during copulation. The **male organs** (Figure 12-3) consist of three pairs of **seminal vesicles** (sperm sacs in which spermatozoa mature and are stored before copulation) which are attached in segments 9, 11, and 12; they lie close to the esophagus. Two pairs of small, branched **testes** are housed in reservoirs in the seminal vesicles, and 2 small sperm ducts connect the testes with **male pores** in segment 15; however, both testes and ducts are too small to be found easily. The **female organs** are also small. Two pairs of small, round **seminal receptacles,** easily seen in segments 9 and 10, store spermatozoa after copulation. You should be able to find the paired **ovaries** that lie ventral to the third pair of seminal vesicles. The paired **oviducts** with ciliated funnels that carry eggs to the female pores in the next segment will probably not be seen.

Earthworm Copulation. When mating, two earthworms, attracted to each other by glandular secretions, extend their anterior ends from their burrows and, with heads pointing in opposite directions, join their ventral surfaces in such a way that the seminal receptacle openings of one worm lie in opposition to the clitellum of the other (Figure 12-4). Each worm secretes quantities of mucus, so that each is enveloped in a slime tube extending from segment 9 to the posterior end of the clitellum. Seminal fluid discharged from the sperm ducts of each worm is carried along the seminal grooves by contraction of longitudinal muscles and enters the seminal receptacles of the mate. After copulation the worms separate, and each clitellum produces a secretion that finally hardens over its outer surface. The worm moves backward, drawing the hardened tube over its head (Figure 12-4C). As it is moved forward, the tube receives eggs from the oviducts, sperm from the seminal receptacles, and a nutritive albuminous fluid from skin glands. Fertilization occurs in the cocoon. As the worm withdraws, the cocoon closes and is deposited on the ground. Young worms hatch in 2 to 3 weeks.

Excretory System. A pair of tubular **nephridia** lies in each segment except the first three and the last one. Each nephridium begins with a ciliated, funnel-shaped **nephrostome,** which projects through the anterior septum of the segment and opens into the next anterior segment.

 Use a dissecting microscope to examine a nephridium. They are largest in the region just posterior to the clitellum. With fine-tipped scissors, carefully remove a nephridium, along with a small portion of the septum through which the nephrostome projects. Mount on a slide with a drop or two of saline solution, cover with a coverslip, and examine with a compound microscope.

Note the slender tubule passing from the nephrostome to the looped nephridium. Note ciliary activity in one narrow portion of the tubule. You may also see parasitic nematodes in the large bladder segment of the tubule. Coelomic fluid is drawn by ciliary activity into the nephrostome and then flows through the narrow tubule, where ions, especially sodium and chloride, are reabsorbed. Urine, containing wastes, collects in the bladder, which empties to the outside through a **nephridiopore.**

Nervous System

 If you have not already done so, extend the dorsal incision to the first segment.

Find a small pair of white **cerebral ganglia** (the brain), lying on the anterior end of the pharynx and partially hidden by dilator muscles; small white **nerves** from the ganglia to the prostomium; a pair of **circumpharyngeal connectives,** extending from the ganglia and encircling the pharynx to reach the **subpharyngeal ganglia** under the pharynx; and a **ventral nerve cord,** extending posteriorly from the subpharyngeal ganglia for the entire length of the animal. Remove or lay aside the digestive tract and examine the nerve cord with a hand lens to see in each body segment a slightly enlarged **ganglion** and **lateral nerves.**

Oral Report

 Be prepared to (1) demonstrate your dissection to your instructor, (2) point out both external and internal structures you have studied, and (3) explain their functions.

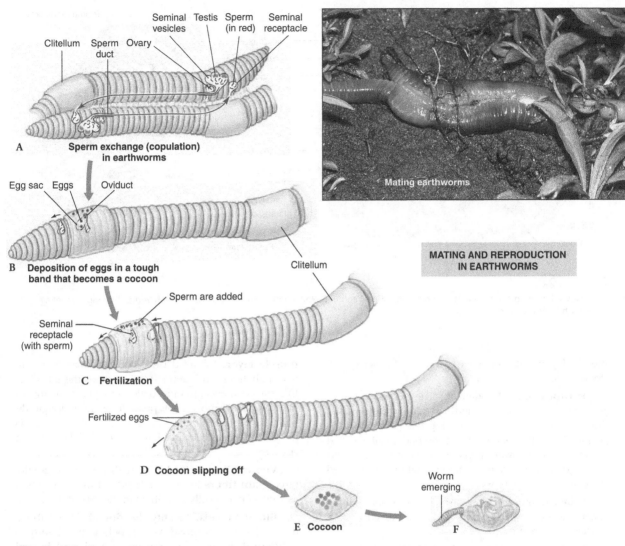

Figure 12-4

Earthworm copulation and formation of egg cocoons. **A,** Mutual insemination; sperm from genital pore (segment 15) pass along seminal grooves to seminal receptacles (segments 9 and 10) of each mate. **B** and **C,** After worms separate, the clitellum secretes first a mucous tube and then a tough band that forms a cocoon. The developing cocoon passes forward to receive eggs from oviducts and sperm from seminal receptacles. **D,** As cocoon slips off over anterior end, its ends close and seal. **E,** Cocoon is deposited near burrow entrance. **F,** Young worms emerge in 2 to 3 weeks. **G,** Two earthworms in copulation. Their anterior ends point in opposite directions as their ventral surfaces are held together by mucous bands secreted by the clitella.

Histology of Cross Section (Figure 12-5)

 Examine a stained slide with low power. Note the tube-within-a-tube arrangement of intestine and body wall. Identify the following.

Cuticle. Thin, noncellular, and secreted by the epidermis.

Epidermis. (Ectodermal.) Columnar epithelium containing mucous gland cells. Mucus prevents the skin from drying out.

Circular Muscle Layer. Smooth muscle fibers running around the circumference of the body. How does their contraction affect body shape? _____

Longitudinal Muscle Layer. Thick layer of obliquely striated fibers that run longitudinally. The

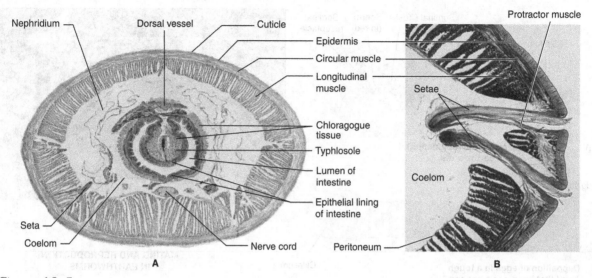

Figure 12-5
A. Cross section of an earthworm through the intestinal region. **B.** Portion of a cross section of an earthworm, showing one set of setae with their protractor muscles.

muscle layers may be interrupted by the setae and dorsal pore.

Peritoneum. (Mesodermal.) The peritoneum (Gr. *peritonaios,* stretched around), a thin epithelial layer lining the body wall and covering the visceral organs (Figure 12-5). Peritoneum lining the body wall is called parietal (L. *paries,* wall) peritoneum. Peritoneum covering the digestive tract and other visceral organs is called visceral (L. *viscera,* bowels) peritoneum.

Setae. If present, they are brownish spines in a sheath secreted by epidermis. They are moved by tiny muscles (Figure 12-5).

Coelom. Space between the **parietal peritoneum,** which lines the body wall, and the **visceral peritoneum,** which covers the intestine and other organs.

Alimentary Canal. The intestine is surrounded by chloragogue tissue. Chloragogue tissue plays a role in intermediary metabolism similar to that of the liver in vertebrates. Inside the chloragogue layer is a layer of **longitudinal muscle.** Why does it appear as a circle of dots? _____ Next is a **circular**

muscle layer, followed by a layer of ciliated columnar epithelium (endodermal), which lines the intestine. Intestinal contents are moved along by peristaltic movement. Is such movement possible without longitudinal and circular muscles? _____ Is peristalsis possible in the intestine of the flatworm or *Ascaris?* _____

Ventral Nerve Cord. Use high power to identify three **giant fibers** in the dorsal side of the nerve cord, as well as nerve cells and fibers in the rest of the cord.

Blood Vessels. Identify the **dorsal** vessel above the typhlosole, **ventral** vessel below the intestine, **subneural** vessel below the nerve cord, and **lateral neurals** beside the nerve cord.

Some slides may also reveal parts of **nephridia, septa, mesenteries,** and other structures.

Drawings

 Sketch and label a cross section of the earthworm as it appears on your slide. Use separate paper.

Phylum _____

Genus _____

Name _____

Date _____

Section _____

Earthworm

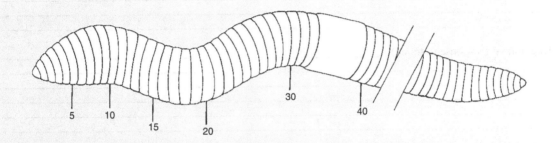

External structure of earthworm, ventral view

Transverse section through the body of earthworm

LAB REPORT

Observations on the Behavioral Responses of an Earthworm

Hydrotaxis _____
_____
_____
_____
_____
_____

Locomotion _____
_____
_____
_____
_____
_____

Thigmotaxis (response to touch) _____
_____
_____
_____
_____
_____
_____

Phototaxis _____
_____
_____
_____
_____
_____

Importance of friction _____
_____
_____
_____
_____
_____

EXERCISE 12C

Class Hirudinida—Leech

Hirudo, Medicinal Leech

Phylum Annelida
   Class Hirudinida
      Order Gnathobdellida
         Genus *Hirudo*
            Species *Hirudo medicinalis*

Where Found

Leeches are predaceous and mostly fluid feeders. Some are true blood suckers, attaching themselves to a host during feeding periods.

   Hirudo is one of the freshwater leeches found in lakes, ponds, streams, and marshes and is native to Europe. *H. medicinalis* (Figure 12-6) is often referred to as the "medicinal leech" because it was formerly used in blood-letting and is still occasionally used in plastic surgery and in the treatment of hematomas. It feeds on the blood of amphibians and mammals. Living leeches are readily available from biological supply houses.

Behavior

Note the use of ventral **suckers**—a smaller oral sucker at the anterior end and a larger caudal sucker at the posterior end.

 Attempt to pull an attached leech free from its substratum.

Are the suckers powerful? The leech combines the use of its suckers with muscular body contractions in creeping.

 Place a leech on a glass plate and watch it move.

The oral sucker attaches and the body contracts; then the caudal sucker attaches and the body extends forward before the oral sucker attaches again. How does movement of a leech on the glass plate compare with movement of the earthworm that you previously observed?

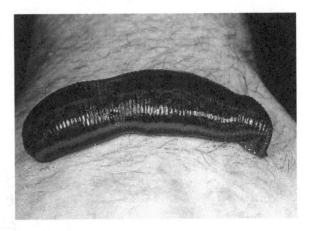

Figure 12-6
Medicinal leech, *Hirudo medicinalis,* feeding on blood from a human arm.

 Drop a leech into the water to observe its undulating, free-swimming motions.

Medicinal leeches are attracted to heat. Why would this be? _____ To investigate this further, see the Experimenting in Zoology feature at the end of the chapter.

External Features

 Study a preserved specimen of *Hirudo* (Figure 12-7).

How does its shape compare with that of an earthworm? Can you distinguish between the dorsal and ventral surfaces? How? _____ A leech is segmented inside and outside, but externally each segment also is marked off into 1 to 5 **annuli,** the larger number being found in segments 9 to 23, inclusive. Each true segment bears a pair of **nephridiopores** and, on one of its annuli, a row of **sensillae** (used mainly to detect water movements) or (at the anterior end) eyespots.

   The oral sucker contains the **mouth.** The **anus** is located in the middorsal line at the junction with the caudal sucker. A **male genital pore** is located ventrally on segment 11, and a **female pore** is on segment 12. Segments 10, 11, and 12 serve as a functional **clitellum,** secreting the capsule in which eggs develop. Leeches are monoecious.

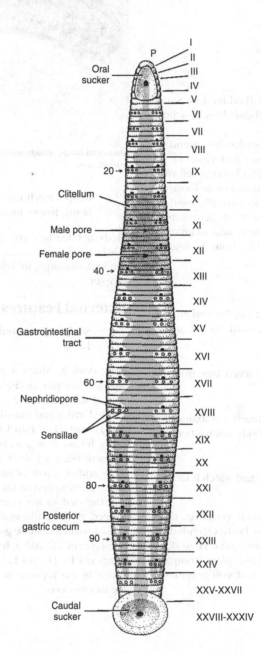

Figure 12-7

External anatomy of *Hirudo medicinalis,* showing segments (Roman numerals) and annuli (Arabic numerals). The position of the gut, not visible externally, is indicated in color.

EXPERIMENTING IN ZOOLOGY
Behavior of Medicinal Leeches,
Hirudo medicinalis

Medicinal leeches, *Hirudo medicinalis,* are best known because of their use in medical procedures. Historically, these leeches were used to draw blood from victims of bites or stings from insects or venomous animals. In addition, during the nineteenth century, leeches were used to draw out "corrupt blood" from people suffering from disease. Today these annelids are frequently used to restore venous circulation after reconstructive surgical procedures, particularly when a finger, a toe, or an ear is surgically reattached after an accident. In 2004 the Food and Drug Administration (FDA) for the first time cleared the commercial marketing of leeches for medicinal purposes. Aside from their use in modern medicine, medicinal leeches are wild animals that have evolved specific adaptations for locating their mammalian prey. Because mammals are endotherms, their body temperatures typically are above ambient water temperatures. Medicinal leeches are able to locate mammals that have entered their ponds or lakes because they have evolved the ability to detect the slightly elevated water temperatures generated by the presence of a mammal.

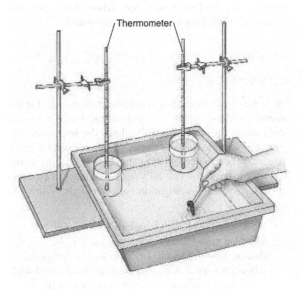

Figure 12-8
Setup for observing the behavior of leeches.

Getting Ready

Work with a partner for this exercise. Obtain a plastic tub approximately 40 cm wide by 60 cm long. Wash the tub and fill it to a depth of 8 to 10 cm using pond water, bottled water, or dechlorinated tap water. After taking the temperature of the water in the tub, fill two 500 ml beakers with water of the same temperature. Place the two filled beakers onto opposite sides of the tub about 30 cm from one end (Figure 12-8). Use ring stands and clamps to suspend thermometers for monitoring the temperatures throughout the experiment. Have a stopwatch available for timing leech behavior.

How to Proceed

Use a short wooden dowel to choose an active medicinal leech. The leech will attach itself to the dowel or balance momentarily on it while you transfer it to your experimental tub. If the leech will not stay on the dowel, gently place it on a paper towel to transfer it to the tub. Release the leech at the end of the tub. Try to release the leech so as not to bias its behavior toward either

of the beakers. How does the leech behave when you release it? Does it go toward the beakers? When leeches find potential prey items or simply want to crawl on a substrate, they first attach to an object using their anterior sucker. Does the leech attach itself to the side of the tub? Does it attach itself to one of the beakers? If so, how much time expires between when you first release the leech and when it attaches itself to a beaker? Once the leech attaches itself to a beaker or the tub, gently remove the leech with the wooden dowel and repeat the trial by replacing the leech at the end of the tub opposite the beakers.

After three trials with the beakers at room temperature, replace the water in one beaker with water warmed to 40° C. Again monitor the temperatures in the beakers. Watch that the temperature in the warm beaker remains at approximately 40° C. Release the leech at the end of the tub opposite the beakers. Does the leech attach itself to one of the beakers? To which beaker does it attach? How much time elapses between release and attachment? Remove the leech from the beaker and conduct at least two more trials.

Does the leech appear to be attracted to the beaker filled with warm water? Compare your results with those of your classmates. Your instructor may want you to combine your data with your classmates' and compare control treatments with experimental treatments, using a statistical test. How many times out of the total control trials does a leech attach to a beaker? How many times in the warm beaker trials? Do the leeches attach to the warm water beakers faster than when there are only beakers filled with room temperature water?

Questions for Independent Investigation

Medicinal leeches are hearty animals that are ideal specimens for these types of experiments. While repeated trials using the same animal violates the important statistical assumption of independence (see Exercise 23A), you may be able to borrow five or six of the other leeches ordered for use by your classmates to conduct an independent investigation on one of the following questions:

1. How small may the temperature difference be between "prey" and the environment to be detected by the leech? How do leeches respond when presented with two beakers, each filled with warm water differing by only a degree or two?

2. Leeches are known to be sensitive to chemical stimuli in the water. Medicinal leeches will feed on beef liver. Can they detect the odor of beef liver? This question may be explored by using a setup similar to that described for examining their sensitivities to temperature differences. Place beef liver inside a plastic beaker that has been pierced repeatedly with a heated pin or needle.

3. How do leeches respond when presented with a choice of attaching either to a beaker filled with warm water (thermal cues) or to one that is releasing food odor (chemical cues)? Which appears to be the more attractive stimulus?

References

Dickinson, M. H., and C. M. Lent. 1984. Feeding behavior of the medicinal leech, *Hirudo medicinalis*. Jour. Comp. Phys. **154**:449–455.

Lent, C. M., and M. H. Dickinson. 1987. On the termination of ingestive behavior by the medicinal leech. Jour. Exp. Bio. **131**:1–15.

Lent, C. M., K. H. Fliegner, E. Freedman, and M. H. Dickinson. 1988. Ingestive behavior and physiology of the medicinal leech. Jour. Exp. Bio. **137**:513–527.

EXERCISE **11**

The Molluscs
Phylum Mollusca
A Protostome Eucoelomate Group

Molluscs, with over 90,000 living species, rank next to arthropods in number of named species. They include chitons, snails, slugs, clams, oysters, squids, octopuses, cuttlefish, and others. They have retained the basic features introduced by the preceding phyla, such as triploblastic structure, bilateral symmetry, cephalization, and a body cavity. The body cavity, though small, is now a **true coelom,** a characteristic shared by all remaining phyla. All organ systems are present.

Molluscs have a specialized, muscular **foot,** generally used in locomotion. A fold of the dorsal wall, called the **mantle,** or **pallium,** encloses a **mantle cavity,** which usually contains the **gills** and secretes an **exoskeleton,** or shell. There is an open **circulatory system** with a pumping **heart** and a complete mouth-to-anus digestive system. Is a circulatory system present in any of the phyla already studied? _____ Most molluscs, with bivalves being a conspicuous exception, have within the mouth a unique rasping organ, the **radula,** used for scraping off food materials. Most molluscs have a well-developed head—again, a feature absent in bivalves.

Classification
Phylum Mollusca

EXERCISE 11A
Class Bivalvia (= Pelecypoda)—Freshwater Clam
Freshwater clam
Projects and demonstrations

EXERCISE 11B
Class Gastropoda—Pulmonate Land Snail
Land snail
Projects and demonstrations

EXERCISE 11C
Class Polyplacophora—Chitons
Chitons

EXERCISE 11D
Class Cephalopoda—*Loligo,* the Squid
Loligo
Demonstrations

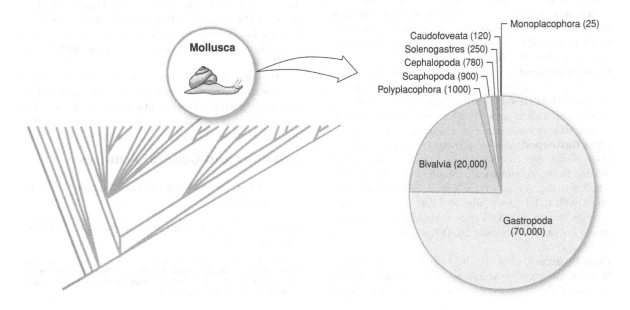

Molluscs have left an extensive fossil record, indicating that their evolution has been a long one. They occupy numerous ecological niches and are found in the sea, in fresh water, and on land. They range from sedentary herbivores to fast-swimming predators.

Classification
Phylum Mollusca

Class Monoplacophora (mon′o-pla-kof′o-ra) (Gr. *monos,* one, + *plax,* plate, + *phora,* bearing). Body bilaterally symmetrical, with broad, flat foot; a single, dome-shaped shell; three to six pairs of gills in shallow mantle cavity; radula present; separate sexes. Example: *Neopilina.*

Class Polyplacophora (pol′y-pla-kof′o-ra) (Gr. *polys,* many, + *plax,* plate, + *phora,* bearing). Chitons. Elongated, dorsally flattened body with reduced head; bilaterally symmetrical; radula present; shell of eight dorsal plates; foot broad and flat; gills multiple, along sides of body between foot and mantle edge; sexes usually separate. Examples: *Katharina, Mopalia.*

Class Caudofoveata (kaw′do-fo-ve-at′a) (L. *cauda,* tail, + *fovea,* small pit). Wormlike; shell, head, and excretory organs absent; radula usually present; mantle with chitinous cuticle and calcareous scales; oral pedal shield near anterior mouth; mantle cavity at posterior end with pair of gills; sexes separate; formerly united with solenogasters in class Aplacophora. Examples: *Chaetoderma, Limifossor.*

Class Solenogastres (so-len′o-gas′trez) (Gr. *solen,* pipe, + *gaster,* stomach). Solenogasters. Wormlike; shell, head, and excretory organs absent; radula usually absent; rudimentary mantle usually covered with scales or spicules; mantle cavity posterior, without true gills but sometimes with secondary respiratory structures; foot represented by long, narrow, ventral pedal groove; hermaphroditic. Example: *Neomenia.*

Class Scaphopoda (ska-fop′o-da) (Gr. *skaphe,* boat, + *pous, podos,* foot). Tusk shells. Body enclosed in a one-piece, tubular shell open at both ends; conical foot; mouth with radula and tentacles; head absent; mantle for respiration; sexes separate. Example: *Dentalium.*

Class Gastropoda (gas-trop′o-da) (Gr. *gaster,* belly, + *pous, podos,* foot). Snails, slugs, conchs, whelks, and others. Body asymmetrical, usually in a coiled shell (shell uncoiled or absent in some); head well developed, with radula; foot large and flat; one or two gills or with mantle modified into secondary gills or lung; dioecious or monoecious. Examples: *Busycon, Physa, Helix, Aplysia.*

Class Bivalvia (bi-val′vi-a) (L. *bi,* two, + *valva,* valve). Bivalves. Body enclosed in a two-lobed mantle; shell of two lateral valves of variable size and form, with dorsal hinge; cephalization much reduced; no radula; foot usually wedge-shaped; gills platelike; sexes usually separate. Examples: *Anodonta, Venus, Tagelus, Teredo.*

Class Cephalopoda (sef′a-lop′o-da) (Gr. *kephalē,* head, + *pous, podos,* foot). Squids, nautiloids, and octopuses. Shell often reduced or absent; head well developed with eyes and radula; foot modified into arms or tentacles; siphon present; sexes separate. Examples: *Loligo, Octopus, Sepia.*

EXERCISE 11A
Class Bivalvia (= Pelecypoda)— Freshwater Clam

Freshwater Clam

Phylum Mollusca
  Class Bivalvia
    Subclass Palaeoheterodonta
      Order Unionoidea
        Genus *Anodonta,* others

Where Found

Bivalves are found in both fresh water and salt water. Many of them spend most of their existence partly or wholly buried in mud or sand. Freshwater clams (also called mussels) are found in rivers, lakes, and streams and were once particularly abundant in the Mississippi River watershed before stream pollution and increasing acidity from acid rain greatly depleted their populations.* Native bivalves are also the biggest losers in the recent invasion of zebra mussels (*Dreissena polymorpha*), unintentionally introduced from Eastern Europe into the Great Lakes in 1988 and now running amok throughout the central United States and Canada. Freshwater clams are overwhelmed by zebra mussels, which attach to their shells in enormous numbers. Some common native freshwater genera are *Anodonta, Lampsilis, Elliptio,* and *Quadrula.*

Traditionally freshwater clams have been used in zoology laboratories because of their availability, but the sea clam, *Spisula,* is quite similar to the freshwater clam and makes a good substitute. Marine mussels, *Mytilus,* or quahogs, *Mercenaria,* can also be substituted.

Behavior and General Features

 Observe living bivalves in an aquarium, if they are available.

Freshwater clams lie half-buried in the sand, and their reactions are slow.

---

*Clams are especially vulnerable to aquatic pollution. Approximately 10% of all freshwater clams became extinct in the twentieth century, and most of the rest are endangered.

What is the natural position of a clam at rest? _____ When moving? _____ Note that it leaves a furrow in the sand when it moves. The soft body is protected by a hard **exoskeleton** composed of a pair of **valves,** or shells, hinged on the dorsal side. When the animal is at rest, the valves are slightly agape ventrally, and you can see at the posterior end the fringed edges of the **mantle,** which lines the valves. The posterior edges of the mantle are shaped so as to form two openings **(apertures)** to the inside of the mantle cavity (Figure 11-1).

 With a Pasteur pipette or hypodermic syringe and needle, carefully introduce a small amount of carmine dye into the water near the apertures. Watch what happens to it.

Which of the apertures has an incurrent flow, and which has an excurrent flow? _____ A steady flow of water through these apertures is necessary to bring oxygen and food to the animal and to carry away wastes. Most bivalves are filter feeders that filter minute food particles from the water, trap them in mucus, and carry them by ciliary action to the mouth.

Some marine clams have the mantle drawn out into long, muscular **siphons.** When the animal burrows deeply into mud or sand, the siphons extend up to the surface to bring clear water into the mantle cavity.

 Gently touch the mantle edge with a glass rod.

What happens? The mantle around the apertures is highly sensitive, not only to touch but also to chemical stimuli, a necessity if the animal is to close its valves to exclude water containing unpleasant or harmful substances.

If the supply of live clams is plentiful, your instructor may want to remove one of the valves from a clam

Figure 11-1

Freshwater clam showing apertures in mantle. The dorsal, or upper, aperture is excurrent; the larger, lower aperture is incurrent.

and sprinkle a few carmine granules on the gills, on the labial palps, and inside of the mantle to let you observe the ciliary action that maintains and controls water flow.

 Lift a clam out of the sand to observe the hasty withdrawal of the foot. Then lay it on its side on the sand to see if it will right itself.

The foot is as soft, flexible, and sensitive as the human tongue. Mucous glands keep the foot well protected with mucus.

 If there is a marine tank containing scallops, compare the method of locomotion of scallops with that of clams.

Written Report

 Report your observations on clam behavior on separate paper.

External Structure

The two valves of the clam are attached by a **hinge ligament** on the dorsal side; the ventral side is free for the protrusion of the foot. A swollen hump, the **umbo** (pl. **umbones**), near the anterior end of the hinge is the oldest and thickest part of the shell and the part most resistant to boring gastropod predators. Concentric **lines of growth** around the umbo indicate growth periods. Where is the youngest part of the shell? _____

The outer, horny layer of the valve is the *periostracum,* which is secreted by a fold at the edge of the mantle. Has any of this layer been eroded away? _____

Now determine the correct orientation of the clam. Note that the umbones are dorsal and located toward the anterior end. Identify the right and left valves.

Internal Structure

The directions that follow apply to living clams (see Appendix A, p. 402) but may be easily adapted to preserved specimens.

 Obtain a living clam that has been heated to about 40° C (104° F), causing the valves to gap slightly. *Caution! Do not overheat.* Your instructor or teaching assistant will open the clam by inserting a strong, short-bladed knife (*not* a scalpel) between the *left* valve and the *left* mantle at the posterior end and cutting the posterior adductor muscle as close as possible to the left valve (Figure 11-2A). Cut the anterior adductor muscle in the same manner. Hold the clam against a firm surface when cutting, and keep your hand clear of the knife blade. The valve will gap open because of the action of the hinge ligament. Separate the

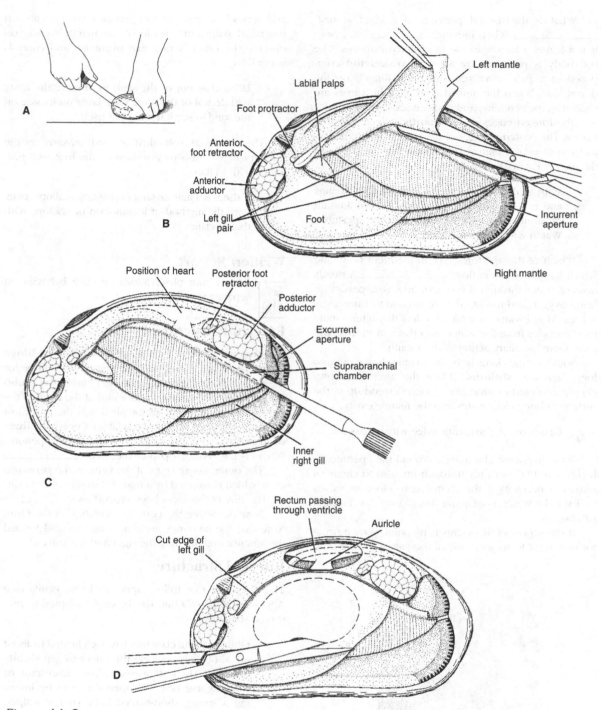

Figure 11-2

Dissection of a freshwater clam. **A,** Cutting the posterior adductor. **B,** Trimming off the left mantle. **C,** Probing the suprabranchial chamber. **D,** Cutting to expose the visceral mass.

mantle completely from the left valve and lift the loosened left valve. Place the clam in a dissecting pan and flood the body with pond or dechlorinated water, allowing the right valve to serve as a container.

The Shell

The bivalve shell protects the animal from predators, serves as a skeleton for muscle attachment, and, in burrowing forms, helps keep mud and sand out of the mantle cavity.

 Examine the inner surface of the left valve.

The inner, iridescent mother-of-pearl surface is the **nacreous layer,** which lies next to the mantle and is secreted continuously by the mantle surface. Between the inner nacreous layer and outer periostracum is a **prismatic layer,** made up of crystalline calcium carbonate. It is secreted by glands in the edge of the mantle.

With the aid of Figure 11-3, locate on the valve the scars of **anterior** and **posterior adductor muscles,** which close and hold the valve together; **anterior** and **posterior foot retractor muscles,** which pull in the foot; and a **foot protractor muscle,** which loops around the visceral mass and helps extend the foot by squeezing the viscera. The shell is opened by the elastic **hinge ligament,** which acts as a spring to force the shells apart when the adductors relax. Are there also muscles to open the shell? _____

Find the **pallial line,** where the pallial muscle of the mantle was attached to the valve.

Identify near the dorsal edge of the valves the teeth, which fit tightly together when the valves are closed, forming an effective locking mechanism. The **pseudocardinal teeth** are pointed projections, and the **lateral teeth** are long ridges along the dorsal edge. Shape and prominence of the teeth vary greatly among different genera.

The Mantle

 With the left valve removed, examine the thin **mantle** covering all the soft tissues of the clam.

Posteriorly the edges of the two mantles are thickened, darkly pigmented, and fused together dorsally to form the ventral **incurrent aperture** and dorsal **excurrent aperture.** The apertures permit a continuous flow of water through the mantle cavity. In many burrowing clams, the apertures are extended into siphons.

 Examine the edge of the mantle, which forms three parallel folds: an outer, a middle, and an inner fold (Figure 11-4).

The outer fold (closest to the shell) secretes the hornlike periostracum as well as the prismatic layer of the shell. The middle lobe is sensory in function; in some bivalves (scallops, for example), it is drawn out into specialized sensory structures, such as tentacles and eyes. The ciliated surface of the inner fold assists in water circulation within the mantle cavity and sweeps out debris; the inner fold also seals the mantle cavity when the clam closes its shell. It is this inner fold that, on the posterior side, forms the clam's incurrent and excurrent apertures.

The mantle is attached to the shell by a muscle along a semicircular line (the **pallial line**) just inside the shell edge (see Figure 11-3). This muscle retracts the mantle folds when valves are closed (if you are dissecting a living clam, you will probably find the mantle edge strongly retracted by this muscle).

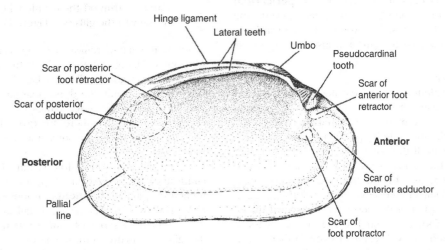

Figure 11-3
Left valve of a freshwater clam, showing the muscle scars.

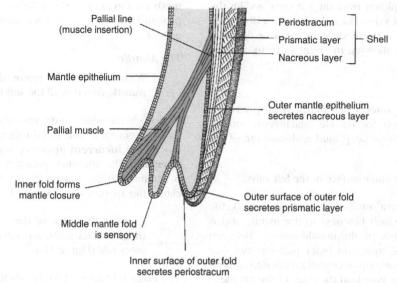

Figure 11-4
Section through margin of freshwater clam shell and mantle.

Sometimes a foreign object, such as a sand grain or parasite, becomes lodged between the mantle and shell. The outer epithelium of the mantle then secretes nacre around the object, forming a pearl. Often, however, the formative pearl becomes fused with the nacreous layer of the shell. Do you find any pearls or other evidence of such irritation in the valve or mantle?

Muscles. Locate the large **adductor muscles,** which close the valves (Figure 11-5). Slightly dorsal to them are the **foot retractor muscles.** The **foot protractor muscle** is small and will be found lying in the visceral mass just posterior to the anterior adductor.

Pericardium. On the dorsal side of the animal, locate the delicate, almost transparent **pericardial membrane** surrounding the heart. In living clams, the beating ventricle is visible through the pericardium. Do not open the pericardium until instructed to do so later.

Mantle Cavity

Lift up the mantle to expose the outer pair of **gills** and body mass beneath. The entire space between the right and left lobes of the mantle is the **mantle cavity.** Cilia on both mantle and gills keep water flowing through the mantle cavity. If the outer gill is much thicker than the inner gill, the animal is probably a female in which the gill is serving as a **brood chamber** for developing embryos. Are clams monoecious or dioecious? _____

The soft portion of the body is the **visceral mass.** The muscular **foot** lies ventral to the visceral mass; it will be retracted but will contract even farther if you touch it with a probe. The foot, much like the mammalian tongue, is a **muscular hydrostat.** It operates by a combination of muscular contraction and hydraulic mechanisms. A clam can extend or enlarge its foot hydraulically by engorgement with blood and uses the extended foot for anchoring itself or drawing its body forward.

Attached to the anterior end of the visceral mass are two pairs of **labial palps,** a pair on each side of the body (see Figure 11-2B). The left and right outer palps join anteriorly to form a protective lip for the slitlike **mouth.** The palps secrete a great amount of mucus and are ciliated to guide food particles trapped in the mucus toward the mouth.

Respiration and the Gills

 Carefully trim off the mantle where it is attached dorsally to the gills (see Figure 11-2B).

With the mantle removed, the gills are conspicuous. Gaseous exchange occurs in both the mantle and the gills. Both mantle and gills are ciliated to promote water flow. Note that only the dorsal margins of the gills are attached; the ventral edge hangs freely in the mantle cavity. Note also that there are *two* gills on each side of the visceral mass, an outer and a somewhat larger inner one.

Each gill is a double fold (Figure 11-6). The walls **(lamellae)** are ridged in appearance, consisting of numerous parallel **filaments** supported by chitinous rods. The two lamellae of each gill are connected to each other by a series of thin partitions, which divide the gill into many vertical spaces, the **water tubes.** Water enters the tubes through innumerable small holes **(ostia)** in the lamellae.

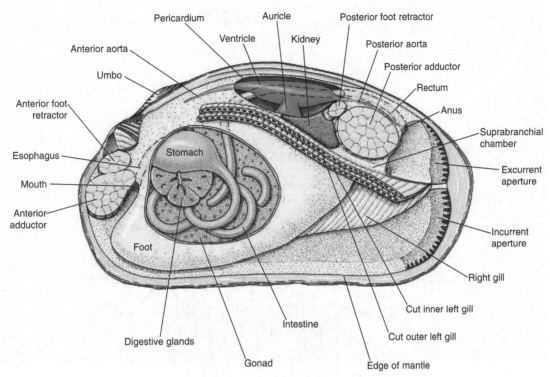

Figure 11-5
Anatomy of a unionid clam.

 Cut a transverse section about 1 mm wide from the lower part of the gill. Lay the section on a slide and examine with a dissecting microscope. Identify lamellae, filaments, and water tubes, as well as the partitions **(interlamellar junctions)** that hold the two lamellae apart (Figure 11-6).

Water tubes connect dorsally with the **suprabranchial chamber,** which in turn empties to the outside through the excurrent aperture.

 Sprinkle a few grains of powdered carmine on the outer gill to see the current produced by the cilia.

Cilia beat constantly, pulling water into the incurrent aperture, through the ostia and into the water tubes, and then into the suprabranchial chamber. From here it is carried out through the excurrent aperture.

 From the excurrent aperture, run a probe into the suprabranchial chamber (see Figure 11-2C). With scissors, slit the suprabranchial chamber to see the tops of the water tubes of the outer gill.

A sedentary animal, such as a clam, which lives half-buried in mud or sand, must have some means of clearing the water passing through the gills of sediment, detritus,

and fecal matter. This is accomplished partially by the small size of the ostia and partially by mucus secreted by glands in the roof of the mantle cavity, which traps particles too large for the ostia. Larger debris drops off the gills, while smaller food particles are carried toward the mouth.

The water tubes in the female serve as brood pouches for eggs or larvae during breeding season.

Circulatory System
Near the dorsal midline, just below the hinge, is the thin-walled **pericardial sac,** within which lies the **heart.**

 Carefully slit open the pericardium, using fine-tipped surgical scissors. Be cautious not to injure the delicate heart inside.

The three-chambered heart is composed of a single **ventricle** and a pair of **auricles** (see Figure 11-5).

 If the ventricle is still beating, count the rate (beats/minute).

Note that the ventricle surrounds the intestine. Two aortae leave the ventricle; the **anterior aorta** passes to the visceral mass and intestine, and the **posterior aorta** runs along the ventral side of the rectum to the mantle.

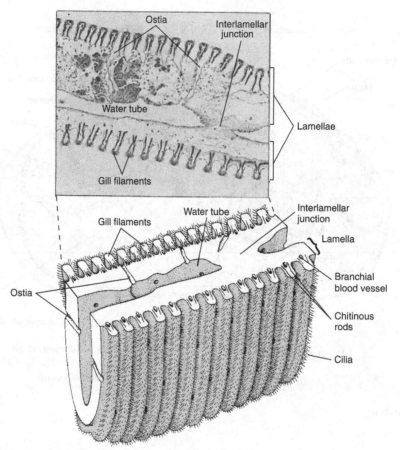

Figure 11-6
Cross section through a portion of the gill of a freshwater clam.

The paired auricles are fan-shaped and very thin-walled. Pass a probe under the uppermost (left) auricle and lift carefully to see its connection to the ventricle.

At your instructor's option, you can inject a small amount of carmine solution into the ventricle using a tuberculin syringe and a small (26 or 27 gauge) hypodermic needle. The carmine solution will flow into and reveal the two aortae.

The pericardial space around the heart is a part of the **coelomic cavity,** greatly reduced in molluscs.

Figure 11-7 shows the general plan of the **open system of circulation** found in a freshwater clam. From the ventricle, the aortae carry blood to sinuses in the body tissues. From the visceral organs, blood is carried first to the kidney for removal of wastes, then to the gills for gaseous exchange, and then back to the auricles and ventricle. Blood from the mantle, rich in oxygen, returns directly to the auricles. Although the blood of molluscs is colorless, it contains either hemoglobin or hemocyanin for oxygen transport. It contains nucleated, ameboid corpuscles.

Coelom
Although molluscs have a true coelom, it is small. The pericardial cavity is part of the coelom, as is the small space around the gonads. A true coelom, you recall, is distinguished from other cavities by being lined with epithelium that arises from the mesoderm. What is the name of the lining of the coelom? _____

Excretory System
A pair of dark kidneys lie under the floor of the pericardial sinus. They are roughly U-shaped tubes. The kidneys pick up waste from blood vessels, with which they are richly supplied, and from the pericardial sinus, with which they connect. Waste is discharged into the suprabranchial chamber and carried away with the exhalant current.

Digestive System
Locate again the **labial palps** and **mouth.**

 To reveal the alimentary canal, cut through the surface tissue on one side of the visceral mass and foot and strip away the epithelium (see Figure 11-2D).

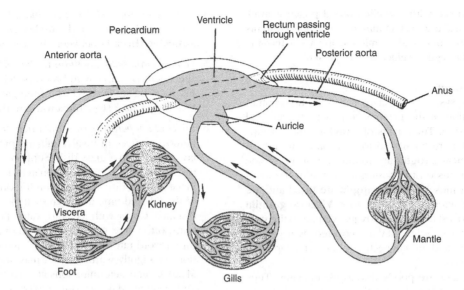

Figure 11-7
Scheme of circulation of a freshwater clam.

The mouth leads into a short **esophagus** that widens into the **stomach,** surrounded by greenish brown **digestive glands.** The stomach narrows into a tubular **intestine,** which can be seen looping back and forth through the visceral mass. The intestine connects to the rectum, seen earlier passing through the ventricle. Trace the rectum as it passes dorsal to the posterior adductor muscle to its end, the **anus,** which empties feces into the exhalant current. Surrounding the intestine is light brown tissue of the **gonad** (see Figure 11-5).

In freshly collected clams, you may find a solid, gelatinous rod, the **crystalline style,** projecting into the stomach. It is composed of mucoproteins and digestive enzymes (chiefly amylase), which are released into the food. The crystalline style disappears within a few days after clams are collected and usually is absent from specimens purchased from biological supply houses.

Clams are suspension feeders (also called filter feeders) that depend on respiratory currents to bring in a food supply, mostly phytoplankton and organic debris. Food particles passed anteriorly along the edge of the gills become entangled in strings of mucus, which are carried into the mouth. Larger particles are dropped to the edge of the mantle and discarded. Digestion is mostly intracellular.

Reproductive System
Sexes are separate but are difficult to distinguish, except by the swollen gills of the pregnant female. The **gonads** (**ovaries** or **testes**) are a brownish mass of minute tubes filling the space between the coils of the intestine.

 Make a wet mount of gonadal tissue and determine whether there are eggs or sperm in it.

The gonads discharge their products into the suprabranchial chamber. Spermatozoa pass into the surrounding water. They enter a female with the inhalant current and fertilize eggs in the suprabranchial chamber. The **zygotes** settle into the water tubes of the outer gill (brood pouch), where each zygote develops into a tiny bivalved larval form known as a **glochidium** (Gr. *glochis,* point, + *idion,* dim.) (found only in freshwater clams) (Figure 11-8). Glochidia, about the size of dust particles, escape through the excurrent siphon. Glochidia have valves bearing hooks, by which they fasten themselves to gills, fins, or skin of a passing fish. Here they encyst and live as parasites for several weeks. After a growth period, the young clams break loose and sink to the bottom sand, where they develop as free-living adults. What advantages do the young clams derive from this relationship with fish? _____

Figure 11-8
Glochidium, larval form of freshwater bivalve molluscs. Each glochidium is about 0.3 mm in diameter.

If a female with a swollen brood pouch is available, make a wet mount of some gill contents and examine with a microscope to determine whether eggs or glochidia are present.

Nervous System

The nervous system of a clam is not highly centralized. Dissection of the nervous system is difficult and often impractical. Three pairs of **ganglia** (small groups of nerve cells) are connected to each other by nerves. **Cerebropleural ganglia** are found one on each side of the esophagus on the posterior surface of the anterior adductor muscle. **Pedal ganglia** are fused and are found in the anterior part of the foot. **Visceral ganglia** are fused into a star-shaped body just ventral to the posterior adductor muscle. They are covered by a yellowish membrane and are connected to the cerebropleural ganglia by nerves.

Sense organs are poorly developed in clams. They are involved with touch, chemical sensitivity, balance, and light sensitivity. They are most numerous on the edge of the mantle, particularly around the incurrent aperture, but you will not be able to see them. However, in scallops, such as *Pecten*, the ocelli are large and numerous, forming a distinctive row of steel-blue "eyes" along the edges of each mantle.

Oral Report

Be prepared to demonstrate your dissection and explain the clam's structures and their functions.

Projects and Demonstrations

1. *Cross section of entire clam after removal from the shell*. This study is made from prepared slides. What you will see in it depends to some extent on the region through which the body was cut. Identify **mantle, mantle cavity, gills, lamellae, water tubes, intestine, foot, suprabranchial space, gonad,** and other structures revealed in the cross section.

2. *Oysters, scallops, and sea clams*. Examine the shells of oysters, scallops, and sea clams.

3. *Shipworm,* Teredo.* Examine a piece of wood into which the wormlike molluscs, *Teredo*, have bored. Examine a preserved specimen of the shipworm. Note the small valves, the small body, and the prolonged siphon that make up the bulk of the shipworm.

---

*See Lane, C. E. 1961 The teredo. Sci. Amer. (Feb.); also interesting Wikipedia entries to shipworms on the web.

4. *Prepared stained slides of glochidia larvae*. Note especially the valves and muscles. Do they have **adhesive threads** between the valves?

5. *Female clam with glochidia in the gills*. Preserved specimens of clams with brood pouches (marsupia) may be studied. Which of the gills serve as brood pouches? How numerous are the glochidia?

6. *Effect of temperature on ciliary action of clam gill*. Remove a piece of bivalve gill and pin out on a layer of wax in a glass dish. Support the gill on two small glass rods approximately 1 cm apart. Place a 1 mm disc of aluminum foil on the surface of the gill and time its progress across a given distance. Cover with ice-cold water. Record rate of transport. As the water warms to room temperature, record rate at intervals of 5°. Judicial additions of slightly warmer water may also be tried. Make several determinations at each temperature and average. Make a diagram plotting mean rates of transport (millimeters/minute [mm/min]) against degrees of temperature.

7. *Experiments with the clam heart*. The heartbeat can be vividly demonstrated by passing a thread under the auricle and recording with a heart transducer and suitable chart recorder. 5-hydroxytryptamine is excitatory and acetylcholine is inhibitory in clam hearts. Both are applied directly on the exposed heart with a pipette as 1:10,000 solutions. Flush with saline (frog Ringers diluted 1:6 with water) after noting the effect of each drug.

EXERCISE 11B

Class Gastropoda— Pulmonate Land Snail

Land Snail

Phylum Mollusca
   Class Gastropoda
      Subclass Pulmonata
         Superorder Stylommatophora
            Genus *Helix, Polygyra*, others

Where Found

Most land snails (Figure 11-9) prefer fairly moist habitats. They are common in wooded areas, where they spend their days in the damp leaf mold on the ground, coming out to feed on the vegetation at night. *Helix* (Gr. *helix*, twisted) (Figure 11-9, top) is a large snail from southern Europe; *Polygyra* (Gr. *poly*, many, + *gyros*, round) is an American land snail.

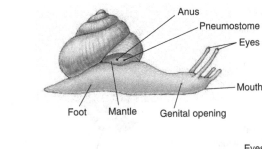

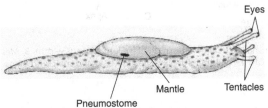

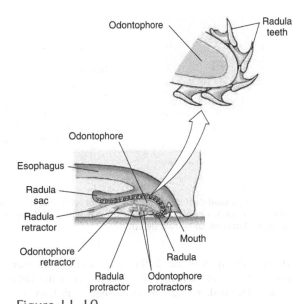

Figure 11-9

Common pulmonates. **Top,** *Helix,* a common land snail. **Bottom,** *Limax,* a common garden slug.

Figure 11-10

Diagrammatic longitudinal section of a gastropod head, showing the radula and radula sac. The radula moves back and forth over the odontophore cartilage. As the animal grazes, the mouth opens, the odontophore is thrust forward against the substratum, the teeth scrape food into the pharynx, the odontophore retracts, and the mouth opens. The sequence is repeated rhythmically.

The subclass Pulmonata constitutes one of three major groups of gastropods. Two other subclasses—Prosobranchia and Opisthobranchia—contain mainly marine snails and marine nudibranchs and tectibranchs.

Behavior

 Place a living snail in a finger bowl and, using the following suggestions, observe its behavior.

Studying a snail will take patience, for snails are unhurried. Can you detect muscular waves along its **foot** as it moves? Does it leave a trail on the glass as it travels? What causes this? _____ Place a piece of lettuce leaf near a snail and see whether it will eat. How long does it take the snail to find the food? _____ Note the **head** with its **tentacles.** How do the two pairs of tentacles differ? _____ Where are the **eyes** located? _____ Touch an anterior tentacle gently and describe what happens. _____ Touch some other parts of the body and note results. _____ Pick up a snail very carefully from the glass on which it is moving and observe exactly what it does.

 Place a land snail on a moistened glass plate and invert the plate over a dish, so that you can watch the ventral side of the foot under a dissecting microscope.

Do you see waves of motion? Can you see evidence of mucus? Of ciliary action? _____ If you are fortunate, you may see the action of the **radula**

(L., scraper) in the mouth. The radula is a series of tiny teeth attached to a ribbonlike organ that moves rapidly back and forth with an action like that of a rasp or file (Figure 11-10).

 Prop up the plate in a vertical position. Which direction does the snail move? Now rotate the plate 90°, so that the snail is at right angles to its former position. When it resumes its travels, in which direction does it move? Now rotate the plate again and observe.

Do you think the snail is influenced in its movements by the forces of gravity (geotaxis; refer to p. 106 for an explanation of taxes and the difference between a positive and a negative taxis)? _____ Try several snails. Do they respond in a similar manner?

The Shell

Examine the shell of a preserved specimen. Note the nature of the spiral shell. Is it symmetrical? _____ To what part of the clam shell does the **apex** correspond? _____ The body of the snail extends through the **aperture.** A **whorl** is one complete spiral turn of the shell. On the whorls are fine **lines of growth** running parallel to the edge of the aperture.

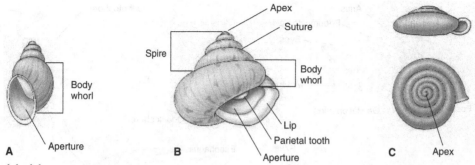

Figure 11-11

Structure of a snail shell. **A,** *Physa,* a sinistral, or left-handed, freshwater snail with lymnaeiform shell (height exceeds width). **B,** *Mesodon* (= *Polygyra*), a dextral (right-handed) snail with heliciform shell (width exceeds height). **C,** *Helicodiscus,* a land snail with planospiral, or flattened, spire (two views).

Holding the apex of the shell upward and the aperture toward you, note whether the aperture is at the right or left. **Dextral,** or right-handed, shells will have the aperture toward the right and **sinistral,** or left-handed, shells toward the left (Figure 11-11). Is your snail dextral or sinistral? _____ Examine a piece of broken shell for the characteristic three layers—the outer **periostracum,** the middle **prismatic layer,** and the shiny inner **nacre.**

Surface Anatomy

If the snail has not contracted enough during killing and preservation* to allow you to slip it carefully from the shell, you may use scissors to cut carefully around the spiral between the whorls, removing pieces of shell as you go and leaving only the central parts, or **columella** (L., pillar). Try not to damage the coiled part of the visceral mass.

The body is made up of **head,** muscular **foot,** and coiled **visceral hump** (Figure 11-12). Identify the **tentacles, eyes,** ventral **mouth** with three lips, and **genital aperture** just above and behind the right side of the mouth. The foot bears a **mucous gland** just below the mouth. Mucous secretions aid in locomotion.

Note the thin **mantle** that covers the visceral hump and forms the roof of the **mantle cavity.** It is thickened anteriorly to form the **collar** that secretes the shell.

Find a small opening, the **pneumostome** (Gr. *pneuma,* air, + *stoma,* mouth), under the edge of the collar (see Figure 11-9). It opens into a highly vascular portion of the mantle cavity, located in the first half-turn of the spiral, which serves as a respiratory chamber **(lung)** in pulmonates. Here diffusion of gases occurs

*Specimens from biological supply houses are usually narcotized before killing, which leaves the animal relaxed and expanded. This is best done by sealing snails in a jar of water, capped so as to exclude all air. Boiling (and then cooling) the water beforehand to drive out oxygen will shorten the asphyxiation time. Animals thus treated will be fully relaxed with antennae and foot extended.

between air and blood. Oxygen is carried by the pigment hemocyanin. Most aquatic gastropods possess gills. The mantle cavity in the second half-turn contains the heart and a large kidney.

The rest of the coiled visceral mass contains the dark lobes of the digestive gland, the intestine, the lighter-colored albumin gland (part of the reproductive system), and the ovotestis (Figure 11-12).

Projects and Demonstrations

1. *Example of a pond snail.* Watch a pond snail attached to the glass side of an aquarium. Note the broad foot by which it clings to the glass. Can you see the motion of the **radula** as the animal eats algae that has settled on the glass?

2. *Examples of other pulmonate snail shells*

3. *Shell-less pulmonate.* Examine a shell-less pulmonate, such as the common garden slug, *Limax* (Figure 11-9).

4. *Examples of shells of prosobranch snails.* Examine some prosobranchs, such as limpets, periwinkles, slipper shells, abalone, oyster drills, conchs, or whelks.

5. *Examples of opisthobranchs.* Examine some nudibranchs, such as sea slugs, and tectibranchs, such as sea hares and sea butterflies.

6. *Masses of fresh snail eggs.* Eggs of freshwater snails are frequently found on vegetation in aquaria where snails are kept or on leaves and stones in streams and ponds. Examine at intervals to follow the development of the embryo and young snails.

7. *Egg cases of marine snails.* Examine some egg cases, such as those of *Busycon* or *Fasciolaria.*

8. *Ciliary action in the intestine of a snail.* Obtain a live aquatic snail (preferably *Lymnaea stagnalis*). Cut open the shell and remove the viscera. Carefully slit open the body and remove the intestine.

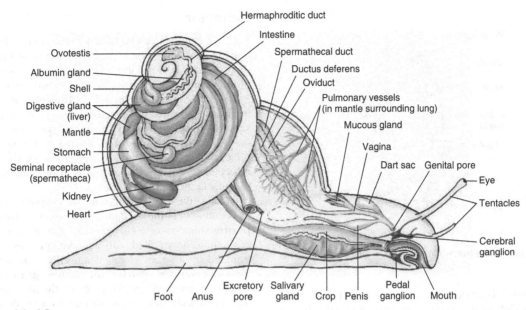

Figure 11-12
Anatomy of a pulmonate snail (diagrammatic).

Slit the intestine and place a small portion, intestinal surface up, on a slide in a drop of saline solution. Examine with high power of your microscope. Note the progressive undulations of cilia over the surface. Ciliary action is best seen some time after you have made the preparation. Are the cilia independent of nerve action? _____ Place a drop of warm (45° C) saline solution on the preparation and note what happens. What is the function of cilia in this region? _____

9. *Isolation of the radula of a snail.* Cut off the head of a snail and soak it in a 10% solution of KOH for 2 or 3 days or until the soft tissues are destroyed and only the radula remains. Transfer the radula to water and wash for 1 or 2 hours in running water. Pieces of attached tissues may be removed by gentle teasing with a needle. With a piece of paper on each side, place the radula between two glass slides bound together by strong rubber bands. In this position, dehydrate it in 50%, 95%, and 100% alcohols, clear in xylol, and mount with mounting medium.

EXERCISE 11C
Class Polyplacophora—Chitons

Chitons

Phylum Mollusca
    Class Polyplacophora
        Family Mopaliidae
            Genus *Katharina,* others

Where Found

Chitons (kyt'ens) are inconspicuous marine animals that live primarily in the rocky intertidal zone. They are "stay-at-homes" that move about mostly at night on short foraging expeditions, returning at night to exactly the same spot. Chitons adhere tightly to rocks with their broad, flat foot, which forms a suction cup that provides a tenacious hold, an important adaptation for an animal that lives in the pounding surf of high-energy, rocky shores. If pried from their resting place, they will curl up like an armadillo, with the eight overlapping dorsal plates providing a protective armor. Chitons feed by scraping algae and diatoms from rocks by a radula-odontophore complex similar to that of gastropod molluscs (see Figure 11-10). A few species are carnivorous.

External Structure

Examine a chiton, such as *Katharina tunicata.* A chiton's thick and leathery margin of the mantle is called the **girdle.** In many species, it partly covers the dorsal plates. Observe the ventral side of the chiton (Figure 11-13). Note the large, muscular foot on which the animal moves by waves of muscular activity, as in gastropods. The **head,** with its central **mouth,** is easily recognized anterior to the foot but is not highly developed. It bears no tentacles or eyes but has a subradular organ that can be extended from the mouth and is thought to be a taste organ (chemosensory). On each side of the body is a distinct groove that separates the foot and head from the mantle; this is the **mantle cavity.** Within this groove lies a single row of many delicate **gills,** or **ctenidia.** Cilia on the gills move a stream of water in

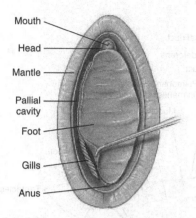

Figure 11-13

Ventral view of the chiton *Katharina tunicata.*

a posterior direction; the water emerges from a small median cleft in the girdle at the posterior end. Locate the **anus** at the posterior end of the mantle cavity. Just anterior to the anus are two excretory pores, one on each side of the foot. In *Katharina* these are located 1 to 2 cm anterior to the anus. Just anterior to each excretory pore is a reproductive pore.

The internal anatomy will not be examined in this exercise. The chiton has a long, coiled intestine with primarily extracellular digestion and a simple, ladder-like nervous system. Most chitons have separate sexes, external fertilization, and a trochophore larval stage that feeds on plankton until it settles and transforms into a juvenile chiton.

EXERCISE 11D

Class Cephalopoda—*Loligo,* the Squid

Loligo

Phylum Mollusca
 Class Cephalopoda
  Subclass Coleoidea
   Order Teuthoidea
    Genus *Loligo*

Where Found

Squids and octopuses are marine animals. Active squids are free-swimming and are found in offshore waters at various depths, whereas octopuses are often found in shallow tidal waters.

Squids range in size from 2 cm up. The giant squid *Architeuthis* (Gr. *archaios,* ancient, + *teuthis,* squid) may measure 15 m from tentacle tip to posterior end. *Loligo* (L., a cuttlefish) averages about 30 cm.

Behavior

Because squids ordinarily do not survive long in aquaria, they may not be available for observation. If they are, notice the swimming movements. A squid can move swiftly, either forward or backward, by using its fins and ejecting water through its **funnel.** When water is ejected forward, the squid moves backward; when water is ejected backward, the animal moves forward—movement by jet propulsion. Even when it is resting, there is a gentle, rhythmical movement of the fins, a muscular movement that also aids in bringing water to the gills in the mantle cavity.

Notice the color changes in the integument caused by contraction and expansion of many **chromatophores** (pigment cells) in the skin. Each chromatophore is a minute organ filled with pigment granules and surrounded by a series of radial muscles. Contraction of the radial muscles stretches the entire organ to form a sheet of pigmented cytoplasm. When the muscles relax, the organ with its pigment shrinks to a small sphere. The pigments, called **ommochromes,** may be black, red, brown, yellow, or orange. Colors appear suddenly when the chromatophores expand and may disappear just as quickly when the chromatophores shrink. Thus, the colors of squids (and those of most other cephalopod molluscs, such as octopuses) can change rapidly. Elaborate color changes that may sweep quickly across a squid's body serve as a complicated and highly developed means of communication. Chromatophores of cephalopod molluscs are quite different from those of vertebrates (frogs, for example), which are irregularly shaped cells containing pigment granules that can be concentrated into a small area or dispersed throughout the cell. No muscles are involved and pigment changes are much slower than those of the cephalopods.

When the animal is attacked, it can emit a cloud of ink from its ink sac through its funnel.

Food is caught by a pair of retractile tentacles extended with lightning speed, then is held and manipulated by the eight arms and killed by a poison injection. Small fishes, shrimps, and crabs are favorite foods.

External Structure

Squids are called "head-footed" because the end of the head, which bears tentacles, is homologous to the ventral side of the clam, and the tentacles represent a modification of the foot. To orient the animal morphologically, hold it with its pointed end uppermost; this is the dorsal "side" of the animal. The head, with the arms, tentacles, and funnel, is the ventral surface. The mouth is on the anterior surface, and the funnel is posterior. Functionally, however, the animal swims horizontally by moving forward and backward. Thus, the *morphological* anterior surface is the *functional* dorsal side, and the *morphological* ventral surface is the *functional* anterior side. We will use the morphological orientation in the following directions, as they are shown in Figure 11-14.

Notice the streamlined body, with the **head** and **arms** at one end and a pair of **lateral fins** at the other (Figure 11-14). The visceral mass, dorsal to the head, is covered with a thick **mantle,** the free end of which forms a loosely fitting **collar** about the neck. The head bears a pair of complex, highly advanced **eyes,** each with pupil, iris, cornea, lens, and retina, which can form clear images. The remarkable similarity of cephalopod and vertebrate eyes is an example of **convergent evolution,** in which two groups of organisms of completely different ancestry develop similar structures.

The head is drawn out into 10 appendages: 4 pairs of **arms,** each with 2 rows of stalked suckers, and 1 pair of long, retractile **tentacles,** with 2 rows of stalked suckers at the ends. The long tentacles can be shot out quickly to catch prey. The arms of males are longer and thicker than those of females. In a mature male, the left fourth arm becomes slightly modified for the transfer of spermatophores to a female. This transition is called **hectocotyly** (Gr. *hekaton,* hundred, + *kotylē,* cup). On the hectocotylized arm, some of the suckers are smaller and form an adhesion area for carrying the spermatophore.

The **mouth** lies within the circle of arms. It is surrounded by a **peristomial membrane,** around which

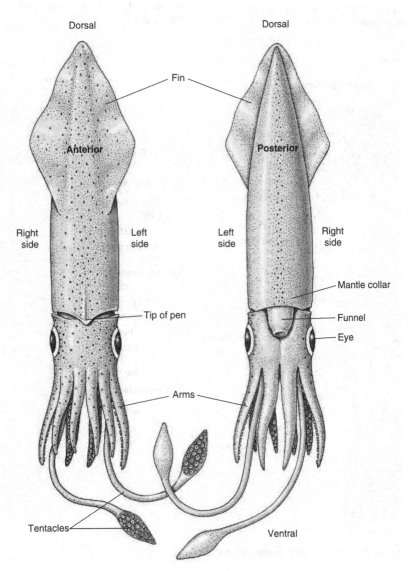

Figure 11-14
External structure of a squid. **Left,** anterior view. **Right,** posterior view.

is a **buccal membrane** with seven projections, each with suckers on the inner surface. Probe in the mouth to find two horny, beaklike **jaws.**

A muscular **funnel (siphon)** usually projects under the collar on the posterior side, but it may be partially withdrawn. Water forced through the funnel by muscular contraction of the mantle furnishes the power for jet propulsion locomotion. Wastes, sexual products, and ink are carried out by the current of water that enters through the collar and leaves through the funnel. The siphon, or funnel, of the squid is not homologous to the siphon of the clam; the clam siphon is a modification of the mantle, whereas the squid siphon, along with the arms and tentacles, is a modification of the foot.

The mottled appearance of the skin is caused by **chromatophores,** pigment cells.

Mantle Cavity

 Beginning near the funnel, make a longitudinal incision through the mantle from the collar to the tip. Pin out the mantle and cover with water.

The space between mantle and visceral mass is the **mantle cavity.** The mantle itself is made up largely of circular muscles covered with integument. The funnel contains both circular and longitudinal muscles.

Locate the interlocking **pallial cartilages** (Figure 11-15). They help support the funnel and close the space between the neck and the mantle, so that water inhaled around the collar can be expelled only by way of the funnel. Lateral to the funnel, find large, saclike valves that prevent outflow of water by way of the collar.

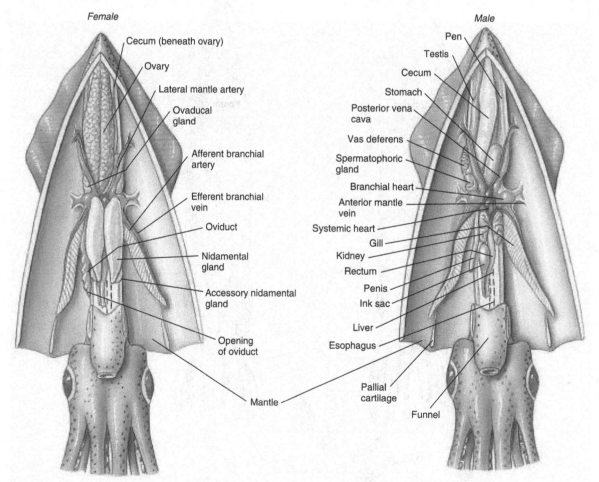

Figure 11-15

Posterior view of mantle cavity of a squid. **Left,** female. **Right,** male.

Slit open the funnel to see the muscular, tongue-like valve that prevents inflow of water through the funnel.

This valve allows a buildup of hydrostatic pressure in the mantle cavity before a jet stream of water is ejected through the funnel.

Locate a large pair of **funnel retractor muscles** and beneath them the even larger **head retractor muscles.** Locate the free end of the **rectum** with its **anus** near the inner opening of the funnel. Between it and the visceral mass is the **ink sac.** Do not puncture it. When a squid is endangered, it can send out a cloud of black ink through the funnel as it darts off in another direction.

A pair of long **gills** is attached at one end to the visceral mass and at the other to the mantle (Figure 11-15). They are located so that water entering the mantle cavity passes directly over them. Unlike in bivalves, the gills are not ciliated. The mantle cavity is ventilated by action of the mantle itself. Contraction of the radial muscles in the body wall causes the wall to become thinner and the capacity of the mantle cavity to become greater, so that water flows in around the collar. Water is then expelled through the funnel when mantle muscles contract. This movement, also used in locomotion, permits very efficient ventilation of the gills.

In most introductory laboratories, observation of the squid will end with study of the mantle cavity. For the more advanced laboratory or for the enterprising student, a study of internal structure follows.

Internal Structure

 A thin skin covers the organs of the visceral mass and encloses the **coelom.** Remove this membrane carefully as you expose the visceral organs. If the specimen is a female, a pair of large, whitish **nidamental** (L. *nidamentum,* nesting materials) glands (which secrete the outer capsules of the egg masses) should be carefully removed (Figure 11-15). Note their location and lay them aside for later study.

Remove the ink sac by separating it carefully from the rectum using fine, sharp-pointed scissors. Do not puncture the ink sac.

Respiratory and Circulatory Systems. At the base of each **gill** is a small, whitish, bulblike **branchial heart** (gill heart) (Figure 11-15). Deoxygenated blood from the branchial heart is carried to the gill by the afferent **branchial artery,** and oxygenated blood is returned by an efferent **branchial vein** to the **systemic heart** (true heart), a larger, whitish organ lying between

the branchial hearts. The systemic heart may be partially hidden by the more anterior **kidneys,** which have a spongelike texture, and the pancreas, seen later in dissection. Each branchial heart receives deoxygenated blood from a large, thin-walled, conical **posterior vena cava.** Each branchial heart also receives blood from a fork of the **anterior vena cava** (cephalic vein, not easily visible) and from a small **anterior mantle vein.** The systemic heart pumps oxygenated blood through the **cephalic aorta** (anterior, not visible in Figure 11-15) and the short **posterior aorta,** which branches immediately to form the **lateral mantle arteries** and the single **median mantle artery** (not shown in Figure 11-15; this artery extends to the mantle and will have been severed when the mantle cavity was opened).

Excretory System. A pair of **kidneys,** somewhat triangular in shape, of spongy texture, and usually white or pale in uninjected specimens, lies between and slightly anterior to the branchial hearts. The kidneys will have the color of the injection fluid, if your specimen was injected. A **renal papilla** lies at the anterior tip of each kidney.

Digestive System.

 Remove the siphon by cutting first the siphon retractor muscles and then the lateral siphon valves and the two small protractor muscles extending between the head and the siphon. Cut between the two ventral arms to expose the **pharynx** (buccal bulb). Cut away the **buccal** and **peristomial membranes** to expose the chitinous **jaws.** Dissect away the overlapping lower jaw and find a tonguelike cartilage, bearing the **radula.** Remove the radula and examine under a microscope, sketching the arrangement of its minute teeth.

The **esophagus** leads down through the cream-colored **liver,** a soft, pale organ lying between the head retractor muscles. It emerges from the posterior end of the liver and passes through the **pancreas,** which is exposed by scraping away kidney tissue between the bases of the gills. The esophagus then leads to a thick-walled, muscular **stomach** (in some specimens, filled with food), which lies somewhat posterior to the systemic heart. By removing some of the pancreatic tissue, the systemic heart now comes into view. The stomach communicates directly with the **cecum,** a large, delicate, thin-walled sac that may, when filled with partially liquified food, fill much of the posterior mantle cavity. The **intestine** leaves the stomach near the entrance of the esophagus and passes *anteriorly* to the **rectum** and **anus.** Open and rinse out the cecum and examine on its ventral surface the fan-shaped **spiral valve,** a complex system of ciliated folds used to sort food particles.

The **ink sac** is a diverticulum of the intestine located back of the rectum and anus. It secretes a dark fluid of melanin pigment that is carried to the rectum by a short duct.

Nervous System. Push the head to one side to see a pair of large **stellate ganglia** on the inner surface of the mantle close to the neck. These ganglia function in movement of the mantle. From each ganglion, several large nerves radiate out over the inner mantle surface. Each nerve contains, along with smaller fibers, one of the giant fibers, which are used in rapid maximal contraction of the mantle. Directions will not be given here for dissection of the brain, which is composed of ganglia lying partly above and partly below the esophagus.

Sense Organs. Sense organs of cephalopods are highly developed. The **eyes** are capable of forming an image. Remove the thin, outer, transparent integument **(false cornea)** to uncover the **true cornea.** Cut away the cornea to observe the circular **iris diaphragm.** Behind the iris is an almost spherical **lens,** suspended by a **ciliary muscle.** Remove the lens to see the darkly pigmented sensory lining **(retina)** of the optic cavity.

A fold of tissue behind each eye and somewhat covered by the edge of the mantle contains a sensory area assumed to be olfactory in function. Sensory cells are numerous in the skin, particularly in the rims of the suckers. **Statocysts** are found embedded in the cartilages on each side of the brain.

Reproductive Organs. In males, the **testis** is an elongated, light-colored organ in the posterior coelomic cavity, usually partly concealed by the cecum (Figure 11-15). Sperm are shed into the coelomic cavity from an opening in the testis and swept by ciliary currents into the enlarged free end of the **vas deferens.** Sperm pass through the convoluted vas deferens to an enlarged, convoluted tubule, the **spermatophoric gland.** Here sperm are packaged into spermatophores (capsules that enclose the sperm), which are stored in the **spermatophoric sac** (not shown in Figure 11-15). The spermatophoric sac lies posterior to the spermatophoric gland and adjacent

to the vas deferens. During copulation, the fingerlike processes at the tip of the hectocotylized arm take the spermatophores from the **penis** and transfer them to the female.

In females, the **nidamental glands** (removed earlier) are conspicuous white organs filling most of the lower part of the mantle cavity. The **ovary** lies posterior and sheds eggs into the coelomic cavity. Push the ovary to one side and try to locate the **oviduct** (it may be covered by the cecum). Near the left branchial heart, the oviduct enlarges into the **oviducal gland,** which secretes the egg shell. The oviduct continues anteriorly beside the nidamental glands to its flared opening, the **ostium,** in the mantle cavity. A mature female has a small pouch, or **sperm receptacle,** on the buccal membrane in the median ventral line, where a male may place the spermatophore. In the process of mating, the male may thrust the spermatophores inside the female's mantle cavity or into the sperm receptacle.

A female uses one of her arms to pick up strings of eggs as they come from her siphon, fertilizes them with spermatozoa from the pouch, and then attaches the strings to some object in the sea. The young hatch in 2 to 3 weeks.

Skeletal System. Dissect out the chitinous **pen** that lies dorsal to the visceral organs and extends from the free edge of the collar to the apex of the mantle. There are also a number of **cartilages** in the head, near the siphon, and in the mantle.

Demonstrations

1. *Microslides showing spermatophores of* Loligo
2. *Preserved octopuses and cuttlefish* (Sepia)
3. *Shells of* Nautilus
4. *Dried cuttlebone of* Sepia
5. *Dissection of an injected cephalopod to show circulatory system*
6. *Dissection of a cephalopod brain*
7. *Living cephalopod, if available*

14

The Crustacean Arthropods

EXERCISE 14A

Subphylum Crustacea—Crayfish, Lobsters, and Other Crustaceans

U ntil recently crustaceans, insects, and myriapods (millipedes and centipedes) were all placed in a single subphylum, Mandibulata, of the phylum Arthropoda because all possess mandibles. However, a growing body of opinion among zoologists contends that the mandibles of the crustaceans and the mandibles of insects and myriapods are not homologous but are the result of convergent evolution from separate origins. Consequently crustaceans are now placed in a separate subphylum, Crustacea.

Crustaceans are **gill-breathing arthropods,** with **two pairs of antennae** and **two pairs of maxillae** on the head and usually a pair of appendages on each body segment. Some of the appendages of present-day adult crustaceans are biramous (two-branched).

Crayfish or Lobster

Phylum Arthropoda
 Subphylum Crustacea
  Class Malacostraca
   Order Decapoda
    Genus *Cambarus*

The following description applies to either crayfish (*Cambarus, Procambarus, Pacifastacus,* and *Orconectes*) or lobsters (*Homarus* and others), for crayfish and lobsters are very similar, except in size.

Where Found

Crayfish, called locally and variously crawfish, crawdads, and mudbugs, are found in freshwater streams and ponds all over the world. *Pacifastacus* (Pacific, fr. L. *pacificus,* peace, + Gr. *astakos,* crayfish) is found mainly west of the Rocky Mountains, *Procambarus* in the southern states, and *Cambarus* (Gr. *kammaros,* lobster) and *Orconectes* are widely distributed east of the Rocky Mountains. There are about 350 species of crayfish in the United States, more species of crayfish than in all the rest of the world. The southern United

EXERCISE 14A

Subphylum Crustacea—Crayfish, Lobsters, and Other Crustaceans
Crayfish or lobster
Other crustaceans
Crustacean development, exemplified by brine shrimp
Projects and demonstrations

EXPERIMENTING IN ZOOLOGY
The Phototactic Behavior of *Daphnia*

States, especially the Gulf Coast, has the largest number of crayfish species. This area also produces most edible crayfish, and millions are raised each year on watery crayfish "farms" in Louisiana.

Crayfish are omnivorous, feeding on all kinds of succulent aquatic vegetation and on animals such as snails, worms, and small vertebrates. Crayfish are hearty animals, able to survive in almost any type of freshwater habitat. Rusty crayfish *(Orocnectes rusticus),* while native to some parts of the Great Lakes, have spread to many habitats where they do not naturally occur. Similarly, the red swamp crayfish*(Procambarus clarkii),* native to the Mississippi drainage, has spread to many western states. In both cases, the crayfish are sold as fishing bait and have likely spread to new locations when fishermen have emptied their bait buckets into habitats where the crayfish do not naturally occur. When nonnative crayfish are introduced into new habitats, they quickly become established and can harm the biological community by feeding on native freshwater invertebrates and amphibians. Crayfish should not be introduced into habitats where they are not naturally found.

The lobster is a marine form. *Homarus americanus* (F. *homard,* lobster) is found along the eastern North American coast from Labrador to North Carolina. Both lobsters and crayfish are widely used for food in various parts of the world. The spiny, or rock, lobster, *Panulirus* (anagram of *Palinurus,* Gr. *palin,* backwards, + *oura,* tail), from the West Coast and southern Atlantic Coast, has no pincers and differs from *Homarus* in several other respects.

Behavior

Place a live crayfish or lobster in a bowl or small aquarium partly filled with water. Provide some shells or stones for shelter.

How are the antennae used? _____ _____What is the response when you stroke the antennae? _____ Notice the compound eyes on the ends of stalks. Are the eyestalks movable? _____ Of what advantage would such eyes be to the animal? _____ _____What evidence of segmentation do you see on the dorsal side of the animal? ____ _____

Note the five pairs of legs. The first pair are called chelipeds because they bear the large claws (chelae). How are the chelipeds used? _____ _____When the animal is startled, what does it do? _____ Is the escape movement forward or backward? _____ How is it accomplished? _____ Is the tail fan involved? _____

Lift up a crayfish and notice the swimmerets on the abdomen. Release it near the surface of the water. Can it swim? _____ How? _____ _____The females use the swimmerets to carry and aerate eggs during the breeding season.

Drop a bit of meat or fish near an undisturbed crayfish in an aquarium. What appendages are used to pick up and handle food? _____ Notice the activity of the small mouth appendages as the animal feeds.

External Features

Place a preserved crayfish or lobster in a dissecting pan and add water to the pan.

The **exoskeleton** is a cuticle secreted by the epidermis and hardened with a nitrogenous polysaccharide called **chitin,** with the addition of mineral salts, such as calcium carbonate. The cuticle must be shed, or **molted** (ecdysis), several times while the crayfish is growing, each time being replaced by a new, soft exoskeleton, which soon hardens. During and immediately after molting, crayfish spend a great deal of time immobile and hiding. Why? _____

The **cephalothorax** is covered by a hard **carapace.** A transverse **cervical groove** marks the head-thorax fusion line. Posterior to this groove are two grooves that separate the median middorsal cardiac area of the carapace, which covers the heart, from the broad lateral extensions of the carapace, which cover the gills. These lateral extensions are also called **branchiostegites** ("gill-cover"). Lift up the edge of the branchiostegite to disclose the **gill chamber** and feathery **gills.**

Extending anteriorly in the head region is the pointed **rostrum** (L., bill, snout), and coming from under the rostrum are the stalked **eyes** and two pairs of **antennae** (the second pair of antennae are also called antennules).

On the ventral side, the five fused segments of the head bear two pairs of antennae and three pairs of small mouthparts. The thorax, made up of eight segments, bears three pairs of **maxillipeds** and five pairs of walking legs.

The **abdomen** is made up of six segments, the first five of which bear the **swimmerets** (also called **pleopods**) (Figure 14-1B). The sixth is a flat process, the **telson** (Gr., extremity), which bears the **anus** on the ventral side and a pair of fan-shaped **uropods.**

Genital Openings. In males the genital openings of the sperm ducts are located medially at the base of each of the fifth walking legs (Figure 14-2). In females the genital openings of the oviducts are located at the base of each third walking leg. Where is the opening of the seminal receptacle? _____ During copulation the male turns the female over and presses the sperm along grooves of the specialized first (copulatory) swimmerets into the seminal receptacle of the female.

Dissection of the Appendages

As you dissect crayfish appendages, you will see how they illustrate the principle of **serial homology.** In crayfish and their relatives, the common biramous appendage became modified into mouthparts, walking legs, chelipeds, and swimmerets with different functions. During evolution some of the biramous branches became lost or modified, and new parts were added. This condition is called **serial homology,** the evolution of a series of structures all homologous to each other but modified for different functions. Crayfish and their relatives possess the best examples of serial homology in the animal kingdom.

From the animal's left side, remove and study each of the appendages. However, do not remove any appendages until you have read the instructions.

Although appendages are numbered consecutively beginning at the anterior end of the animal, it is easier to remove them by beginning at the **posterior** end and proceeding forward. To remove an appendage, grasp it at the base with forceps as near the body as possible and work it loose gradually by gently manipulating the forceps back and forth. Some of the appendages are quite small and feathery, and some are attached to gills. *Be very careful to remove all of the parts of each appendage together* (Figure 14-3). As you remove each one, identify its **medial** and **lateral** sides. Pin the appendages in order on a sheet of paper in the bottom of a dissecting pan. Keep covered with water. Alternatively, the

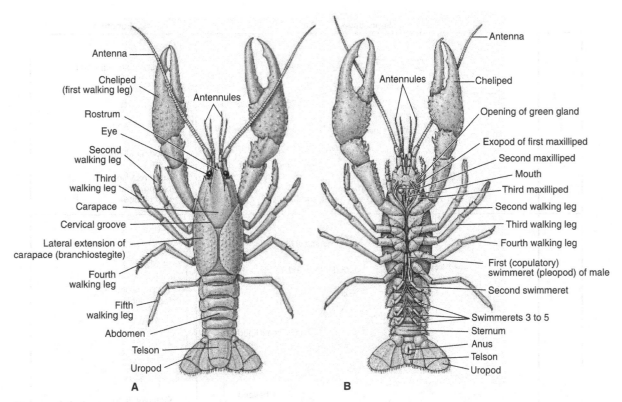

Figure 14-1
External structure of crayfish. **A,** Dorsal view. **B,** Ventral view.

appendages may be glued (e.g., with Elmer's Glue-All) in order on a piece of white cardboard and labeled.

Uropods. The broad uropods (Gr. *oura,* tail, + *pous,* foot) on the most posterior segment are biramous; together with the medial telson, they make up the strong

tail fan that is used in the rapid backward movements so important in escape. The tail fan also helps protect eggs and young on the female's swimmerets.

Swimmerets (Pleopods). Swimmerets illustrate the biramous plan.

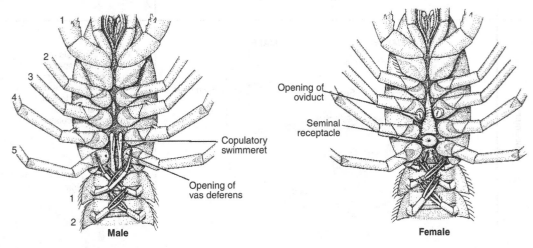

Figure 14-2
Ventral views of crayfish, male and female.

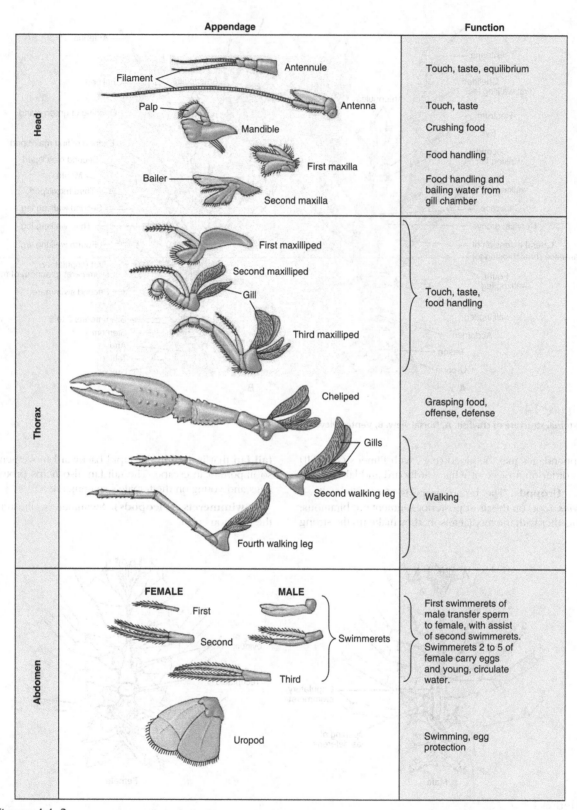

Appendage	Function

Head

Antennule — Touch, taste, equilibrium

Filament

Palp

Antenna — Touch, taste

Mandible — Crushing food

First maxilla — Food handling

Bailer

Second maxilla — Food handling and bailing water from gill chamber

Thorax

First maxilliped

Second maxilliped

Gill

Third maxilliped — Touch, taste, food handling

Cheliped — Grasping food, offense, defense

Gills

Second walking leg

Fourth walking leg — Walking

Abdomen

FEMALE   MALE

First

Second — Swimmerets — First swimmerets of male transfer sperm to female, with assist of second swimmerets. Swimmerets 2 to 5 of female carry eggs and young, circulate water.

Third

Uropod — Swimming, egg protection

Figure 14-3
Appendages of crayfish. Protopod in pink; endopod in blue; exopod in yellow.

The first two pairs in males are modified as **copulatory organs.** They are large and grooved and used to direct sperm onto females (see Figure 14-2). The first pair in the female is usually reduced in size. What is the function of the swimmerets? _____

The part of the appendage attached to the body is called the **protopod.** The medial branch is the **endopod,** and the lateral branch is the **exopod.**

Walking Legs (Pereiopods). The first (most anterior) pair of walking legs are **chelipeds,** with enlarged claws **(chelae)** used in defense. The other four pairs are used in walking and food handling. There is no exopod, so they are called **uniramous** (single-branched). The first four pairs are attached to gills. Which of the four pairs of walking legs bear chelae? _____

Maxillipeds. Each of the three paired maxillipeds (L. *maxilla,* jaw, + *pes,* foot) has an endopod and a very slender exopod. Be sure to obtain both in removing the appendage. Remove the third (most posterior) maxilliped and its attached gill.

The second and first maxillipeds are similar to the third but smaller. The first maxilliped bears no gill. The maxillipeds are food handlers that break up food and move it to the mouth.

Maxillae. The maxillae anterior to the maxillipeds are foliaceous (thin and leaflike) and direct food toward the mouth. On the second maxilla, the protopod is expanded into four little processes, the endopod is small and pointed, and the exopod forms a long blade called the **gill bailer,** which beats to draw currents of water from the gill chambers.

Mandibles. The mandibles on each side of the mouth are heavy, triangular structures, bearing teeth on their inner edges. These are protopods. A little palp folded above each tooth margin represents the endopod. The exopod is absent. Mandibles work from side to side to direct food into the mouth and to hold it while the maxillipeds tear it up. Pry the mandibles apart and remove the left mandible carefully. A strong mandibular muscle attached to the base may tear off with the mandible.

Antennae. The endopod of each antenna is a very long, many-jointed filament. The exopod is a broad, sharp, movable projection near the base. On its broad protopod on the ventral side of the head is the **renal opening** from the excretory gland. Antennae and antennules are sensitive to touch, vibrations, and the chemistry of the water (taste). When you fed the crayfish, how were the antennae used? _____

Antennules. Each antennule has a three-jointed protopod as well as two long, many-jointed filaments. The antennules are also concerned with equilibrium.

Branchial (Respiratory) System

Remove part of the carapace on the animal's right side and note the feathery **gills** lying in the branchial chamber. You have already seen that some of the gills are attached to certain appendages. These outer gills are called the foot gills. How many appendages have gills attached? _____ Move the appendages to determine this. Separate the gills carefully, laying aside the foot gills. Another row of gills underneath is attached to membranes that hold the appendages to the body. These gills are called joint gills. Some genera, but not *Cambarus,* have a third row of gills (side gills) attached to the body wall.

 Remove a gill, place it in a watch glass, cover with water, and examine with a hand lens. Now cut the gill in two and look at one of the cut ends.

The **central axis** bears **gill filaments** that give it a feathery appearance. Notice that the central axis and the little filaments contain canals. These represent blood vessels (afferent and efferent) that enter and leave the filaments. What do the terms "afferent" and "efferent" mean? _____ What happens to blood as it passes through the filaments? _____ Water enters the gill chamber by the free ventral edge of the carapace and is drawn forward over the gills by action of the gill bailer of the second maxilla, facilitated by movements of the other appendages.

Internal Structure

 Remove the dorsal portion of the exoskeleton by inserting the point of a scissors under the posterior edge of the lateral carapace about 1.3 cm to one side of the medial line. Cut forward to a point about 1 cm posterior to the eye. Do the same on the other side, thus loosening a dorsal strip about 2.5 cm wide. Carefully remove this center portion of the carapace, a little at a time, being careful not to remove the underlying **epidermis** and **muscles,** which cling to the carapace, especially in the head region. Loosen such tissue with a scalpel and push it carefully back into place.

 Remove the dorsal portion of the abdominal exoskeleton in the same way, uncovering each segment carefully so as not to destroy the long **extensor muscle** lying underneath.

The thin tissue covering the viscera is **epidermis,** which secretes the exoskeleton. Notice the position of the pinkish portion of the epidermis, which lies in the same position as the cardiac region of the carapace. This covers the **pericardial sinus** containing the **heart.** The sinus may be filled with colored latex if the circulatory system has been injected for easy identification.

 Remove the epidermis carefully with forceps to expose the viscera.

The large **stomach** lies in the head region, anterior to the heart (Figure 14-4). On each side of the stomach and heart are large, cream-colored lobes of the **hepatopancreas** (digestive gland). They extend the full length of the thorax. This gland is the largest organ in the body.

Muscular System. As you removed the carapace, you noticed the tendency of certain muscles in the head region to cling to it. These are **gastric muscles,** which attach the stomach to the carapace (Figure 14-4B). On each side of the stomach lies a little mass of muscle, **mandibular muscles,** which move the mandibles. One of these may have been removed when the mandible was removed. On each side of the thorax, a narrow band of muscles runs longitudinally to the distal end of the abdomen. These are **extensor muscles,** which are used to straighten the abdomen. In the abdomen, lying ventrally to the extensors and nearly filling the abdomen, are **flexor muscles,** which flex the abdomen (bend it ventrally). Why are these muscles so large?

Circulatory System. The small, angular **heart** is located just posterior to the stomach. If the circulatory system has been injected, the heart may be filled and covered with a mass of colored injection fluid or latex filling the sinus. Remove the latex carefully bit by bit, being careful not to destroy the tiny blood vessels leaving the heart. The heart lies in a cavity called the **pericardial sinus,** which is enclosed in a membrane, the **pericardium.** The pericardium may have been removed with the carapace.

This is an open type of circulatory system. The hemolymph leaves the heart in arteries but returns to it by way of venous sinuses, or spaces, instead of veins. Hemolymph enters the heart through three pairs of slit-like openings, **ostia,** which open to receive hemolymph and then close when the heart contracts to force out hemolymph through the arteries.

Your instructor may want to demonstrate the heartbeat of a living crayfish (instructions given on p. 220).

Five arteries leave the anterior end of the heart (Figure 14-4): a median **ophthalmic artery** (Gr. *ophthalmos,* eye) extends forward to supply the cardiac stomach, esophagus, and head; a pair of **antennal arteries,** one on each side of the ophthalmic, passes diagonally forward and downward over the digestive gland to supply the stomach, antennae, antennal glands, and parts of the head; and a pair of **hepatic arteries** (Gr. *hepatos,* liver) from the ventral surface of the heart supplies the hepatopancreas.

Leaving the posterior end of the heart are the **dorsal abdominal artery,** which extends the length of the abdomen, lying on the dorsal side of the intestine, and the **sternal artery,** which runs straight down (ventrally) to beneath the nerve cord, where it divides into

the **ventral thoracic** and **ventral abdominal arteries,** which supply the appendages and other ventral structures (Figure 14-4). Do not attempt to find these ventral arteries now. They will be referred to later.

Reproductive System. The **gonads** in each sex lie just under the heart. Their size and prominence will depend on the season in which the animals were killed. To find them, lay aside the heart and abdominal extensor muscle bands. The gonads are very slender organs, usually slightly different in color from the digestive glands, lying along the medial line between and slightly above the glands. The gonads are sometimes difficult to distinguish from the digestive glands.

In females the gonads, or **ovaries,** are slender and pinkish, lying side by side, with anterior ends slightly raised. In some seasons, the ovaries may be swollen and greatly distended with eggs, appearing orange. A pair of **oviducts** leaves the ovaries and passes laterally over the digestive glands to the genital openings on the third walking legs.

Male gonads, or **testes,** are white and delicate. **Sperm ducts** pass diagonally over the digestive glands and back to the openings in the fifth walking legs (Figure 14-4A).

Digestive System. The **stomach** is a large, thin-walled organ, lying just back of the rostrum. It is made up of two parts—anteriorly a large, firm **cardiac chamber** and posteriorly a smaller, soft **pyloric chamber.** These will be examined later.

Sometimes a mass of calcareous crystals (**gastroliths**) is attached to each side of the cardiac chamber near the time of molting. These limy masses are thought to have been recovered from the old exoskeleton by the blood and used in making the new exoskeleton.

The **intestine,** small and inconspicuous, leaves the pyloric chamber, bends down to pass under the heart, and then rises posteriorly to run along the abdominal length above the large flexor muscles. The intestine ends at the **anus** on the telson.

The large **hepatopancreas,** also called **liver** or **digestive glands** (Figure 14-4), furnishes digestive secretions that are poured through hepatic ducts into the pyloric chamber. The hepatopancreas also is the chief site of absorption and storage of food reserves.

 To see the whole length of the digestive system, remove the left lobe of the hepatopancreas and gonad and push aside the left mandibular muscle.

You can now see the **esophagus,** connecting the stomach and mouth, and the intestine, arising from the stomach and running posteriorly to the abdomen, where it lies just ventral to the dorsal abdominal artery. You can also see the **sternal artery** descending ventrally.

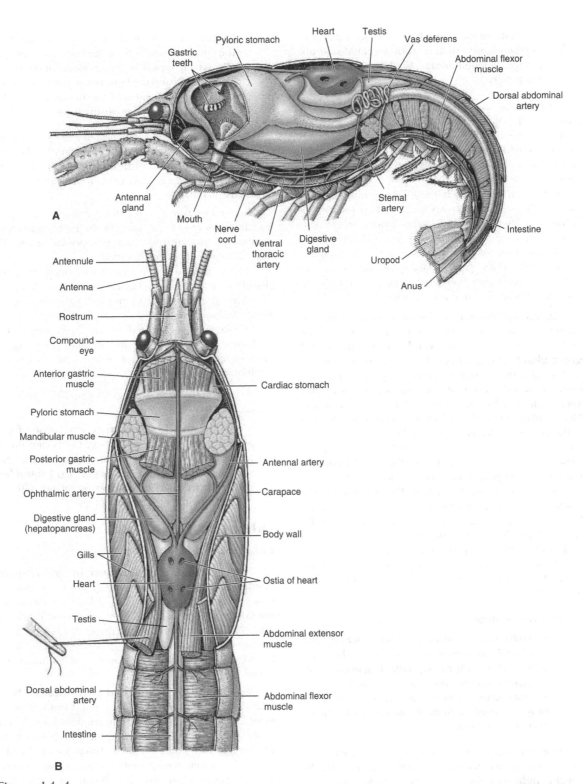

Figure 14-4

Internal structure of male crayfish. **A,** Lateral view. **B,** Dorsal view. What median artery extends forward from the heart to supply the cardiac stomach, esophagus, and head? _____ What pair of arteries pass diagonally forward and downward over the digestive gland to supply the stomach, antennae, antennal glands, and part of the head? _____ What artery leaves the posterior of the heart? _____

Now remove the stomach by severing it from the esophagus and intestine, turn it ventral side up, and open it longitudinally. Wash out the contents, if necessary.

The cardiac chamber of the stomach contains a **gastric mill,** which consists of a set of three chitinous teeth, one dorsomedial and two lateral, which are used for grinding food. They are held by a framework of ossicles and bars in the stomach and operated by the gastric muscles.

In the cardiac stomach, the food is ground up and partially digested by enzymes from the hepatopancreas before it is filtered into the smaller pyloric stomach in liquid form. Large particles must be egested through the esophagus. Rows of setae and folds of the stomach lining strain the finest particles and pass them from the pyloric stomach into the hepatopancreas or into the intestine, where digestion is completed.

Excretory System. In the head region anterior to the digestive glands and lying against the anterior body wall is a pair of **antennal glands** (also called **green glands,** though they will not appear green in the preserved material) (Figure 14-4). They are round and cushion-shaped. In crayfish each gland contains an **end sac,** connected by an excretory tubule to a bladder. Fluid is filtered into the end sac by hydrostatic pressure in the hemocoel. As filtrate passes through the excretory tubule, reabsorption of salts and water occurs, leaving urine to be excreted. A duct from the bladder empties through a renal pore at the base of each antenna.

How would urine production differ between freshwater crayfish and marine lobster? _____ Why? _____ The role of the antennal glands seems to be largely regulation of the ionic and osmotic composition of body fluids.

Excretion of nitrogenous wastes (mostly ammonia) occurs by diffusion in the gills and across thin areas of the cuticle.

Nervous System.

Carefully remove all of the viscera, leaving the esophagus and sternal artery in place. The brain is a pair of **supraesophageal ganglia** that lie against the anterior body wall between the antennal glands. Can you distinguish three pairs of nerves running from the ganglia to antennae, eyes, and antennules?

From the brain, two connectives pass around the esophagus, one on each side, and unite at the **subesophageal ganglion** on the floor of the cephalothorax.

Chip away the calcified plates that cover and conceal the double ventral nerve cord in the thorax and follow the cord posteriorly. By removing the big flexor muscles in the abdomen, you can trace the cord for the length of the body. Note the ganglia, which appear as enlargements of the cord at intervals. Observe where the nerve cord divides to pass on both sides of the sternal artery. Note the small lateral nerves arising from the cord.

In annelids there is a ganglion in each segment, but in arthropods there is some fusion of ganglia. The brain is formed by the fusion of three pairs of head ganglia, and the subesophageal ganglion is formed by the fusion of at least five pairs.

Sense Organs. Crayfish have many sense organs: **tactile hairs** over many parts of the body, **statocysts, antennae, antennules,** and **compound eyes.** The eyes have already been observed.

Tactile hairs are specialized for touch reception, detection of water currents, and orientation. A number of chemoreceptors are present on the antennae, antennules, and mouthparts.

A **statocyst** is located in the basal segment of each antennule. The pressure of sand grains against sensory hairs in the statocyst gives crayfish a sense of equilibrium.

Oral Report

Be prepared to demonstrate any phase of your dissection to your instructor. (1) Locate on the dissection any structure mentioned in the exercise and (2) explain its function. (3) Explain how the appendages of crayfish or lobster illustrate the principle of serial homology.

Other Crustaceans

Class Branchiopoda

Fairy Shrimp, *Eubranchipus* or *Branchinecta* (Order Anostraca). Fairy shrimp have 11 pairs of basically similar appendages used for locomotion, respiration, and egg carrying. They swim ventral side up. They have no carapace. Note the dark eyes borne on unsegmented stalks. Females carry eggs in a ventral brood sac, which can usually be seen when the animal is moving (Figure 14-5).

Water Flea, *Daphnia* (Order Cladocera). Water fleas (Figure 14-5) are common in pond water. Mount a living *Daphnia* on a slide, using enough water to prevent crushing but not enough to allow free swimming. *Daphnia* is 1 to 3 mm long and, except for the head, is covered by a thin, transparent carapace. Large biramous second antennae are the chief organs of locomotion. There are five pairs of small, leaflike swimmerets on the thorax. These are used to filter microscopic algae from the water for food. Blood in the open system is red from the presence of hemoglobin. The paired eyes are fused.

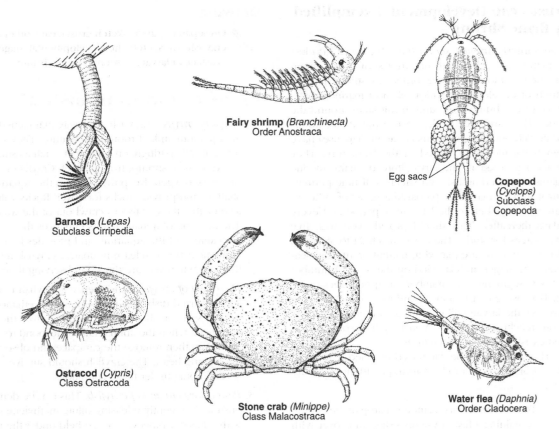

Figure 14-5
Some representative crustaceans.

The brood pouch in females is large and posterior to the abdomen. They can reproduce parthenogenetically. (See p. 220 for demonstration of heartbeat.)

See the Experimenting in Zoology feature at the end of this chapter for a study of the phototactic behavior of *Daphnia.*

Class Maxillopoda

Subclass Ostracoda. Ostracods with their transparent bivalved carapace resemble tiny clams (1 to 2 mm). They have a median eye and seven pairs of appendages, including large antennules and antennae (Figure 14-5).

Subclass Copepoda. *Cyclops* and other copepods are found everywhere in fresh and brackish water. *Cyclops* has a median eye near the base of the rostrum and long antennae, modified in males. The cephalothorax bears appendages; the abdomen has none. The sixth thoracic segment in females carries large, pendulous egg sacs. The last abdominal segment bears a pair of caudal projections covered with setae (Figure 14-5).

Subclass Cirripedia. Barnacles (all marine) might be mistaken for molluscs because they are enclosed in a calcareous shell. *Balanus,* the acorn barnacle, has a six-piece shell that surrounds the animal like a parapet. The animal protrudes its six pairs of biramous appendages through the opening at the top to create water currents and sweep in plankton and particles of detritus.

The gooseneck barnacle, *Lepas* (Figure 14-5), attaches to floating objects by a long stalk, the drawnout front part of the head. The body proper is enclosed in a bivalve carapace strengthened by calcareous plates. Six pairs of delicate filamentous and biramous appendages can be protruded from the carapace. Feathery with long setae, the appendages form an effective net to strain food particles from the water.

Class Malacostraca

Class Malacostraca is a large group. It includes the Isopoda (sow bugs, pill bugs, wood lice, and others with a dorsoventrally flattened body); Amphipoda (beach fleas, freshwater *Gammarus,* and others that are laterally compressed); and Decapoda (shrimps, crabs, crayfish, and lobsters).

 Examine a crab (Figure 14-5) and compare its structure and appendages with those of crayfish.

Crustacean Development, Exemplified by Brine Shrimp

Brine shrimp, *Artemia salina* (Gr. *Artemis,* a goddess of mythology), which are not true shrimp but members of the more primitive order Anostraca, have a pattern of development typical of most marine crustaceans. Brine shrimp are found in salt lakes around the world. They are filter feeders. Since the 1930s, adults and cysts (containing nauplius larvae in diapause) have been harvested and cultured in the laboratory. They are used as food in the larviculture of many marine organisms, including fish and shellfish. If time permits, your instructor may have prepared a series of cultures, started 10 days before the laboratory period and every 2 days thereafter. This should provide you with five larval stages for study. The larvae hatch 24 to 48 hours after the dry cysts are placed in natural or artificial seawater. The stages are classified on the basis of number of body segments and number of appendages present. Because growth cannot continue without molting (ecdysis), the larvae will go through a number of molts before reaching adult size. You may find some of the shed exoskeletons in the cultures.

The animals can be narcotized or killed if you add a few drops of ether or chloroform per 10 ml of culture water.

 To observe the larvae, mount a drop of the culture containing a few larvae on a slide and cover with a coverslip. Try to identify the stages listed in the following text.

Nauplius. A newly hatched larva, called a nauplius, has a single median ocellus and three pairs of appendages (two pairs of antennae and one pair of mandibles), and the trunk is still unsegmented.

Metanauplius. The first and second maxillae have developed, and there is some thoracic segmentation.

Protozoea. There are now seven pairs of appendages because the first and second pairs of maxillipeds have been added. Compound eyes are developing.

Zoea. The third pair of maxillipeds has now appeared. The eyes are complete and there are several thoracic segments.

Mysis. Most or all of the 19 body segments and 11 pairs of appendages found in the adult are now present. In these transparent forms, you should be able to see the digestive tract and, in live specimens, its peristaltic movements.

Brine shrimp attain adulthood at about 3 weeks and can be maintained on a diet of yeast, fed sparingly. Adults closely resemble their much larger freshwater cousins—fairy shrimp, *Eubranchipus* (Figure 14-5).

Drawings

 On separate paper, sketch crustaceans other than crayfish, or sketch the developmental stages of crustacean larvae, as seen in brine shrimp.

Projects and Demonstrations

1. *Keeping crayfish.* Crayfish are easily maintained in an aquarium tank at room temperature. They will thrive if fed sparingly on raw meat, such as small pieces of fish, shrimp, frog, or beef. Crayfish need plenty of oxygen. Keep the water in the aquarium shallow and provide rocks for cover. Rocks will also enable the crayfish to crawl out of the water. The addition of aquatic plants enhances the appearance of the aquarium and provides food. Remember not to release nonnative crayfish into the wild when you are through observing them.

2. *Heartbeat of crayfish.* Anesthetize a crayfish in a suitably sized dish by immersing in 15% ethanol, or club soda, freshly opened. Remove from the anesthetic when the animal fails to respond to prodding; then remove the carapace and observe the beating heart. The crayfish should survive several hours under these conditions.

3. *Respiratory current of crayfish.* This can be demonstrated by gently releasing dilute methylene blue with a Pasteur pipet or syringe held under the rear of the animal's carapace. The ink or dye emerges anteriorly as two colored jets.

4. *Organization of antennal glands.* These can be identified by injecting into the hemocoel of a crayfish 0.25 ml of 0.5% aqueous solution of Congo red. After 18 to 24 hours, remove one of the glands and examine under a dissecting microscope. Cells of the end sac (coelomosac) should be red; channels of the labyrinth, blue.

5. *Heartbeat of* Daphnia. Place a small drop of petrolatum (Vaseline) in the center of a Syracuse watch glass. Fasten *Daphnia* by one valve of its carapace to the petrolatum, but be careful that water circulates between the valves. Observe the heartbeat. Start with water at 0° C. As the water slowly rises to room temperature, record the heartbeats at the different temperatures. Determine the number of heartbeats in 15 seconds at each 2° or 3° rise in temperature.

6. *Tree hermit crabs. Coenobita clypeatus* are available from biological supply companies (e.g., Carolina Biological) and make interesting displays for the laboratory. They are easily maintained in a sand-based terrarium, where they can be fed dry toast, lettuce, bananas, and the like.

7. *Blood cells in arthropods.* Unlike vertebrate blood, arthropod blood contains no erythrocytes. The respiratory pigment, usually hemocyanin, is dissolved in the plasma rather than carried in cells. Arthropods possess a variety of leukocytes or amebocytes. Because their blood clots much more rapidly than does vertebrate blood, their observation is sometimes more difficult.

To observe in the natural state, place a drop of paraffin oil on a clean slide and focus on the drop. Snip off the tip of an antenna with petroleum-jellied scissors, place the tip in the oil drop, and observe and sketch the cells as they emerge.

Phagocytosis in crayfish cells may be observed by injecting the animal with a suspension of carmine or India ink. Examination of the blood an hour or so later may reveal particles ingested by leukocytes.

8. *Other suitable demonstrations*
   a. Female crayfish carrying eggs and young; preserved specimens are available from biological supply companies
   b. Various kinds of barnacles
   c. Various kinds of crabs
   d. Cross section of crayfish gill

EXPERIMENTING IN ZOOLOGY
The Phototactic Behavior of *Daphnia*

Many species of freshwater zooplankton move toward light (positive phototaxis). In nature, movement toward light often means movement toward shallower, warmer water that is rich in algae and microorganisms. However, most zooplankton have few defense mechanisms and are very vulnerable to predators. Movement toward light would seem to make them more visible to potential predators. Thus, natural selection might favor one type of response to light when no predation risk is apparent and a different response to light when predation risk exists.

Getting Ready

Work with a partner for this exercise. Try to work in a room that can be darkened. Obtain an open-ended glass tube 2 to 3 cm in diameter and 25 to 30 cm long (Figure 14-6). Wash the tube and place a black rubber stopper tightly into one end. Use a wax pencil to mark off three equal sections of tube: left, middle, and right. Fill the tube to within 3 to 4 cm of the top with bottled water or dechlorinated tap water. Have a second rubber stopper available for the open end. Have a stopwatch available for timing the experiment.

How to Proceed

Use a pipette to count out 20 *Daphnia* and add them to the tube. Place the second stopper firmly into the open end. Clamp the tube to the ring stand, so that it is horizontal. Turn out the room lights and allow the *Daphnia*

to acclimate to the tube for the next 10 minutes. At the end of each minute for the next 10 minutes, record where the *Daphnia* are distributed in the tube (left, middle, right). If light from the windows is insufficient

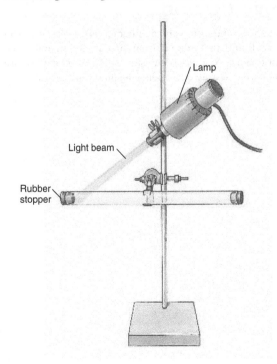

Figure 14-6
Setup for observing the phototactic behavior of *Daphnia*.

to see the *Daphnia,* use diffuse lighting from a lamp some distance from the tube. Turn the lamp on just long enough to count the *Daphnia* and then turn it off until the next observation. After the tenth observation, calculate the mean percentage of *Daphnia* in each section of the tube over the 10 minutes. Wash out the tube and fill it with clean water and 20 new *Daphnia* and repeat the experiment. Calculate the mean distribution of *Daphnia* for the two trials.

After two trials with *Daphnia* in the dark, repeat the experiment with a dissecting scope illuminator (Figure 14-6) clamped at an angle, so that it illuminates the end of one stopper, making it visible to the *Daphnia.* Clamp it 4 to 5 cm away from the tube, so that it does not heat the water. Again record the distribution of *Daphnia* in the tube over the next 10 minutes and repeat the experiment. Calculate the mean distribution of *Daphnia* for the two trials.

Compile the data from the entire class and calculate overall means for all control trials and all lighted trials.

Do *Daphnia* appear to respond to light? Do they exhibit negative or positive phototaxis? In the light trials, do you notice any change in distribution over the 10 minutes?

Questions for Independent Investigation

Recent studies on vertical migrations in zooplankton have found that stimuli from predators can influence phototaxis. Aquatic organisms such as *Daphnia* are often very sensitive to chemical stimuli in the water.

1. Design an experiment to test how fish odor might affect phototaxis in *Daphnia*. Try adding a small amount of water (40 to 50 ml) from a tank that contains a bass or sunfish to your experimental tube containing the *Daphnia*. What would be a good control for this experiment?

2. Do *Daphnia* respond the same to chemical cues from bass or sunfish as they do to cues from frog tadpoles? Why might there be a difference?

3. *Daphnia* also have many invertebrate predators (e.g., hydra, midge larvae—*Chaoborus*). Do chemical cues from invertebrate predators have an effect on their phototactic behavior?

4. How might the effects of gravity impact phototaxis? Design an experiment to examine the effects of both gravity and light on *Daphnia* behavior.

References

DeMeester, L. 1991. An analysis of the phototactic behaviour of *Daphnia magna* clones and their sexual descendants. Hydrobiologia **225:**217–227.

DeMeester, L. 1993. Genotype, fish-mediated chemicals, and phototactic behavior in *Daphnia magna*. Ecology **74:**1467–1474.

Neill, W. 1990. Induced vertical migration in copepods as a defense against invertebrate predators. Nature **345:**524–525.

Parejko, K., and S. Dodson. 1991. The evolutionary ecology of an antipredator reaction norm: *Daphnia pulex* and *Chaoborus americanus*. Evolution **45:**1665–1674.

EXERCISE 13

The Chelicerate Arthropods
Phylum Arthropoda
Subphylum Chelicerata

There are approximately a million named species of arthropods, a huge and diverse phylum that includes chelicerates (spiders, scorpions, and their allies), crustaceans, myriapods (millipedes, centipedes), and hexapods (insects, and their kin).

Arthropods have **jointed appendages,** a fact that gave them their name (Gr. *arthron,* joint, + *pous, podos,* foot). Like that of annelids, the arthropod body is constructed of an extended series of repeated segments. This design principle is called **metamerism** = serial segmentation. However, unlike annelids, the initial array of repeated segments has, through fusion, reduction, and specialization, evolved into the many divergent anatomies of advanced arthropods. A major evolutionary shift was the fusion of segments into discrete, functional units called **tagmata** (sing. **tagma;** Gr. *tagma,* arrangement, order, row)—for example, head, thorax, and abdomen of insects or cephalothorax and abdomen of spiders and ticks. Another important evolutionary trend is specialization of appendages. You will see several examples of appendage specialization among the three arthropod subphyla to be studied in this exercise and Exercises 14 and 15.

> ### Classification
> Phylum Arthropoda
>
> ### EXERCISE 13A
> Chelicerate Arthropods—Horseshoe Crab and Garden Spider
> Horseshoe crab
> Garden spider
> Demonstrations

In addition to features shared by previous phyla, such as **triploblastic development, true coelom, bilateral symmetry, cephalization,** and **all organ systems,** arthropods have developed **striated muscle** for rapid movement; an **exoskeleton,** or cuticle, containing the tough nitrogenous polysaccharide **chitin** for support and protection; **gills** and a very efficient **tracheal system** for gaseous exchange; and **greater specialization** of body organs, especially specialization of form and function among the appendages. The coelom is much reduced. Instead, the major body space is a **hemocoel** derived from fusion of the embryonic blastocoel with the developing coelom. It is filled with

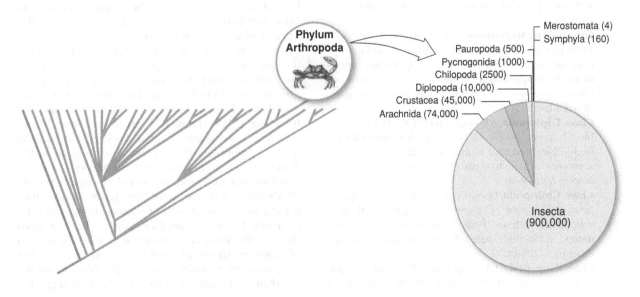

blood, called **hemolymph,** which circulates through an arthropod's "open" circulatory system.

Classification

Phylum Arthropoda

Subphylum Trilobita (tri′lo-bi′ta) (Gr. *tri,* three, + *lobos,* lobe). Trilobites. All extinct forms; Cambrian to Carboniferous; body divided by two longitudinal furrows into three lobes; distinct head, thorax, and abdomen; biramous (two-branched) appendages.

Subphylum Chelicerata (ke-liss′uh-ra′ta) (Gr. *chēlē,* claw, + *keras,* horn, + *ata,* group suffix). Eurypterids, horseshoe crabs, spiders, and ticks. First pair of appendages modified to form chelicerae; pair of pedipalps and four pairs of legs; no antennae, no mandibles; cephalothorax and abdomen usually unsegmented.

    Class Merostomata (mer′o-sto′ma-ta) (Gr. *mēros,* thigh, + *stoma,* mouth, + *ata,* group suffix). Aquatic chelicerates that include horseshoe crabs *(Limulus)* and extinct Eurypterida.

    Class Pycnogonida (pik′no-gon′i-da) (Gr. *pyknos,* compact, + *gony,* knee, angle). Sea spiders.

    Class Arachnida (ar-ack′ni-da) (Gr. *arachnē,* spider). Spiders, scorpions, and their allies. Segments fused into cephalothorax; head with paired chelicerae and pedipalps; four pairs of legs; abdomen segmented or unsegmented, with or without appendages; respiration by gills, tracheae, or book lungs. Example: *Argiope.*

Subphylum Crustacea (crus-ta′she-a) (L. *crusta,* shell, + *acea,* group suffix). Crustaceans. With gills; body covered with carapace; exoskeleton with limy salts; appendages currently considered biramous and variously modified for different functions; head with two pairs of antennae. Examples: *Cambarus, Homarus.*

Subphylum Myriapoda (mir-ee-ap′o-da) (Gr. *myrias,* a myriad, + *podus,* foot). Centipedes, millipedes, pauropods, and symphylans. All appendages uniramous; head appendages consisting of one pair of antennae, one pair of mandibles, and one or two pairs of maxillae.

Class Diplopoda (di-plop′o-da) (Gr. *diploos,* double, + *pous, podos,* foot). Millipedes. Subcylindric body elongated and wormlike; variable number of segments; usually two pairs of legs to a segment. Example: *Spirobolus.*

Class Chilopoda (ki-lop′o-da) (Gr. *cheilos,* lip, + *pous, podos,* foot). Centipedes. Elongated with dorsoventrally flattened body; variable number of segments, each with pair of legs; tracheae present. Example: *Lithobius.*

Class Pauropoda (pau-rop′o-da) (Gr. *pauros,* small, + *pous, podos,* foot). Pauropods. Minute, soft-bodied forms with 12 segments and 9 or 10 pairs of legs. Example: *Pauropus.*

Class Symphyla (sym′fy-la) (Gr. *syn,* together, + *phylon,* tribe). Garden centipedes. Centipede-like bodies of 15 to 22 segments and usually 12 pairs of legs. Example: garden centipede, *Scutigerella.*

Subphylum Hexapoda (hek-′sap′oda) (Gr. *hex,* six + *pous, podus,* foot). Insects. Body with distinct head, thorax, and abdomen; thorax usually with two pairs of wings; three pairs of jointed legs. Example: lubber grasshopper, *Romalea.*

EXERCISE 13A

Chelicerate Arthropods— Horseshoe Crab and Garden Spider

The chelicerates include horseshoe crabs, sea spiders, spiders, scorpions, mites, ticks, and some others. These arthropods do not possess mandibles (jaws) for chewing. Instead, the first pair of appendages, called chelicerae (ke-liss′er-uh), are feeding appendages adapted for seizing and tearing. Most chelicerates have a two-part body of cephalothorax (prosoma) and abdomen (opisthosoma). There are no antennae.

Horseshoe Crab

Phylum Arthropoda
   Subphylum Chelicerata
      Class Merostomata
         Subclass Xiphosurida
           Genus *Limulus*
             Species *Limulus polyphemus*

Where Found

Horseshoe crabs are not really crabs at all but members of an ancient group of chelicerates, Merostomata (mer′o-sto′ma-ta; Gr. *mēros,* thigh, + *stoma,* mouth), most of which are long extinct.

Horseshoe crabs are called "living fossils" because they are survivors of a group that was abundant during the Silurian period, 425 million years ago. The genus *Limulus,* to which the living horseshoe crab *Limulus polyphemus* belongs, arose 250 million years ago and has changed little during this vast span of time. Horseshoe crabs are marine bottom dwellers that feed on molluscs, worms, and dead fish. They live along the Atlantic Coast from Nova Scotia to Mexico's Yucatan peninsula but are historically abundant along the coasts of Virginia, Delaware, and New Jersey, where they come ashore in great numbers during spring high tides to spawn. In recent years their numbers have declined dramatically. Their eggs are important food for millions of migratory shorebirds, which feast on the eggs and may more than double their weight before continuing their northward migration. It has been suggested that recent declines in horseshoe crab numbers may be impacting the success of migratory bird species. Until recently, horseshoe crabs were used by farmers as fertilizer and as feed for farm animals. Today, horseshoe crabs are important for biomedical research on vision and for drug testing.

External Features

The entire body of a horseshoe crab is covered with a tough, leathery **exoskeleton** that contains chitin, a tough polysaccharide. Among products made from horseshoe crab chitin is surgical suture thread that promotes healing as it slowly dissolves. As a horseshoe crab grows, it must shed (molt) the exoskeleton, a process called **ecdysis.**

Cephalothorax (Prosoma). Covering the cephalothorax dorsally and laterally is a hard, horseshoe-shaped **carapace** (F. from Sp. *carapacho,* shell), concave below and convex above. A pair of lateral compound eyes and a pair of median simple eyes are on the dorsal side.

On the ventral side are six pairs of appendages, located around the **mouth** (Figure 13-1). The first pair, called **chelicerae** (ke-liss'uh-ree; sing. **chelicera;** Gr. *chēlē,* claw,+ *keras,* horn), are small and are used to detect and manipulate food. The second pair are called **pedipalps** (L. *pes, pedis,* foot,+ *palpus,* stroking). The next four pairs of appendages are **walking legs.** All appendages except the last pair of walking legs and pedipalps of the male are chelate—that is, they bear pincers, or **chelae** (ke'lee; sing. **chela;** Gr. *chēlē,* claw), and all except the chelicerae have spiny masticatory processes called **gnathobases** (Gr. *gnathos,* jaw, + *basis,* base) on the basal segments. Move the appendages and note how these processes would tear up food and move it toward the mouth. The chelae of the appendages pick up food and pass it to the gnathobases. Note that the last pair of walking legs has no chelae; instead, each has four movable, bladelike processes, one of which is tipped with a pair of spines. These legs are used to push against the sand to help in forward movement and in burrowing. Between the last pair of walking legs is a small, rudimentary pair of appendages called **chilaria.**

Abdomen (Opisthosoma). The abdomen bears six pairs of spines along the sides and, on its ventral side, six pairs of flat, platelike appendages. The first of these forms the **genital operculum,** on the underside of which are two **genital pores.**

The other five abdominal appendages are modified as **gills.** Lift up one of these flaps to see the many (100 to 150) leaflike folds called **lamellae** (la-mel'ee; sing. **lamella;** L. dim. of *lamina,* plate). Because of this leaflike arrangement, such gills are called **book gills** (Figure 13-1). Exchange of gases between blood and surrounding water takes place in the lamellae.

Movement of the gills not only circulates water over them but also pumps blood in and out of the lamellae. The blood contains **hemocyanin,** a respiratory pigment used in oxygen transport, as well as an amebocyte that kills invading bacteria. A chemical extracted from the amebocytes is now used to assure absence of harmful bacteria in intravenous drugs, vaccines, and implantable medical devices. Each summer, blood is collected from thousands of horseshoe crabs for extraction of amebocytes; the crabs are returned to the sea after bleeding.

Beating of the abdominal flaps can also be used in swimming and may aid the animal in burrowing by creating a water current that washes out mud or sand posteriorly.

Telson. The long, slender **telson** (Gr., extremity), or tail spine, is used for anchoring when the animal is burrowing or plowing through the sand or in righting itself when turned over. The **anus** is located under the proximal end of the telson.

Reproduction

During mating, horseshoe crabs aggregate in shallow water. A male clasps a female's carapace with his modified pedipalps and is carried around by the larger female. The female lays eggs in a depression in the sand near the high-tide mark while the male sprays sperm on the eggs as they emerge. After several weeks, the eggs hatch as free-swimming **trilobite larvae** (Figure 13-2), so-named because of their superficial resemblance to a trilobite. A larva looks much like an adult except that it lacks the tail spine and has only two of the five pairs of book gills. As it develops through a series of molts, segments and appendages are added until the young animal reaches adult form.

Behavior

 If live horseshoe crabs are available in a marine aquarium, you may make some observations.

Where do you find the resting animals? Swimming about, resting on the sand, or covered with sand? Before disturbing them, drop some bits of fresh shrimp, oyster, or fish meat near them. Do they respond? How? (Normally they do most of their feeding at night.)

To observe their respiratory gill movements, lift an animal in the water, so that you can watch the beating of the gills. Gill movement is probably faster than when the animal is resting. Why? Each time the flaps move forward, blood flows into the gill lamellae; as the flaps move backward, the blood flows out.

Free the animal near the surface of the water and see how it swims. Does it turn over? Which appendages does it use in swimming? As it settles to the sandy bottom, watch its reactions. Does it try to burrow? How? Can you see the use of the last pair of legs? Does the animal arch its back? Does it use the telson?

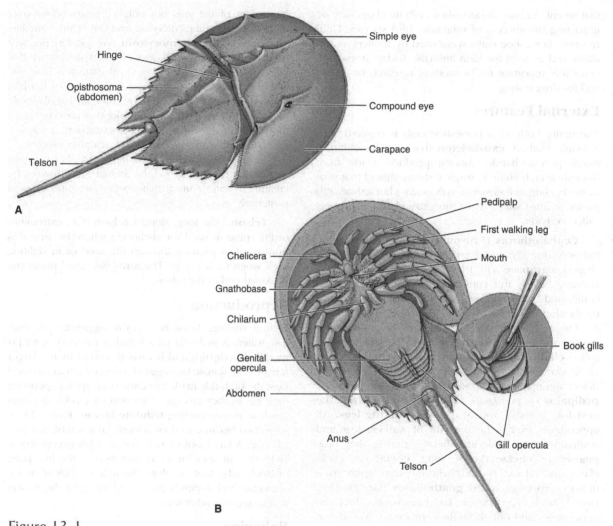

Figure 13-1

A, Dorsal view of *Limulus*, the horseshoe crab. **B,** Ventral view of a female. The inset shows an operculum lifted to reveal the location of book gills.

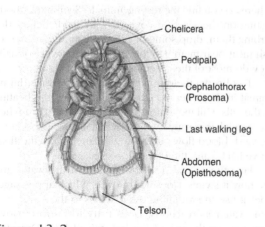

Figure 13-2

Trilobite larva of the horseshoe crab.

Written Report

Record your observations on separate paper.

Garden Spider

Phylum Arthropoda
   Subphylum Chelicerata
      Class Arachnida
         Order Araneae
            Genus *Argiope*

Where Found

Spiders are distributed in all kinds of habitats, such as forests, deserts, mountains, swamps, land, and water. The garden spider (*Argiope,* ar-ji′uh-pee; Gr., nymph of mythology), which builds its orb webs in sunny places in gardens and tall grass, is found throughout the United

States. Two common species are *A. aurantia,* with a mottled black and yellow abdomen (Figure 13-3), and *A. trifasciata,* with black and yellow bands on the abdomen. The males are about one-fourth the size of the females (4 to 8mm) and are rarely seen. They spin smaller webs near those of the female.

Behavior

A garden spider will spin its orb web in captivity, and, if the spider is kept in a large glass container with tall grass or twigs and covered with screen or cheesecloth, the process can be watched. The spider spins a symmetric orb web and prefers to hang head downward in the center, holding its forelegs and hind legs close together (Figure 13-3). If web building can be observed, note the process—how the spider makes a supporting framework, then the radial spokes, and finally the spiral—first a temporary spiral beginning outside and then a permanent spiral beginning at the center. If possible, examine bits of the silk under a microscope. Is there more than one kind of silk? _____

Adding insects to the terrarium containing the spider may allow you to witness a capture in the net, biting of the prey to paralyze it, and then securing of the prey with silken thread.

Spiders secrete enzymes to begin digestion outside the body. *Argiope* can apparently crush and tear the prey as well as suck out the liquid parts. How long does it take the spider to complete a meal? _____
_____

Can you see the eyes? _____ Most spiders have poor vision (jumping spiders an exception) but

Figure 13-3

Black and yellow garden spider, *Argiope aurantia,* which builds its orb web in gardens or tall grasses and then hangs there, head down, awaiting an unwary insect.

are covered with sensory hairs and are very sensitive to touch and vibration.

External Features

 Study a preserved specimen and handle gently. There is always danger of breaking off appendages or the abdomen from the rest of the body. Use a hand lens or dissecting microscope to examine the parts. Keeping the specimen moist will help prevent its becoming brittle.

The chitinous **exoskeleton** is hard, thin, and somewhat flexible. **Sensory hairs** project from all parts of the body. The tagmata of the arachnid include the anterior **cephalothorax** and the posterior **abdomen** joined by a slender waist, or **pedicel.**

Cephalothorax. Most spiders have six to eight **eyes** on the anterior dorsal surface, but some have fewer. Spiders do not have compound eyes; all are simple ocelli. How many eyes does your specimen have? _____ Use a dissecting microscope to find them.

Identify the paired chelicerae, which are vertically oriented on the front of the face. The terminal segment of a chelicera is a **fang,** by which the spider ejects poison from its poison gland (Figure 13-4B). Does the spider have true jaws (mandibles)? _____ Pedipalps are six-jointed and used for gripping prey. In males the pedipalp is modified as an intromittant organ to transfer sperm to a female. The basal parts (coxal endites) of the pedipalps are used to squeeze and chew food. Find the mouth between the pedipalps. Can the spider ingest only liquid food? _____

How many pairs of **walking legs** are there? _____ Each leg is made up of seven segments, as follows (from base to distal end): **coxa, trochanter, femur, patella, tibia, metatarsus,** and **tarsus.** The tarsus has claws and a tuft of hair at its terminal end.

Abdomen. On the ventral surface at the anterior end, find two lateral, slitlike openings that mark the location of the **book lungs.** Book lungs are fashioned very much as are the book gills of horseshoe crabs, except that they are enclosed internally in pockets. The inner walls of these pockets are folded into long, thin plates (leaves of the "book") held apart by bars, so that there are always air spaces between them. Gas exchange occurs between blood circulating inside the lamellae and air flowing in the spaces between the lamellae. These air spaces connect with a small air chamber in each lung that opens to the outside through the slitlike openings, or spiracles, already observed (Figure 13-4). Some spiders—the tarantula, for example—have two pairs of book lungs. By peeling forward the cover of the lung and examining with a dissecting microscope, you should be able to see many thin respiratory leaves.

Locate, between the spiracles, the **epigynum** (e-pij'in-um; Gr. *epi,* on, + *gynē,* woman), which conceals

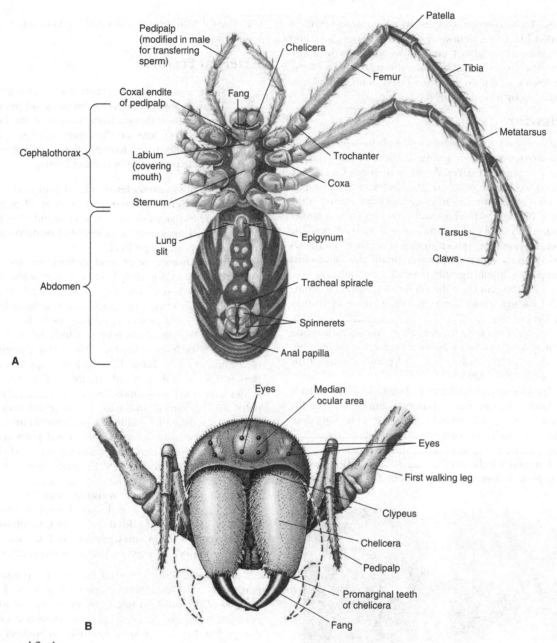

Figure 13-4

A, Ventral view of a female garden spider, *Argiope aurantia*. **B,** Anterior, or "face," view.

the female genital pore. Preserved specimens are probably all females.

Posteriorly on the abdomen, just in front of the spinnerets, is a small **tracheal spiracle.** This is an opening into a small chamber from which tracheal tubes extend into the body. What is the function of the tracheal system?_____ Arachnid tracheal systems are similar to those of insects but less extensive. Garden spiders have both book lungs and tracheae, but not all spiders do; some have only one type of respiratory organ.

There are three pairs of **spinnerets** on a raised surface. The middle pair is quite small, but the other two pairs are rather large, conical, and readily movable. The ends of the spinnerets have a variety of tiny silk spouts, each producing a particular type of silk. The silk is secreted as a fluid by the silk glands and hardens with exposure to air. Examine the spinnerets with a dissecting microscope.

A small, fleshy papilla just posterior to the spinnerets bears the **anus.**

EXERCISE 15

The Arthropods
Myriapods and Hexapods

EXERCISE 15A
Myriapods—Centipedes and Millipedes

The subphylum **Myriapoda** (Gr. *myries,* myriad, numberless, + *podos,* foot) includes several groups (Chilopoda, Diplopoda, Pauropoda, and Symphyla). They have two tagmata—head and trunk. There is one pair of antennae, and the trunk bears paired appendages on all but the last segment (Figure 15-1).

Class Chilopoda—Centipedes

Phylum Arthropoda
   Subphylum Myriapoda
      Class Chilopoda
         Order Scolopendromorph
            Genus *Scolopendra* or *Lithobius*

Centipedes, or "hundred-leggers," are active predators that live in moist places under logs, stones, and bark, where they feed on worms, larvae, and insects.

 If living examples are available, watch their locomotion and note the agile use of the body and legs.

Note the general shape of the body and arrangement of segments and appendages. Is the body circular or flattened in cross section? _____

 On a preserved specimen of *Lithobius* (Gr. *lithos,* stone, + *bios,* life) or *Scolopendra* (Gr., a kind of centipede) (Figures 15-1 and 15-2), examine the head.

Some species have simple **ocelli;** others have large, faceted **eyes** resembling the compound eyes of insects. Which does your specimen have? _____

 Pull aside the large poison fangs to uncover the mouth area and examine under a dissecting microscope.

Find the **antennae; labrum,** anterior to the mouth; **mandibles** and **first maxillae,** lateral to the mouth;

EXERCISE 15A
Myriapods—Centipedes and Millipedes
Class Chilopoda—centipedes
Class Diplopoda—millipedes

EXERCISE 15B
Insects—Grasshopper and Honeybee
Romalea, lubber grasshopper
Apis, honeybee
Projects and demonstrations

EXERCISE 15C
Insects—House Cricket
Acheta domesticus, house cricket

EXERCISE 15D
Metamorphosis of *Drosophila*
Drosophila, fruit fly

EXERCISE 15E
Collection and Classification of Insects
Key to the Principal Orders of Insects

and **second maxillae,** bearing a long palp and a short labial portion just posterior to the mouth.

The first trunk appendages are the prehensile **maxillipeds,** each bearing a terminal **poison fang.** Do the rest of the trunk appendages bear legs? _____
The last segment bears the **gonopores,** and the **anus** is located on a short telson. Find the **spiracles.** In *Lithobius* they are located near the bases of the legs. In *Scolopendra* the spiracles are located more dorsally and are present on alternate segments.

Class Diplopoda—Millipedes

Phylum Arthropoda
   Subphylum Myriapoda
      Class Diplopoda
         Subclass Chilognatha
            Order Juliformia
               Genus *Julus* or *Spirobolus*

Millipedes, or "thousand-foot worms," are found throughout the world, usually hiding in damp woods

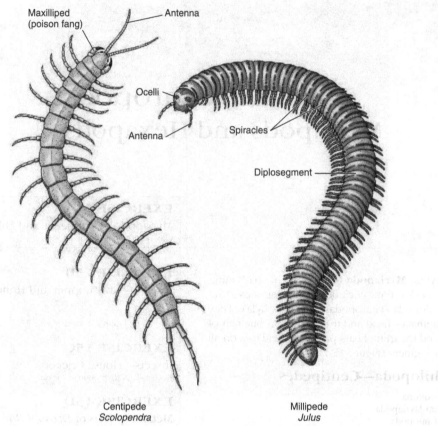

Figure 15-1
Examples of myriapods—centipede and millipede.

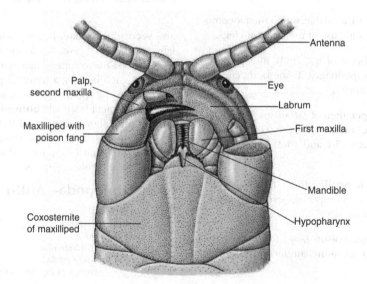

Figure 15-2
Mouthparts of *Scolopendra*, ventral view.

under bark, leaves, rocks, and logs. They are herbivorous, feeding on decaying wood or leaves. Their most distinguishing feature is the presence of diplosegments, which are double trunk segments possibly derived from the fusion of two single segments and each bearing two pairs of legs. The name "Diplopoda" comes from Greek *diploos*, double, and *pous, podos*, foot (see Figure 15-1).

 If living millipedes such as *Spirobolus* (L. *spira*, coil, + Gr. *bōlos*, lump) or *Julus* (Gr. *iulus*, plant-down) are available, note the shape of the body, use of the antennae, use of the legs, and ability to roll up.

Notice the rhythm of the power and recovery strokes of the legs with opposite sides of each segment exactly out of phase. It is similar to that seen in the polychaete *Nereis*. The movements of the legs pass in regular, successive waves toward the anterior end. If a specimen has been chilled, you should be able to determine the number of legs working together in each wave and the number of segments between waves.

 Study a preserved specimen, and locate on the head the **ocelli, antennae, labrum, mandibles,** and **labium** (fused second maxillae).

Are there appendages on the first trunk segments? _____ How many pairs on the next three segments? _____ The **gonopores** open on the third trunk segment at the bases of the legs. How does this compare with the centipede? _____ The dorsal overlapping of the exoskeletal plates provides full protection for the animal, even when rolled into a ball. Notice that each of the diplosegments has two pairs of **spiracles.**

EXERCISE 15B
Insects—Grasshopper and Honeybee

Insects are by far the largest group of animals. It is estimated that there are 1.1 million named species of insects—more than all other named animals combined—and that several million species of insects remain to be discovered and described.

Among their chief characteristics are **three pairs of walking legs; one pair of antennae;** a body typically divided into **head, thorax,** and **abdomen;** and a respiratory system of **tracheal tubes.** Most insects are also provided with one or two pairs of **wings.** Their sense organs are often specialized and perhaps account for much of their success in the competition for ecological niches.

Most insects are less than 2.5 cm long, but they range from 1 mm to 20 cm, with the largest insects usually living in tropical areas.

A grasshopper has a fairly typical insect body plan. A honeybee, on the other hand, has become specialized for particular conditions. Not only is its morphology modified for special functions and adaptations, but it is a social insect in which patterns of group organization involve different types of individuals and division of labor.

Romalea, Lubber Grasshopper

Phylum Arthropoda
  Subphylum Hexapoda
    Class Insecta
      Order Orthoptera
        Genus *Romalea*

Behavior of a Grasshopper

 If living grasshoppers are available, observe them in a terrarium or place one in a glass jar with moist paper towel in the bottom and a stick or another object to perch on.

Is the color adaptive, given its natural habitat? _____ Can it move its head? _____

Observe how the grasshopper moves and how it uses its legs. How does it crawl up a stick? _____ _____ How does it use its claws? _____ _____ What position does it assume when quiescent in the jar? _____ How does it jump? _____ How are its legs adapted for jumping? _____ Does it use its wings? _____

Note movements of the body while it is at rest. Are the movements related to breathing? _____ _____ How does the grasshopper breathe? _____ How does it get air into its body? _____ What is the common food of grasshoppers? _____ Observe how one eats a piece of lettuce leaf. Watch how it moves its mouthparts.

Take a specimen from the jar. Note that it will regurgitate its greenish digestive juices and food on a glass plate. Is this a defensive adaptation?

Written Report

 Record your observations on p. 232.

External Structure

 Study a preserved specimen of a grasshopper. It is a model of compactness, so use a dissecting microscope or hand lens to observe smaller structures.

Note the division of the body into three tagmata: **head, thorax,** and **abdomen.** Is the grasshopper segmented throughout, or is segmentation more apparent in certain regions of the body? _____

The chitinous **exoskeleton** is secreted by the underlying epidermis. It is composed of hard plates, called **sclerites,** which are bounded by sutures of soft cuticle.

The Head of the Grasshopper. The head of the grasshopper is freely movable. Notice the **compound eyes, antennae,** and three **ocelli,** one dorsal to the base of each antenna and one in the groove between them. Lift the movable, bilobed upper lip, or **labrum** (L., lip) (Figure 15-3), and observe the toothed **mandibles.** The mouth contains a membranous **hypopharynx** for tasting food. The bilobed lower lip, or **labium** (L., lip), is the result of the fusion of the second maxillae. The labium bears on each side a three-jointed labial palp. Between the mandible and labium are paired **maxillae** (L., jawbone), each with a maxillary palp, flat lobe, and toothed jaw. Note how the mouthparts are adapted for biting and chewing.

In summary, the insect head has four pairs of true appendages: antennae, mandibles, maxillae, and labium (fused second maxillae). There are at least six segments in the head region, although some of them are apparent only in the insect embryo.

 After you study the rest of the external features, if time permits, your instructor may ask you to use forceps and teasing needles to carefully remove all the mouthparts and arrange them in their relative positions on a sheet of paper. Permanent demonstration mounts can be made very easily by a method given in Appendix A, p. 406.

Thorax of the Grasshopper. The thorax is made up of three segments: **prothorax, mesothorax,** and **metathorax,** each bearing a pair of legs (Figure 15-4). The mesothorax and metathorax also bear a pair of wings. **Spiracles** (external openings of the insect's tracheal system) are located above the legs in the mesothorax and metathorax. Note the leathery **forewings** (on the mesothorax) and the membranous **hindwings** (on the metathorax). Which is more useful for flight? _____ What appears to be the chief function of the forewings? _____ The small **veins** in the wings, or tracheal tubes, are used by entomologists in the identification and classification of insects.

Examine the grasshopper's legs and identify the basal **coxa** (L., hip); small **trochanter** (Gr., ball of hip joint); large **femur;** slender, spiny **tibia;** and five-jointed **tarsus** with two **claws** and a terminal pad, the **arolium.** Which pair of legs is most specialized, and for what function? _____

Abdomen of the Grasshopper. There are 11 segments in the abdomen of the grasshopper. Notice the large **tympanum,** the organ of hearing, one located on each side of the first abdominal segment. On which of the abdominal segments are the paired spiracles located? _____ In both sexes, segments 2 to 8 are similar and unmodified, and segments 9 and 10 are partially fused.

The eleventh segment forms the genitalia (secondary sex organs). On each side behind the tenth segment is a projection, the **cercus** (pl. **cerci;** Gr. *kerkos,* tail). In females the posterior end of the abdomen is pointed and consists of two pairs of plates, with a smaller pair between, with the whole forming the **ovipositor.**

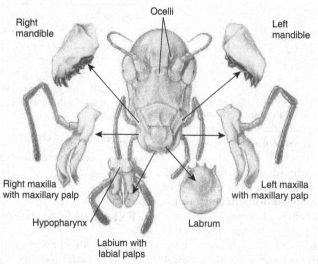

Figure 15-3
Head and mouthparts of grasshopper.

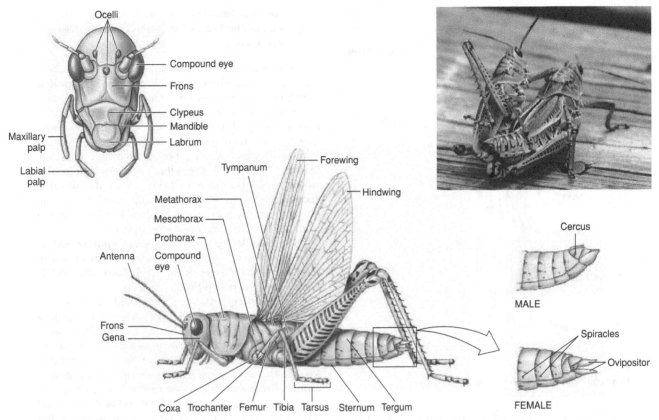

Figure 15-4
External features of female grasshopper. The terminal segments of a male with external genitalia are shown in the inset.

Between the plates is the opening of the **oviduct.** The end of the abdomen in males is rounded. What is the sex of your specimen? _____

Drawings

 Label the external view of the grasshopper on p. 231.

Apis, Honeybee

Phylum Arthropoda
   Subphylum Hexapoda
      Class Insecta
         Order Hymenoptera
           Genus *Apis*
              Species *Apis mellifera*

External Structure

 Examine a preserved or freshly killed honeybee. Use a dissecting microscope or hand lens to study smaller structures.

The body of a honeybee, like that of a grasshopper, is divided into three tagmata: **head, thorax,** and **abdomen.**

Head of a Honeybee. Identify **antennae, compound eyes,** and three **ocelli,** located dorsally between the compound eyes. The mouthparts can be used for both chewing and sucking (Figure 15-5). Observe the narrow upper lip, or **labrum,** with a row of bristles on its free margin. Below the labrum are brownish **mandibles.** From its mouth projects a sucking apparatus made up of a long, slender, hairy **tongue** (or **labium**); paired **labial palps,** one on each side of the tongue; and paired, broad **maxillae,** one on each side of the labial palps.

Thorax of a Honeybee. The thorax is composed of three segments: **prothorax, mesothorax,** and **metathorax,** but the lines of division between the segments are less distinguishable than on a grasshopper. A honeybee's first abdominal segment is also a part of the thorax, lying anterior to its narrow "waist." Each segment bears a pair of legs, and the mesothorax and metathorax each bear a pair of wings. Note that both pairs of wings are thin and membranous, unlike those of a grasshopper, in which only the hindwings are membranous. How would this difference affect the wings' function? _____

Notice small hooks on the front margin of the hindwing. During flight the hooks catch hold of a groove

Use your hand lens, or remove the legs from one side of the bee and examine under a dissecting microscope.

Note hairs on the **foreleg.** Are they branched? _____ These hairs collect pollen. The **pollen brush** (Figure 15-6) consists of long hairs on the proximal end of the tarsus. Pollen brushes on the forelegs and middle legs brush pollen off the body hairs and deposit it on the pollen combs of the hindlegs (Figure 15-6).

At the distal end of the tibia is a movable spine, the **velum** (L., covering). The velum covers a **semicircular notch,** which bears a row of stiff bristles, the **antenna comb.** The velum, notch, and comb together make up the **antenna cleaner.** The antenna is freed from pollen as it is drawn through this antenna cleaner.

The **middle leg** has a long, sharp **spur** projecting from the end of the tibia that is used to remove pollen from the pollen basket of the leg behind. The middle leg also bears a pollen brush.

The **hindleg** is the largest leg and the most specialized. One of its striking adaptations is the **pollen basket,** a wide groove with bristles on the outer surface of the tibia. By keeping these bristles moist with mouth secretions, the bee can use the basket for carrying pollen. On the inner surface of the metatarsus are **pollen combs,** which are composed of rows of stout spines. Large spines found along the distal end of the tibia and the proximal end of the metatarsus make up the **pollen packer.** The pecten (pollen rake) removes pollen from the pollen brush of the opposite leg; then, when the leg is bent, the auricle packs it into the pollen basket. The bee carries her baskets full of protein-rich pollen back

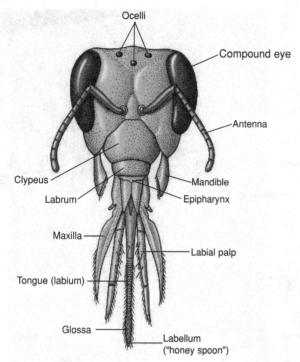

Figure 15-5
Head and mouthparts of honeybee.

near the margin of the forewing. The wings of a bee may vibrate 400 times or more per second during flight.

The legs of a honeybee have the same segments as those of a grasshopper but are adapted for specific functions.

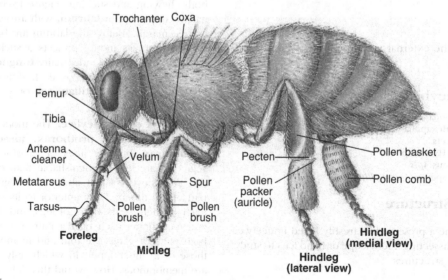

Figure 15-6
Adaptive legs from the left side of worker honeybee.

to the hive and pushes the pollen into a cell, where it will be cared for by other workers.

Abdomen of a Honeybee. The abdomen of a bee has 10 segments, the first of which is actually part of the thorax, as mentioned before. The last three segments are modified and hidden within the seventh segment. Can you identify five pairs of spiracles on the abdomen? _____

Honeybee Sting. The amazingly intricate **sting** is a modified ovipositor that has evolved for defense. It consists of a large **poison gland** that receives secretions (a mixture of proteins, peptides, and other compounds) from two acid glands by way of a common duct (Figure 15-7). The poison sac discharges into the cavity of a sting bulb; from there the poison passes through the canal of the sting shaft and into the wound. The sting bulb also receives a short alkaline gland of uncertain function.

When a honeybee stings, it thrusts the barbs of the sting into the victim's flesh. The entire sting apparatus is torn out of the bee's abdomen, fatally wounding the bee. The sting actually consists of a sting shaft together with two barb lancets that are moved rapidly back and forth on the stylet by the action of protractor and retractor muscles. Therefore, even after the bee has hurriedly departed, the self-sacrificial sting continues to work in deeper and poison continues to be injected into the wound for 30 to 60 seconds.

The sting of the queen bee is used only against rival queens and can be withdrawn and reused many times. It is more firmly attached within the queen's abdomen, and the lancets have fewer and smaller barbs.

Honeybees as Social Animals. In the hive of a honeybee, there are three **castes: workers, queen,** and **drones. Workers** are sexually inactive genetic females and make up most of the society. They do most of the work of the hive, except lay eggs. They collect food, clean out the hive, make honey and wax, care for the young, guard the hive, and ventilate the hive.

The single **queen** is a sexually mature female that lays the eggs, which may or may not be fertilized by sperm stored in her spermatheca.

Drones are males; all develop from unfertilized eggs and consequently are haploid (workers and the queen are diploid). There are usually only a few hundred drones in a hive. Their main duty is to fertilize the queen during the nuptial flight, although usually only one is required to provide the queen enough sperm to last her lifetime.

Internal Structure of an Insect

Study of the internal structures of a grasshopper is not always satisfactory because the various organs appear somewhat poorly defined. Internal structures are more easily studied in an anesthetized cricket, instructions for which are given in Exercise 16C.

Oral Report

 Be prepared to (1) identify the major external features of a grasshopper and/or honeybee, (2) explain the adaptations of a worker honeybee appendages, and (3) explain the sting of a worker honeybee.

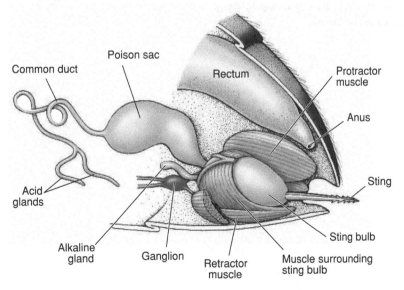

Figure 15-7
Sting of worker honeybee.

Projects and Demonstrations

1. *Capillary circulation in a cockroach wing.* Use adults of *Periplaneta* or tropical cockroach *Blaberus*. From a small piece of Styrofoam or balsa wood, hollow out a depression about the size of the cockroach. Anesthetize the roach with CO_2 and place it in the depression. Pin a piece of paper across the head and pronotum; pin a second piece of black paper across the abdomen, leaving one of the wings exposed *above* the paper in its normal resting position. Slip a piece of shiny white paper under the wing. Shine a focused beam of intense light on the wing from a low angle and observe the wing with a dissecting microscope. The circulating blood in the capillaries should now be visible. The light must be intense, and it may be necessary to adjust the angle of light for best effect. Visibility depends on reflection of light from circulating blood cells. Sometimes it is easier to see circulation in the hindwing (flow stops if the forewing is extended into the flying position).

2. *Real-life study of cecropia or polyphemus moth life cycles.* Both large larvae and cocoons of cecropia and polyphemus moths can be collected in fall. The larvae feed on leaves of dwarf willow. To observe the spinning of the cocoons, collect large larvae and place them in a rearing cage in the laboratory. The rearing cage can be an aquarium tank with 1 inch of moist sand in the bottom and a jar of water or wet sand to contain fresh willow branches. Place cotton around the mouth of the jar to prevent larvae from falling into it. Place the larvae on the willow leaves and cover the aquarium with a glass plate. Replace the willow leaves when they wilt or are eaten by larvae.

Collected cocoons can be stored in a box of moss, which must always be kept slightly moist. If the box is stored in a cool cellar or unheated room, adults will emerge in spring. If kept in a warm room, they will probably emerge in midwinter. Before adults emerge, place the cocoons in a large cage or screened box containing branches to which the moths can cling while drying their wings.

3. *Demonstration of insect eggs and egg cases.* Eggs of walkingsticks and egg masses (oothecae) of praying mantids can be obtained from biological supply companies and kept in a refrigerator until a few weeks before their hatching is desired. Place in a terrarium or any glass container that can be covered with cheesecloth or fine-meshed wire screening.

   Mantids are carnivorous and have voracious appetites. If not provided with sufficient food (*Drosophila* or other insects), they will devour each other. The nymphs should not be kept in direct sun or drafts, as they require enough natural humidity to protect them during molts. If the skins they are molting are too dry, they may not be able to free themselves and consequently die during the process.

   Grasshopper eggs are sometimes available and will hatch if kept in damp soil at room temperature. The nymphs can be fed fresh lettuce.

4. *Firefly luminescence.* Dried firefly lanterns together with ATP and all necessary material for demonstrating the emission of light can be obtained from biological supply companies. ATP supplies the energy needed for the oxidation of the luciferin. Instructions are included.

Phylum _____

Subphylum _____

Genus _____

Name _____

Date _____

Section _____

Lubber Grasshopper

External view of female (male abdomen at bottom left)

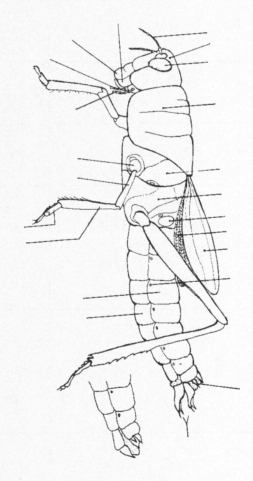

Behavior of Grasshoppers

LAB REPORT

Name _____

Date _____

Section _____

Comparing Characteristics of Annelida and Arthropoda

	Annelida	Arthropoda
Segmentation		
Body covering		
Main body cavity		
Appendages		
Circulatory system		
Respiration		
Excretory organs		
Sense organs		
Method of growth		
Division of animal kingdom (protostome/deuterostome)		

EXERCISE 15C
Insects—House Cricket*

Acheta Domesticus, House Cricket

Phylum Arthropoda
   Subphylum Hexapoda
      Class Insecta
         Order Orthoptera
           Genus *Acheta*
              Species *Acheta domesticus*

House crickets, or gray crickets, commercially available as fish bait, are a European import and are not native to this country. Although crickets have functional wings, the flight muscles do not completely develop and crickets never fly. Adult house crickets live an average of 2 months, during which time females will deposit up to 2000 eggs. Only adult males sing (more accurately, stridulate), and one of the functions of their stridulating is to attract females. At a rearing temperature of 30° C, the eggs hatch in 13 days. There are eight larval instars (growth stages) before the final ecdysis (molt) to the adult 48 days later.

External Structure

 Examine several alcohol-preserved crickets. Determine the sex of the crickets (Figures 15-8E and 15-9C), and determine which are larval instars and which are adults.

Only adult crickets have fully developed wings. The last two or three larval instars of crickets have external wing pads (buds). Crickets have **gradual metamorphosis.** The animal grows by successive molts (ecdysis), with each stage called a larval instar; after the last molt, the insect is called an adult.

 Pin an adult male or female preserved cricket lateral side up in the dissecting dish.

Note that the basic 18 segments of the insect are functionally organized into three body regions, or tagmata: **head** (5 segments), **thorax** (3 segments), and **abdomen** (10 segments). Feeding and sensory organs are on the head, locomotory organs (wings and legs) are on the thorax, and digestive and reproductive organs are in the abdomen. All head segments are fused into a unit head capsule, and the mouthparts represent the modified appendages. The 3 thoracic segments are the **prothorax, mesothorax,** and **metathorax.** The abdominal segments are simply numbered 1 through 9 (the cerci represent segment 10). The entire dorsum is called the **tergum** (L., back) (or notum), and any 1 specific segment of the dorsal plate is called a **tergite.** The lateral body surface is the **pleuron** (Gr., side) (**pleurite**

*Exercise contributed by J. P. Woodring of Louisiana State University.

for 1 segment), and the ventral body surface is the **sternum** (L., breastbone) (**sternite** for 1 segment). Find and identify all of these parts.

 Cut off a prothoracic leg and identify all of the segments and the tympanic membrane (Figure 15-8). Cut off the mesothoracic wing of a male cricket (Figure 15-8A), and determine how male crickets are able to stridulate. Place a cricket ventral side up, bend the head back, fold out the labrum, and pin the head in this position (Figure 15-8C). Identify all the mouthparts by moving each with fine forceps. Carefully remove one maxilla and the labium to see the **hypopharynx.**

The hypopharynx acts as a tongue and bears the openings of the **salivary glands.**

Functional Observations

 Work in pairs. Anesthetize two crickets with carbon dioxide. Immobilize one cricket ventral side up by crossing insect pins over the insect (do not stick the pins through the cricket). When the cricket recovers from the anesthetic, feed it some colored, moistened food and observe the action of the mouthparts under a dissecting microscope.

The heart is an almost transparent tube visible through the intersegmental membranes along the middorsal line. Cut the wings off the other cricket and immobilize it *dorsal side up* with insect pins crossed over the body. When the cricket recovers from the anesthetic, determine the ventilation rate (abdominal contractions) and the heart rate in ventilations and beats per minute.

Internal Anatomy

 If necessary, reanesthetize the cricket from which the wings have been removed, and pin the animal *dorsal side up* through the head and epiproct (Gr. *epi,* upon, + *proktos,* anus) (see Figure 15-9C and D) onto the wax in the dish. Flood the entire animal with saline and cut the cricket open with fine-tipped scissors. Pin open the cricket with insect pins.

Observe **peristalsis** of the gut and movement of the **malpighian tubules.** The cricket will remain alive and the organ systems will function normally for several hours under these conditions. The chalky white **fat body,** which functions as a liver, is spread throughout the body and will vary greatly in amount and location according to age and diet of the cricket. Note the **tracheal tubes,** which appear silvery because of contained air. These branch throughout the body.

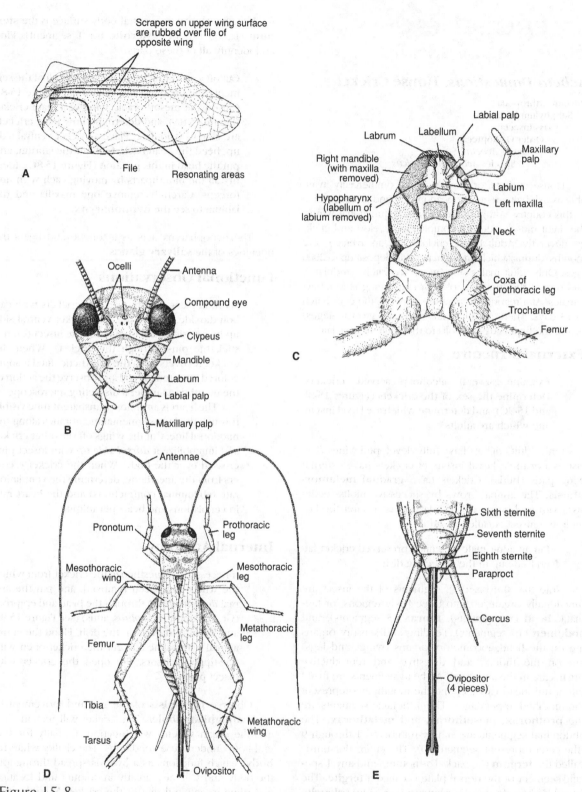

Scrapers on upper wing surface
are rubbed over file of
opposite wing

File

Resonating areas

A

Ocelli

Antenna

Compound eye

Clypeus

Mandible

Labrum

Labial palp

Maxillary palp

B

Labial palp

Labrum   Labellum

Maxillary
palp

Right mandible
(with maxilla
removed)

Hypopharynx
(labellum of
labium removed)

Labium

Left maxilla

Neck

Coxa of
prothoracic leg

Trochanter

Femur

C

Antennae

Pronotum

Prothoracic
leg

Mesothoracic
wing

Mesothoracic
leg

Femur

Metathoracic
leg

Tibia

Tarsus

Metathoracic
wing

Ovipositor

D

Sixth sternite

Seventh sternite

Eighth sternite

Paraproct

Cercus

Ovipositor
(4 pieces)

E

Figure 15-8

External structure of cricket. **A,** Undersurface of male mesothoracic wing. **B,** Frontal view and **C,** ventral view of head. **D,** Dorsal aspect of adult female. **E,** Ventral aspect of adult female abdomen.

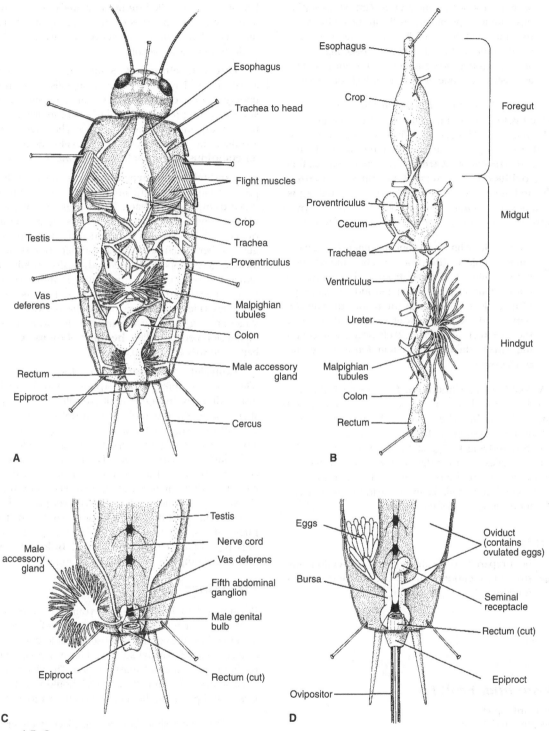

Figure 15-9

A, Internal anatomy of cricket (fat bodies not shown). **B,** Isolated gut. **C,** Male reproductive anatomy. **D,** Female reproductive anatomy.

Sever the esophagus and rectum. Grasp the esophagus with forceps and gradually lift the entire digestive tract out by carefully cutting each tracheal connection to the gut (use a dissecting microscope). Stretch and straighten out the gut and pin it as illustrated to one side of the dish (Figure 15-9B).

Identify all structures labeled in Figure 15-9. Note that the **ureter** arises in the middle of the hindgut.

Both male and female reproductive systems are best seen after the digestive tract has been removed. Identify the gonads (**testes** or **ovaries**), gonoducts (**vas deferens** or **oviducts**), **accessory gland, bursa** or **genital bulb,** and genitalia. The genitalia are the **aedeagus** (e-de'a-gus; Gr. *aidoia,* genitals) of males and the **ovipositor** (L. *ovum,* egg, + *ponere,* to place) of females.

 Pour off the saline from your specimen, but leave it pinned in place. Rinse out the debris and fat body with a mild jet of water from a plastic squeeze bottle. Pour off all the water and add several drops of methylene blue dye to the tissues to stain the nerve cord and ganglia. Wait 1 minute; then cover the specimen with water. Pick away tissue covering parts of the nervous system. Rinse and restain if necessary.

A double ventral **nerve cord** passes back through the body. In the thorax are three pairs of large, fused **segmental ganglia.** The nerve cords are widely separated. In the abdomen are five smaller ganglia; the fifth ganglion (overlying the genital bulb in males and the bursa in females) is larger than the rest and supplies all the posterior end of the body (Figure 15-9C and D).

Two cerebral ganglia lie in the head but are not visible without dissection of the head.

Oral Report

 Be prepared to locate on your dissection any structure mentioned in the exercise and state its function.

EXERCISE 15D
Metamorphosis of *Drosophila*

Drosophila, Fruit Fly

Phylum Arthropoda
  Subphylum Hexapoda
    Class Insecta
      Order Diptera
        Genus *Drosophila*

Metamorphosis

Early development of an insect occurs within the egg. Most insects change form during the growth stages after hatching. This is called **metamorphosis.** As it grows, an insect undergoes a series of molts; each stage between molts is called an **instar.** Insect young vary in the degree of development of hatching.

Direct Development. Some wingless insects, such as silverfish (Thysanura) and springtails (Collembola), undergo direct development rather than metamorphosis. The young resemble adults except in size and sexual maturity and are called juveniles. The stages are egg, juvenile, and adult. This type of development is called **ametabolous** (Gr. *a,* without, + *metabolē,* change).

Gradual Metamorphosis. In gradual, or incomplete, metamorphosis, the immature forms are commonly called **nymphs** (or **larvae**). Their wings develop as external outgrowths that increase in size as the animal grows by successive molts. Larvae of aquatic forms have tracheal gills or other modifications for aquatic life. Terrestrial forms include grasshoppers, locusts and the like (Orthoptera), termites (Isoptera), and true bugs (Hemiptera). Those having aquatic larvae include mayflies (Ephemeroptera), stoneflies (Plecoptera), and dragonflies (Odonata). The stages are egg, larva (several instars), and adult. This type of development is called **hemimetabolous** (Gr. *hemi,* half, + *metabolē,* change).

Complete Metamorphosis. Most insects (about 88%) have complete metamorphosis. A series of larval instars different from the adult are followed by a pupal stage and finally the adult. The wormlike larvae, called caterpillars, maggots, bagworms, grubs, and so on, usually have chewing mouthparts. Wings develop internally during the larval stages. The larva forms a cocoon, or case, about itself and becomes a pupa. At the final molt, the adult emerges fully grown. Flies and fruit flies (Diptera), butterflies and moths (Lepidoptera), beetles (Coleoptera), and the like undergo complete metamorphosis. Thus, the stages are egg, larva, pupa, and adult. This type of development is called **holometabolous** (Gr. *holo,* complete, + *metabolē,* change).

Procedure

Beginning 7 to 10 days before your laboratory period, your instructor will have placed in each of several vials a pair of fruit flies and a microscope slide covered with a thick layer of banana-agar medium (or a commercial medium) and a drop of yeast solution. The vials will have been stoppered with cotton. There should now be eggs, larvae, and pupae in the medium on the various slides.

 Remove a slide from a vial, place it under a dissecting microscope, and study its contents.

A female deposits **eggs** on food appropriate to feed her growing larval young. These hatch in about 24 hours into wormlike **larvae.** Larvae of flies are often called maggots. The larvae eat and grow for about 5 days and then become inactive **pupae,** each enclosed in a brownish case, within which final metamorphosis occurs. About 4 days after pupae are formed, **adults** emerge. Adults are full-size when they appear.

 To study adults, you may kill them by placing a few drops of ether on the cotton plug in the vial.

Can you distinguish sexual differences in the adults? _____ Compare the structure of a fruit fly with that of a honeybee and a grasshopper. What difference do you note in the wings? _____ _____ Fruit flies belong to the order Diptera (Gr. *di-,* two, + *pteron,* wing). Is the order well named?

_____

Drawings

 On separate paper, sketch eggs, larvae, and pupa of developing *Drosophila.*

EXERCISE 15E
Collection and Classification of Insects

Where to Collect Insects

1. Using a sweep net, sweep over grass, alfalfa, or weed patches.
2. Spread a cloth, a newspaper, or an inverted umbrella under a bush or shrub; beat or shake the plant vigorously.
3. Overturn stones, logs, bark, leaf mold, and rubbish; look under dung in pastures.
4. Watch for butterflies to alight; then drop a net over them.
5. Look around outdoor lights at night.
6. At night, suspend a sheet from a limb or clothesline, with the lower part of the sheet spread on the ground. Direct automobile headlights or a spotlight on the sheet. The insects will be attracted to the white light, hit against the sheet, and drop onto the cloth below.
7. Moths may be baited by daubing a mixture of crushed banana or peach and molasses or sugar on the bark of trees; visit the trees at night with a flashlight to collect the moths.
8. Locate soil insects by placing humus and leaf matter in a Berlese funnel.
9. Water insects may be seined with a water net. Aquatic insect larvae may be found in either quiet or running water, attached to plants and leaves, or under stones or may be sieved out of bottom mud.
10. In early spring, the sap exuding from stumps and tree trunks attracts various insects.

Killing Insects

If an insect is to be preserved, it must be killed in such a way as not to damage it. Killing bottles of various sizes and shapes may be used. Wide-mouthed plastic jars, such as peanut butter jars with screw-top lids, are best. Each jar should be conspicuously labeled POISON.

A temporary killing bottle can be made quickly by wetting a piece of cotton with a fumigant, such as ethyl acetate (nail polish remover); placing it in the bottom of a bottle; covering it with several discs of blotting paper; and screwing on the lid. *Do not inhale* the fumigant. Half-pint or pint jars are satisfactory. The fumigant must be replenished before each collecting trip. A few loose strips of paper towel added to the bottle will help absorb moisture and protect small insects. Replace the paper as it becomes moist.

A more permanent killing jar can be made by cementing a snap-cap vial to the underside of the lid of a wide-mouthed jar, with the vial opening facing down. The vial is filled with cotton saturated with ethyl acetate before use. When the killing jar is not in use, the cap may be snapped on the vial to retard evaporation. Similar killing jars may be purchased from biological supply houses.

Hard-bodied insects may require an hour or so to ensure death. If you are collecting many kinds of insects, it is good to have several killing bottles so that large insects, such as butterflies, dragonflies, and large beetles, may be kept in separate jars, away from smaller, more fragile insects.

To transfer an insect from a net to the killing jar, fold the net over, uncover the jar, work the jar into the net, and place its mouth over the insect as it clings to the cloth; hold the lid over the jar for a few seconds until the insect is quiet before removing it from the net and placing it in the jar. Remove the insect from the killing jar when it is dead and place it between layers of paper towel or in paper envelopes to prevent damage.

Soft-bodied insects and especially larval forms should not be put into the killing jar. They are killed by dropping them into 70% to 80% ethyl alcohol or by injecting their bodies with alcohol. The alcohol should be changed after a few days because it becomes diluted by the body fluids of the animals.

Relaxing

Insects that have dried out are fragile and easily broken. If an insect cannot be mounted before it has become dry, it can be relaxed. Prepare a relaxing jar by placing a layer of wet sand or wet paper towel in the bottom of a glass jar, adding a few drops of formalin or carbolic acid to discourage mold, and covering the sand with a disc of blotting paper to protect the insect. The insect may be left in the relaxing jar for 1 to 3 days, as necessary.

Displaying Insects

1. Insects can be mounted in shallow boxes on a layer of cotton and covered with glass plates or sheets of acetate. An attractive box of this kind can be made by cutting out the main portion of the lid of the box, so that a 1.5- to 2.5-cm rim, or "frame," remains around each side, then gluing a piece of glass or acetate to the inside of the lid behind the frame. The box itself is lined with cotton, and the insects are held in place on the cotton by the acetate or glass in the lid.

2. Pinned insects can be displayed in purchased Schmitt boxes, cigar boxes, or cardboard boxes deep enough to take an insect pin. Balsa wood or layers of soft corrugated cardboard should be glued to the bottom of the box.

   Pin insects with regular insect pins, which are longer and thinner than common pins. Sizes 2 and 3 are convenient sizes for general use.

   Pin grasshoppers through the posterior part of the pronotum, a little to the right of the midline (Figure 15-10D). Butterflies and moths are pinned through the center of the thorax, whereas bees, wasps, and flies are pinned through the thorax but a little to the right of midline. Pin bugs (hemipterans) through the scutellum, a bit to right of midline, and beetles through the right elytron (forewing), halfway between the two ends of the body. To insert the pin, hold the insect between the thumb and forefinger of one hand and insert the pin with the other. Mount all specimens at a uniform height—about 2.5 cm above the point of the pin.

A tiny label with date, place, and name of the collector can be added to the pin under the insect, with another label giving the scientific name of the insect placed under the first.

A very small insect can be mounted on the point of an elongated, triangular piece of light cardboard about 8 to 10 mm long and 3 to 4 mm wide at the base (Figure 15-11). After putting the triangular cardboard mount on the pin, hold the pin and touch the tip of the cardboard triangle to the glue; then touch the insect with the gluey tip. Use as little glue as possible to hold the insect.

Many winged insects, such as butterflies, moths, and mayflies, are usually mounted first on a spreading board, which has a groove into which the body is pinned. The wings are then spread out and held in the proper position to dry. Care must be taken not to damage the insect or to rub off the scales of a lepidopteran. The wings are carefully moved into position by pins and held by strips of paper pinned to the board. For butterflies, moths, and mayflies, the rear margins of the forewings should be straight across, at right angles to the body; the hindwings should be far enough forward so that there is no gap between the forewings and hindwings. The forewing should overlap the front edge of the hindwing a little. With damsel-flies, dragonflies, grasshoppers, and most other insects, the front margins of the hindwings should be straight across, with the front wing far enough forward so that forewings and hindwings do not touch.

Try to maneuver the wings by means of a pin held near the base of the wings—not through the

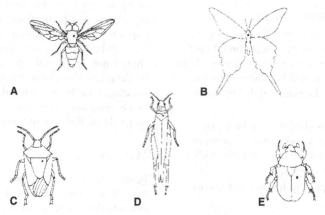

Figure 15-10

How to pin insects. The dots indicate the location of pins. **A,** Flies. **B,** Butterflies and moths. **C,** Bugs. **D,** Grasshoppers. **E,** Beetles.

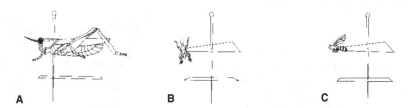

Figure 15-11

Pinning and labeling insects. **A,** Larger insects are pinned through the body. Minute ones can be glued to a paper point, either **B,** dorsal side up or **C,** laterally. Dates, places, and scientific names may be printed on slips of paper beneath the insect.

wings, because that would make holes in them. Pin the wings securely with paper strips, using several strips if necessary. When completed, hold the body down with forceps and remove the pin from the thorax.

If the specimen is to be displayed on cotton under glass, the spreading board is not necessary. Pin the insect upside down (feet up) on a flat

pinning surface, such as corrugated cardboard, and pin the wings with strips of paper as before.

Drying may take several days. If the abdomen, when touched gently with a pin, can be moved independently of the wings, the specimen is not dry enough; wait until the body is stiff before removing the pins and strips of paper.

Key to the Principal Orders of Insects*

The following key will enable you to place your insects in the correct order. The use of a two-choice, or dichotomous, key such as this one is explained in Chapter 5. This key is designed for use with adult (final instar) insects and is therefore not suitable for identification of insect larvae. If you wish to carry identification to family, genus, or species, consult one of the references listed at the end of this key.

Terms Used in the Key

Cercus (pl. cerci) One of a pair of jointed anal appendages

Tarsus (pl. tarsi) The leg segment distal to the tibia, consisting of one or more segments or subdivisions

Lepidoptera

1   With functional wings 2
     Without functional wings, or with
     forewings thickened and concealing
     membranous hindwings 15

2 (1)   Wings covered with minute scales;
         mouthparts usually a coiled tube
         (butterflies, moths) . . . . **Lepidoptera**
         Wings usually clear, not covered with
         scales; mouthparts not a coiled tube 3

Diptera

3 (2)   With one pair of wings (true flies) . . . . . . **Diptera**
         With two pairs of wings 4

4 (3)   Wings long, narrow, fringed with long
         hairs, body length 5 mm or less
         (thrips) . . . . **Thysanoptera**
         Wings not narrow and fringed, body
         usually longer than 5 mm 5

Thysanoptera

5 (4)   Abdomen with two or three threadlike "tails";
         hindwings small (mayflies) . . . . . **Ephemeroptera**
         Abdomen with only short filaments
         or none; hindwings larger 6

6 (5)   Forewings clearly longer and with
         greater area than hindwings 7
         Forewings not longer, or only slightly
         longer than hindwings, and with same or
         less area than hindwings 9

Ephemeroptera

7 (6)   Forewings noticeably hairy; antennae as long
         or longer than body (caddis flies) . . . **Trichoptera**
         Wings transparent or translucent, not
         hairy; antennae shorter than body 8

Trichoptera

*Key adapted from Borror, D. J., and R. E. White. 1970. A field guide to the insects of America north of Mexico. Boston, Houghton Mifflin Company.

8 (7)   Tarsi two-segmented or three-segmented;
        body not wasplike or beelike 14
        Tarsi five-segmented; usually wasplike or
        beelike (sawflies, ichneumons, winged
        ants, wasps, bees) . . . . **Hymenoptera**

Tarsi

Hymenoptera

9 (6)   Head prolonged ventrally into a beaklike
        structure (scorpionflies) . . . . **Mecoptera**
        Head not prolonged ventrally 10

Mecoptera

10 (9) Antennae very short and bristlelike; eyes
        large; abdomen long and slender
        (dragonflies, damselflies) . . . . **Odonata**
        Antennae not short and bristlelike; eyes
        moderate to small 11

Odonata

11 (10) Hindwings broader than forewings; cerci
        present (stoneflies) . . . . **Plecoptera**
        Hindwings little if any broader than
        forewings; cerci absent 12

Plecoptera

12 (11) Mothlike; wings noticeably hairy and
        opaque; antennae as long or longer than
        body (caddis flies) . . . . **Trichoptera**
        Not mothlike; wings not noticeably hairy,
        usually clear; antennae shorter than
        body 13

Trichoptera

13 (12) Wings with few cross veins; tarsi
        four-segmented; length to 8 mm
        (termites) . . . . **Isoptera**

Isoptera

continued

Wings with numerous cross veins;
tarsi five-segmented; length to 75 mm
(fishflies, dobsonflies, lacewings,
ant lions) . . . . **Neuroptera**

Neuroptera

14 (8)   Mouthparts sucking, beak arising from
rear of head (cicadas, hoppers,
aphids) . . . . **Hemiptera,
suborder Auchenorrhyncha**
Mouthparts chewing, beak absent; body
length less than 7 mm (book lice,
bar lice) . . . . **Pscoptera**

Auchenorrhyncha

15 (1)   Wings entirely absent 16
Wings modified, forewings hard and
leathery and covering hindwings 27

16 (15)   Narrow-waisted, antlike (ants, wingless
wasps) . . . . **Hymenoptera**
Not narrow-waisted or antlike 17

Hymenoptera

17 (16)   Body rarely flattened laterally; usually do
not jump 18
Body flattened laterally; small jumping
insects (fleas) . . . . **Siphonaptera**

Siphonaptera

18 (17)   Parasites of birds and mammals; body
nearly always flattened dorsoventrally 19
Never parasitic; body usually not flattened 20

19 (18)   Head as wide as or wider than thorax
(chewing lice) . . . . **Phthiraptera**

Phthiraptera

Head narrower than thorax
(sucking lice) . . . . **Phthiraptera,
suborder Anoplura**

Anoplura

20 (18) Abdomen with stylelike appendages
or threadlike tails (silverfish,
bristletails) . . . . **Thysanura**
Abdomen with neither styles nor tails 21

Thysanura

21 (20) Abdomen with a forked, tail-like jumping
mechanism (springtails). . . . . **Collembola**
Abdomen lacking a jumping
mechanism. 22

Collembola

22 (21) Abdomen usually with two short tubes;
small, plump, soft-bodied (aphids,
others) . . . . **Hemiptera,
suborder Sternorrhyncha**
Abdomen without tubes; usually not
plump and soft-bodied 23

Sternorrhyncha

23 (22) Lacking pigment, whitish; soft-bodied 24
Distinctly pigmented; usually
hard-bodied 25

Isoptera

24 (23) Antennae long, hairlike; tarsi two-segmented
or three-segmented (psocids) . . . . . . **Psocoptera**
Antennae short, breadlike; tarsi
four-segmented (termites) . . . .**Isoptera**

25 (23) Body shape variable; length over
5 mm. 26
Body narrow; length less than 5 mm
(thrips). . . . . **Thysanoptera**

Heteroptera

26 (25) Antennae four-segmented or five-segmented;
mouthparts sucking (wingless bugs) . . **Hemiptera,
suborder Heteroptera**
Antennae many-segmented; mouthparts
chewing. 31

Phasmatodea

continued

27 (15)   Abdomen with forcepslike cerci
(earwigs) . . . . **Dermaptera**
Abdomen lacks forcepslike cerci 28

28 (27)   Mouthparts sucking; beak usually
elongate 29
Mouthparts chewing 30

Dermaptera

29 (28)   Forewings nearly always thickened at
base, membranous at tip; beak rises from
front or bottom of head (true bugs)
. . . . **Hemiptera, suborder Heteroptera**

Heteroptera

Forewings of uniform texture throughout;
beak arises from hind part of head
(hoppers) . . . . **Hemiptera, suborder
Auchenorrhyncha**

Auchenorrhyncha

30 (28)   Forewings with veins, at rest held rooflike over
abdomen or overlapping, hind legs modified for
jumping (grasshoppers, crickets, katydids)
. . . . **Orthoptera**

Orthoptera

Forewings without veins, meeting in a
straight line down back
(beetles) . . . .**Coleoptera**

Coleoptera

31 (26)   Body oval and flattened (cockroaches)
. . . . **Blattodea**
Body slender and elongate 32

32 (31)   Stick-like body (Walking Sticks) . . . **Phasmatodea**
Elongate body with raptorial front
legs (mantids) . . . . **Mantodea**

References

Note that, in addition to the following general guide-books, regional guides are often useful for surrounding areas.

Arnett, R. H. 1985. American insects: a handbook of the insects of America and Mexico. New York, Van Nostrand Reinhold Company.

Arnett, R. H., Jr., and M. C. Thomas, eds. 2000. American beetles, vol. 1. Boca Raton, Florida, CRC Press.

Borror, D. J., and R. E. White. 1970. A field guide to the insects of America north of Mexico. Boston, Houghton Mifflin Company.

Chu, H. F. 1949. How to know the immature insects. Dubuque, Iowa, Wm. C. Brown Company.

Claassen, P. W. 1931. Plecoptera nymphs of America (north of Mexico). Springfield, Ill., Pub. of the Thomas Say Foundation, by Charles C. Thomas.

Covell, C. V., Jr. 1984. A field guide to the moths of eastern North America. Boston, Houghton Mifflin Company.

Dillon, E. S., and L. S. Dillon. 1972. A manual of common beetles of eastern North America. New York, Dover Publications, Inc.

Edmunds, G. F., Jr., S. L. Jensen, and L. Berner. 1976. The mayflies of North and Central America. Minneapolis, University of Minnesota Press.

Ehrlich, P. R., and A. H. Ehrlich. 1961. How to know the butterflies. Dubuque, Iowa, Wm. C. Brown Company.

Harris, J. R. 1952. An angler's entomology. New York, F. A. Praeger.

Hogue, C. L. 1993. Insects of the Los Angeles Basin. Los Angeles, Natural History Museum of L.A. County.

Holland, W. J. 1968. The moth book: a popular guide to a knowledge of the moths of North America. New York, Dover Publications, Inc.

Jaques, H. E. 1947. How to know the insects, ed. 2. Dubuque, Iowa, Wm. C. Brown Company.

Jaques, H. E. 1951. How to know the beetles. Dubuque, Iowa, Wm. C. Brown Company.

Jewett, S. G. 1959. The stoneflies (Plecoptera) of the Pacific Northwest. Corvallis, Oregon State College.

Klots, A. B. 1951. A field guide to the butterflies of North America east of the great plains. Boston, Houghton Mifflin Company.

LaFontaine, G. 1981. Caddisflies. New York, Lyons & Burford.

Lehmkahl, D. M. 1979. How to know the aquatic insects. The pictured key nature series. Dubuque, Iowa, Wm. C. Brown Company.

McPherson, J. E. 1982. The Pentatomoidea (Hemiptera) of northeastern North America. Carbondale, Ill., Southern Illinois University Press.

Merritt, R. W., and K. W. Cummins. 1996. An introduction to the aquatic insects of North America, ed. 3. Dubuque, Iowa, Kendall/Hunt Publishing Company.

Miller, P. L. 1984. Dragonflies. New York, Cambridge University Press.

Milne, L., and M. Milne. 1980. The Audubon Society field guide to North American insects and spiders. New York, Alfred A. Knopf, Inc.

Needham, J. G., and M. J. Westfall, Jr. 1975. A manual of the dragonflies of North America (Anisoptera): including the Greater Antilles and the provinces of the Mexican border. Berkeley, University of California Press.

Opler, P. A. 1992. A field guide to eastern butterflies. The Peterson field guide series. Boston, Houghton Mifflin Company.

Otte, D. 1981–84. The North American grasshoppers. Vol. 1: Acrididae (Gomphocerinae and Acridinae); Vol. 2: Acrididae (Oedipodinae). Cambridge, Mass., Harvard University Press.

Pyle, R. M. 1981. The Audubon Society field guide to North American butterflies. New York, Alfred A. Knopf, Inc.

Sborboni, V., and S. Forestiero. 1998. Butterflies of the world. Buffalo, N.Y., Firefly Books Inc.

Schuh, R. T., and J. A. Slater. 1995. True bugs of the world. Ithaca, N.Y., Cornell University Press.

Scott, J. A. 1986. The butterflies of North America: a natural history and field guide. Stanford, Calif., Stanford University Press.

Smart, P. 1975. The international butterfly book. New York, Crowell Company.

Stehr, F. W. (ed.). 1991. Immature insects. Vols. 1 & 2. Dubuque, Iowa, Kendall/Hunt Publishing Company.

Swan, L. A., and C. S. Papp. 1972. The common insects of North America. New York, Harper & Row, Publishers.

Triplehorn, C. A., and N. F. Johnson. 2005. Borror and DeLong's introduction to the study of insects. ed. 7. Belmont, Calif., Brooks/Cole.

White, R. E. 1983. A field guide to the beetles of North America. Boston, Houghton Mifflin Company.

Wiggins, G. B. 1977. Larvae of the North American caddisfly genera (Trichoptera). Toronto, University of Toronto Press.

NOTES

10

Five Small Protostome Phyla
Phylum Nematoda
Phylum Rotifera
Phylum Gastrotricha
Phylum Nematomorpha
Phylum Acanthocephala

All bilateral animal phyla except the acoelomates possess a **body cavity** belonging to one of two types: (1) **true coelom,** in which a peritoneum (an epithelium of mesodermal origin) covers both the inner surface of the body wall and the outer surface of the visceral organs in the cavity, or (2) **pseudocoel,** a body cavity not entirely lined with peritoneum.

A body cavity of either type is an advantage because it provides room for organ development and storage and allows some freedom of movement within the body. Because the cavity is often fluid-filled, it also provides for a hydrostatic skeleton in those forms lacking a true skeleton.

EXERCISE 10A

Phylum Nematoda—*Ascaris* and Others
Ascaris, intestinal roundworm
Some free-living nematodes
Some parasitic nematodes
Projects and demonstrations

EXERCISE 10B

A Brief Look at Some Other Protostomes
Phylum Rotifera
Phylum Gastrotricha
Phylum Nematomorpha
Phylum Acanthocephala

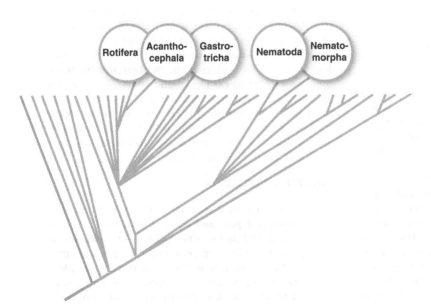

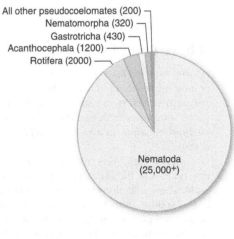

Four of the five phyla considered in this exercise are pseudocoelomate (the exception, phylum Gastrotricha, is acoelomate). Of these four, phylum Nematoda is by far the largest and most important economically.

All pseudocoelomate phyla are at the **organ-system level of organization.** Pseudocoelomates tend to be cylindrical in body form, to be unsegmented, and to have a complete (mouth-to-anus) digestive tract (this is absent in acanthocephalans). The epidermis is usually covered with a cuticle. There are both aquatic and terrestrial members, and parasitism is fairly common.

EXERCISE 10A
Phylum Nematoda—
Ascaris and Others

Nematodes are an extensive group with worldwide distribution. They include terrestrial, freshwater, marine, and parasitic forms. They are elongated roundworms covered with a flexible, nonliving cuticle. Circular muscles are lacking in the body wall and, in *Ascaris,* longitudinal muscles are arranged in four groups separated by epidermal cords (some nematodes have six or eight groups of longitudinal muscles). Cilia are completely lacking. Are cilia present in any acoelomates? _____ In cnidarians? _____ Nematodes—both parasitic and free-living—are incredibly abundant. A handful of good garden soil contains thousands of nematodes. Some 50 species of nematodes occur in humans, most of them nonpathogenic.

Ascaris, Intestinal Roundworm

Phylum Nematoda
    Class Rhabditea
        Order Ascaridida
            Genus *Ascaris*
                Species *Ascaris suum*

Where Found

Ascaris lumbricoides (Gr. *askaris,* intestinal worm) is a common intestinal parasite of humans. *A. suum,* which parasitizes pigs, is so similar to the human parasite that it was long considered merely a different strain of *Ascaris lumbricoides. Ascaris megalocephala* is common in horses.

Ascaris infections are extremely common—nearly one-quarter of the human population is infected worldwide. These infections were once common in rural areas in the southeastern United States. The present number of infected persons in the United States is unknown but has been estimated to be as high as 4 million. Infections are most common among immigrants, travelers, and refugees. Careless defecation near habitation by individuals harboring worms seeds the soil with eggs that may

remain infective for years. The eggs are extraordinarily resistant to chemicals, remaining viable in 2% formalin and in 50% solutions of the common laboratory acids. Moderate to heavy infections cause malnutrition and underdevelopment in children, and the worms' metabolites may cause immune reactions. Heavy infections can lead to fatal intestinal blockage or to wandering of overcrowded worms; the psychological trauma caused by the latter can only be imagined.

General Features

 Place a preserved *Ascaris* in a dissecting pan and cover with water. A word of caution: although the chance of infection from eggs from formalin-preserved female *Ascaris* is remote, be sure to wash your hands after dissecting the worm.

Females, which run 20 to 40 cm in length, are more numerous and are larger than males, which average 15 to 31 cm in length. Males have a curved posterior end and two chitinous **spicules** projecting from the anal region. The spicules are used to hold the female's vulva open during copulation. How long is your *Ascaris* specimen? _____ Is the body segmented? _____ Compare your specimen with one of the other sex.

With a hand lens, find the **mouth,** with three **lips,** one dorsal and two ventral (Figure 10-1). Find the ventral **anus** at the posterior end. The anus in a male not only discharges feces from the rectum but also serves as a genital opening. The female genital opening **(vulva)** is located on the ventral side about one-third the length of the body from the anterior end. It may be hard to distinguish from scars. Use a hand lens or dissecting microscope.

Note the shiny **cuticle** that covers the body wall. It is nonliving and consists primarily of **collagen,** which also is found in vertebrate connective tissue.

Four **longitudinal lines** run almost the entire length of the body—**dorsal** and **ventral median lines** and two **lateral lines.** Dorsal and ventral lines, which indicate location of bundles of nerve fibers, are very difficult to see on preserved specimens. However, along the lateral lines, the body wall is thinner, and the lines usually appear somewhat transparent. Excretory canals are located inside the lateral lines.

Internal Structure

 Select a female specimen, place the worm in a dissecting pan, and cover it with water. Locate the lateral lines, where the body wall seems somewhat thinner. Now find the anus and vulva on the ventral side. This should help you identify the opposite, or middorsal, line. Now, with a razor blade, slit open the body wall *along the*

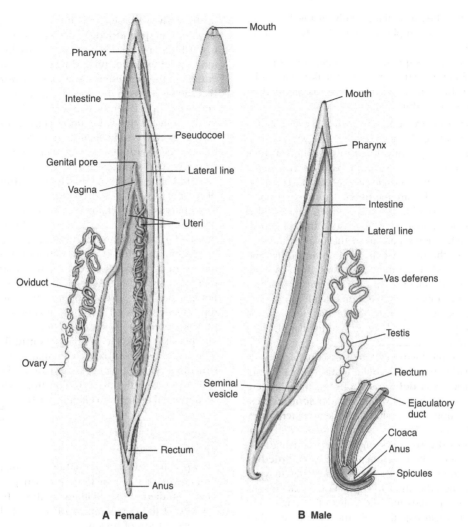

Figure 10-1

Ascaris. **A,** Internal structure of female, with insert showing detail of anterior end. **B,** Internal structure of male, with insert showing detail of cloacal region.

middorsal line, being careful to avoid injuring the internal structures. Pin back the body wall to expose the viscera, *slanting the pins outward* to allow room for dissection.

Body Wall and Pseudocoel. Note the body cavity. Why is it called a **pseudocoel?** _____ How does it differ from a true coelom? _____ _____ Note fluffy masses lining the body wall. These are large, nucleated cell bodies of the **longitudinal muscle cells,** whose fibers extend longitudinally in the body wall. With your teasing needle, tease out some of the fibers from the cut edge of the wall. Examine fibers and cells under the microscope. Absence of circular muscles accounts for the thrashing movements of these animals. Note the absence of muscle cells along the **lateral lines.**

Excretory System. Excretory canals located in the lateral lines unite just back of the mouth to empty ventrally through an **excretory pore.** The canals are largely osmoregulatory in function. Excretion also occurs through the cuticle. Flame cells are lacking in *Ascaris* and other nematodes, although they are found in some other pseudocoelomate phyla.

Digestive System. The mouth empties into a short, muscular **pharynx,** which sucks food into the ribbon-like **intestine** (Figure 10-1A). The intestine is thin-walled for absorption of digested food products into the pseudocoel. Trace it to the **anus.** What is meant by "tube within a tube" construction? _____

Does *Ascaris* fit this description? _____ Does the planarian? _____

Digestion is begun extracellularly in the lumen of the intestine and is completed intracellularly in cells of the intestinal wall.

There are no respiratory or circulatory organs. Oxygen is obtained mainly from the breakdown of glycogen within the body, and distribution is handled by the pseudocoelomic fluid.

Reproductive System. The female reproductive system fills most of the pseudocoel. The system is a Y-shaped set of long, convoluted tubes. Unravel them carefully with a probe. The short base of the Y, the **vagina,** opens to the outside at the **vulva.** The long arms of the inverted Y are the **uteri.** These extend posteriorly and then double back as slender, much-coiled **oviducts,** which connect the uteri with the threadlike terminal **ovaries.** Eggs pass from the ovaries through the oviducts to the uteri, where fertilization occurs and shells are secreted. Then they pass through the vagina and vulva to the outside. The uteri of an ascaris may contain up to 27 million eggs at a time, with as many as 200,000 eggs being laid per day. Study the life history of *Ascaris* from your text. Is there an intermediate host in the life cycle? _____

The male reproductive system is essentially a single, long tube made up of a threadlike **testis,** which continues as a thicker **vas deferens.** Both are much-coiled. The vas deferens connects with the wider **seminal vesicle,** which empties by a short, muscular **ejaculatory duct** into the anus. Thus, the male anus serves as an outlet for both digestive system and reproductive system and is often called a **cloaca** (L., sewer). **Spicules** secreted by and contained in spicule pouches may be extended through the anus. In copulation a male inserts the copulatory spicules into the vulva of a female and discharges spermatozoa through the ejaculatory duct into the vagina.

What is meant by "sexual dimorphism"? _____ _____How does *Ascaris* illustrate this?_____ How is *Ascaris* transmitted from host to host? _____ How can infestation be prevented? _____ In what ways is *Ascaris* structurally and functionally adapted to life as a parasite in the intestine? _____ _____

Transverse Sections of *Ascaris*

 Study a prepared stained slide, at first under low power. If both female and male cross sections are present, examine first the larger female cross section.

Note the thick, noncellular **cuticle** on the outside of the body wall (Figure 10-2). Below the cuticle is a thinner syncytial **epidermis,** which contains nuclei but few cell walls. **Longitudinal muscles** making up most

of the body wall appear as fluffy, irregular masses dipping into the **pseudocoel,** with tips of the cells directed toward the nearest nerve cord. Muscle continuity is interrupted by **longitudinal lines.** Look for **excretory canals** in the lateral lines and look for **dorsal** and **ventral nerve cords** in the dorsal and ventral lines. The lateral lines appear free of muscle cells. In the pseudocoel of the female, the large **uteri** (Figure 10-2) are filled with eggs enclosed in shells and in cleavage stages. The thin-walled **oviducts** also contain eggs, whereas the wheel-shaped **ovaries** are composed of tall epithelial cells and have small lumens. The **intestine** is composed of a single layer of tall, columnar cells (endodermal). The pharynx and rectal region of the intestine are lined with cuticle. Why? _____ Why is *Ascaris* not digested in the human intestine? _____

Examine the male cross section. It is similar to the female in all respects except for the reproductive system. You should see several rounded sections of **testes** packed with spermatogonia (precursors to male reproductive cells). There may also be several sections of **vas deferens** containing numerous spermatocytes and possibly a section of a large **seminal vesicle** filled with mature spermatozoa. Note that male reproductive structures visible in the cross section of the roundworm will depend on the body region from which the cross section is taken (refer to Figure 10-1B).

Table of Comparison

On pp. 169 and 170 is a table for comparing representatives of three of the metazoan phyla that you have studied so far. Filling in this table affords a survey of the development of these phyla and is an excellent form of review.

Some Free-Living Nematodes

Vinegar Eels
Turbatrix aceti (tur-ba'tricks; L. female that disturbs), the vinegar eel (Figure 10-3), is often found in fermented fruit juices, particularly the sediment of nonpasteurized vinegar, where it feeds on the yeasts and bacteria found there. As in *Ascaris,* females are larger than males.

 Place a drop of the culture containing worms on a clean glass slide and examine with a compound microscope.

Notice the violent thrashing movements, the body bending in S and C shapes. Because they have only longitudinal muscles in the body wall, vinegar eels, like other nematodes, can flex their body only from side to side. Locomotion is especially inefficient in free water, in which they can make little directional progress.

Add a pinch of sand to the slide and observe again. The worms are now able to use the sand grains as fulcra to make forward progress. In this manner, nematodes can readily move through the interstitial fluids of soils or between the cells of tissues. Now place another drop of culture on a clean slide and cover with a coverslip. Quiet the worms for study by *gently* warming the slide over a small flame or an incandescent lamp. Worms also may be quieted by adding a drop of 1N HCl to the culture.

Note the blunt anterior end, the **mouth, pharynx,** and **pharyngeal bulb.** This leads into a long, straight **intestine,** which ends at the ventral **anus,** located a short distance from the pointed tail end.

Select a female specimen. Large females will contain two to five developing juveniles in the **uterus.** *Turbatrix* is **ovoviviparous** (L. *ovum,* egg, + *vivere,* to live, + *parere,* to bring forth), giving birth to about 45 living young during its average life span of 10 months. Note the **vulva** on the ventral side, which receives sperm in copulation and through which the young worms are born. The **seminal receptacle** lies just behind the uterus. The **ovary** extends anteriorly from the uterus and doubles back dorsally.

Males can usually be identified by their **copulatory spicules,** which may protrude from the anal opening. They are used for holding the female during copulation. It may be possible to see the filamentous **testis** extending forward from about the middle of the body, then bending back on itself. It leads, by way of a sperm duct, to the cloaca.

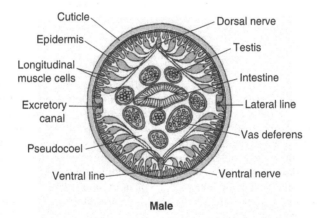

Male

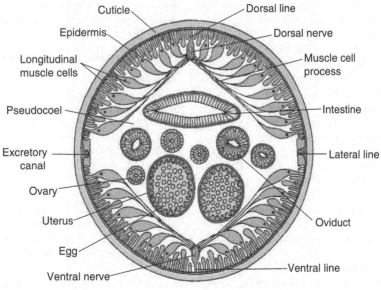

Figure 10-2

Transverse sections through male and female *Ascaris* worms.

Female

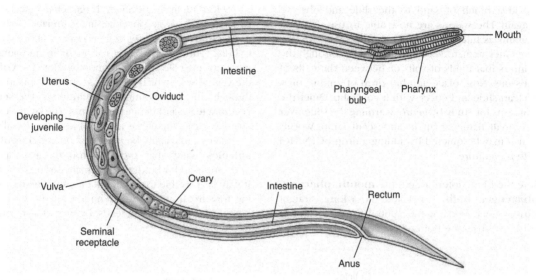

Figure 10-3
Turbatrix aceti, the vinegar eel (female).

Soil Nematodes

Nematodes are present in almost every imaginable habitat. N. A. Cobb emphasized their abundance in this quotation from a 1914 U.S. Department of Agriculture yearbook: "If all the matter in the universe except the nematodes were swept away, our world would still be dimly recognizable, and if, as disembodied spirits, we could then investigate it, we should find its mountains, hills, vales, rivers, lakes, and oceans represented by a thin film of nematodes. The location of towns would be decipherable, since for every massing of human beings there would be a corresponding massing of certain nematodes. Trees would still stand in ghostly rows representing our streets and highways. The location of the various plants and animals would still be decipherable, and, had we sufficient knowledge, in many cases even their species could be determined by an examination of their erstwhile nematode parasites."

The main limiting factor is presence of water because nematodes are aquatic animals in the strictest sense. They are capable of activity only when immersed in fluid, even if it is only the microscopically thin film of water that normally covers soil particles. If no water film is present, nematodes either die or pass into a quiescent resting stage.

Soil nematodes are more abundant among roots of plants than in open soil, so the best collecting source is probably the top few centimeters of a long-established meadow turf.

Some nematodes are herbivorous, feeding on algae, fungi, and higher plants; many feed on plant roots. Examples are species of *Tylenchus, Heterodera, Dorylaimus,* and *Monhystera.* Carnivorous nematodes feed on other nematodes, rotifers, small oligochaetes, and so on. These include species of *Dorylaimus, Diplogaster,* and *Monochus.* Some nematodes are **saprophagous** (suh-prof'uh-gus; Gr. *sapros,* rotten, + *phagos,* to eat), such as *Rhabditis, Cephalobus,* and *Plectus,* which probably live on bacteria or other microorganisms. Some species are omnivorous. Some soil nematodes are parasitic on plant or animal life.

Soil samples may be brought in from a wide variety of places. Methods that you may use to collect nematodes, as well as many annelids and arthropods, for study under the microscope are found on p. 166. Methods are also given for obtaining *Rhabditis* from the nephridia of earthworms.

Some Parasitic Nematodes

Hookworms

Hookworms, *Necator americanus* ("American killer"), live in the intestines of their vertebrate hosts. They attach themselves to the mucosa and suck up the blood and tissue fluids from it. The species most important to humans are *N. americanus* and *Ancylostoma duodenale* (an-ke-los'ta-muh; Gr. *ankylos,* crooked, + *stoma,* mouth). Hookworms infect about 4% of the population in the southern United States, where 95% of the cases are *Necator* infections. White people are more susceptible to hookworm than are black people and prevalence is higher among whites than blacks. *A. caninum* is a common hookworm of domestic dogs and cats (Figure 10-4).

Hookworms mature and mate in the small intestine of the host. Developing eggs are passed out in the feces. On the ground they require warmth (preferably

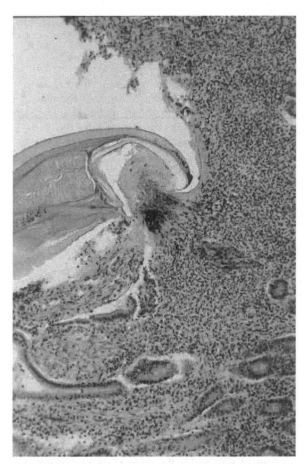

Figure 10-4

Section through anterior end of *Ancylostoma caninum,* the dog hookworm, in the intestine. Note the lacerating cutting plates, used for attachment to the intestinal mucosa.

20° to 30° C), shade, and moisture for continued development. They hatch in 24 to 48 hours into young juveniles, which feed on fecal matter, molt their cuticles twice, and in a week or so are ready to infect a new host.

If the ground surface is dry, they migrate into the soil, but after a rain or morning dew they move to the surface, extend their bodies in a snakelike fashion, and wave back and forth. Thousands may group together, waving rhythmically in unison. Under ideal conditions, they may live for several weeks.

Infection occurs when juveniles contact the host's skin and burrow into it. Those that reach blood vessels are carried to the heart and then to the lungs. There they are carried by ciliary action up the respiratory passages to the glottis and swallowed. In the small intestine, they grow, molt, mature, and mate. Five weeks after entry, they are producing eggs.

Whether hookworm disease results from infection depends on number of worms present and nutritional

condition of the infected person. Massive infections in the lungs may cause coughing, sore throat, and lung infection. In the intestinal phase, moderate infections cause an iron-deficiency anemia. Severe infections may result in severe protein deficiency. When accompanied by chronic malnutrition, as in many tropical countries, there may be irreversible damage, resulting in stunted growth and below-average intelligence.

 Examine prepared slides of hookworms.

Adult males of *Necator* are typically 7 to 9 mm long; females, 9 to 11 mm long. Specimens of *Ancylostoma* are slightly longer. The anterior end curves dorsally, giving the worm a hooklike appearance. Note the large buccal capsule, which bears a pair of dorsal and a pair of ventral cutting plates surrounding its margin (Figure 10-4). A stout, muscular esophagus serves as a powerful pump.

Note on males a conspicuous copulatory bursa consisting of two lateral lobes and a smaller dorsal lobe, all supported by fleshy rays. Needlelike spicules are present, which in *Necator* are fused at the distal ends to form a characteristic hook. In females the vulva is located in about the middle of the body.

Trichina Worm

The trichina worm, *Trichinella spiralis* (Gr. *trichinos,* of hair, + *ella,* dim. suffix), is a nematode parasite in humans, hogs, rats, and other omnivorous or carnivorous mammals.

 Study a slide of larvae encysted in pork muscle (Figure 10-5).

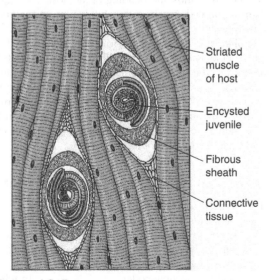

Striated muscle of host

Encysted juvenile

Fibrous sheath

Connective tissue

Figure 10-5

Trichinella spiralis, the trichina worm. Juveniles are shown encysted in skeletal muscle.

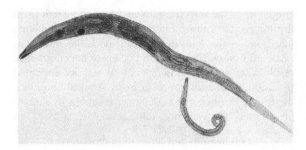

Figure 10-6
Pinworms, *Enterobius vermicularis*. The male is smaller and has a curled posterior end.

How many cysts does your slide show? _____ Would you be able to see the cysts in meat with the naked eye? _____ The cyst wall is made of fibrous tissue that gradually becomes calcified from the host's immune reactions. How many worms are coiled in a cyst? _____ Study the life cycle of *Trichinella* in your text. Are they oviparous or ovoviviparous? _____ How can you prevent trichinosis? _____ Study a slide showing male and female adults. Where would the adults live in the human host? _____

Pinworm
Pinworms, *Enterobius vermicularis* (en-te-robe′ee-us; Gr. *enteron*, intestine, + *bios*, life) (Figure 10-6), are the most common nematode parasite of humans in the United States. They live in the large intestine and cecum. Females, up to 12 mm in length, lay their eggs at night around the anal region of their host. A single female may lay 4600 to 16,000 eggs. Scratching contaminates the hands and bedding of the host. The eggs, when swallowed, hatch in the duodenum and mature in the intestine.

Unlike hookworms, pinworms are often found at high socioeconomic levels. Although approximately one-third of the human population in the United States is infected with pinworms, their presence is mainly an irritation and an embarrassment because pinworms cause no obvious debilitating effects. But unmeasurable is the mental stress suffered by families in their efforts to rid their households of the worms.

Projects and Demonstrations

1. *Prepared slide of* Wuchereria bancrofti *(wu-ka-rir′ ee-a; after Otto Wucherer, nineteenth-century German physician)*. Examine prepared slides of the filarial worm, *Wuchereria bancrofti*. Consult your textbook for the life cycle. What disease is caused by this nematode? _____ In what climate is infestation common? _____ What is the alternate host? _____ What control methods might be used? _____

2. *Prepared slides of* Dracunculus medinensis *(dra-kunk′ u-les; L. dim. of* draco, *dragon)*. Examine prepared slides of the guinea worm, *Dracunculus medinensis*. Consult your textbook for the life cycle of this worm. In what part of the world is this nematode common? _____ Where do the larvae develop? _____ How is this parasite acquired? _____ What control methods would you use to prevent infestation?

3. *Prepared slides of other nematode parasites.* Examine prepared slides of eggs, larvae, or cysts of any nematode parasites.

4. *Prepared slide of* Dirofilaria immitis *(dog heartworm)*. Examine a prepared slide of microfilariae in a smear of dog blood. Heartworm is especially prevalent along the Atlantic and Gulf Coast states and northward along the Mississippi River drainage, where dogs are infected by mosquitoes that ingest and transmit the microfilariae with their blood meals. The worms mature in the right heart and pulmonary artery. Heavy infestations cause cardiopulmonary failure.

5. *Methods for collecting soil nematodes.* Nematode populations in soil often reach enormous proportions and are of great importance both in the ecology of soils and in the economic cost nematodes inflict on agriculture. Either of these procedures will give students an impression of the abundance of soil nematodes.

   a. Boiled potato. Leave some pieces of boiled potato for several days in various places—under a rock, plank, or bit of soil or in a garden, a meadow, a marsh, or an empty lot—and then place them in sterile test tubes, plug with cotton, and set in a warm room for several days before examining.

   b. Baermann apparatus. Wrap a sample of soil in several layers of cheesecloth and suspend from the arm of a ring stand. Fit a short rubber tube with petcock clamp to the spout of a funnel, and attach the funnel to an arm of the ring stand below the bag of soil. Pour warm water (20° to 26° C) into the funnel, so that 4 to 6 cm of the soil in the bag is immersed. After 1 to several hours, drain off a little of the water from the tube into a small test tube. Let the nematodes settle, and then pipette off the supernatant fluid. Examine the nematodes under the microscope.

More information on the use of the Baermann apparatus for collecting soil nematodes is provided by Goldstein, P., and J. Metzner. 1971. Experiments with microscopic animals. Garden City, N.Y., Doubleday & Company, Inc.

6. *Methods for demonstrating* Rhabditis maupasi. The larval stages of *Rhabditis maupasi* are a common nematode parasite living in the nephridia of earthworms (other congenerics occur in fresh water and in soil). The larvae never develop to adults in living earthworms, but after the earthworm's death the nematodes feed on bacteria in the decaying tissue and rapidly mature to adults. Fill some Petri dishes half-full of agar jelly (made by boiling 2 g of agar per 100 ml of water) and allow to cool. Into each dish, cut 6 mm lengths from the posterior third of several fresh earthworms. Cover and leave for 2 to 5 days or until nematodes are seen on the putrefying pieces of earthworm. Adding small bits of raw meat from time to time and subculturing will maintain cultures indefinitely.

Another method is to slit freshly killed *Lumbricus* down the middorsal line posterior to the fifteenth segment. Pin back the walls, cover with water, and examine the nephridia. Larval nematodes may be found in or on some nephridia. Encysted stages also occur in coelomic "brown bodies." If parasites are found, place the earthworm in a jar on wet paper toweling and cover. Keep the preparation wet for 2 to 4 days, depending on the temperature, while the earthworm decomposes and the nematodes reproduce. Examine some of the culture in a few drops of water. There should be much of the life cycle present in the culture: fresh eggs, eggs containing larvae, immature worms, and mature worms. To preserve the worms for storage, put the culture into a test tube and let settle. Pour off most of the water and add an equal amount of boiling 10% formalin to kill and straighten the worms.

EXERCISE 10B
A Brief Look at Some Other Protostomes

Phylum Rotifera
Philodina and Others

 Place a drop of rotifer culture on a depression slide, cover, and examine with subdued light under low power.

How does the animal attach itself? _____ Is it free-swimming? _____ Does it have a definite head end? _____ Note the anterior discs of cilia (**corona**) that give the impression of wheels turning. Are they retractile? _____ The cilia function both in swimming and in feeding.

The tail end (or **foot**) bears slender toes. How many? The foot contains a pedal gland that secretes a cement used for clinging to objects.

Locate the pharynx (**mastax**), which is fitted with jaws for grinding up food particles. The mastax is conspicuous in living rotifers because of its rhythmic contractions (Figure 10-7). Rotifers feed on small plankton organisms swept in by cilia. Can you identify the digestive tract?

In *Philodina* (fill-uh-dine'uh; Gr. *philos*, fond of, loving, + *dinos*, whirling) (Figure 10-7), the **cuticle** is ringed (annulated), so that it appears segmented. From watching its movements, would you say it had circular muscles? Longitudinal? Oblique? _____ Estimate the size of the rotifers. Is there more than one variety in the culture? _____

In many rotifers, the cuticle is thickened and rigid and is called a **lorica.** *Monostyla* and *Platyias* are examples. Some rotifers, such as *Floscularia* (Figure 10-7), live in a secreted tube. Most rotifers live in fresh water.

Phylum Gastrotricha
Chaetonotus and Others

Gastrotrichs include both freshwater and marine organisms. In size and general habits, they are similar to the rotifers and are often found in the same cultures.

 Place a drop of culture on a slide, cover, and study first with low and then with high power.

Observe the manner of locomotion of gastrotrichs. They glide along on a substratum by means of ventral cilia. *Chaetonotus* (NL. *chaeta*, bristle, + Gr. *notos*, back), a common genus, is covered with short, curved dorsal spines (Figure 10-7). The rounded head bears cilia and little tufts of sensory bristles. The tail end is forked and contains cement glands similar to those of rotifers. Do gastrotrichs use the forked tail in the same manner as rotifers use the toes? _____

Gastrotrichs have a syncytial epidermis covered with a cuticle. In feeding they use the head cilia to sweep algae, detritus, and protozoans into the mouth. How long are the specimens? _____

Most marine gastrotrichs are hermaphroditic, but in freshwater species only parthenogenetic females are known.

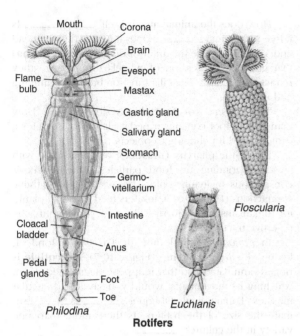

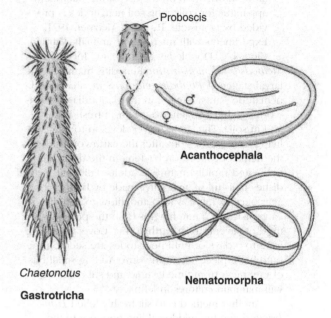

Figure 10-7
Some representative protostomes.

Phylum Nematomorpha

Threadworms, or "Horsehair" Worms

Threadworms, or "horsehair" worms (Figure 10-7), such as *Paragordius* and *Gordius,* are long, cylindrical, hair-like worms often found wriggling in watering troughs, puddles, ponds, and quiet streams. Most range between 0.5 and 3 mm in diameter and from 10 to 300 mm in length, but some reach a length of 1 m.

How long are your specimens? _____ Is the diameter uniform throughout? _____ If you have live specimens, what would you conclude about their muscular makeup, judging from their movements? _____

Nematomorphs have no lateral lines or excretory system, and in adults the digestive system is degenerate. They differ from nematodes in having a cloaca in both sexes. Females lay long, gelatinous strings of eggs on water plants. Larvae, which are encysted on plants, are sometimes eaten by arthropods, in which the larvae are parasitic for a while.

---

*L. *Gordius,* after Gordius, king of Phrygia, who tied an intricate knot that, according to legend, could be untied only by one destined to rule Asia. Many generic names have been taken from mythology, and in many cases their application is quite obscure. Because horsehair worms often become inextricably entangled in knots comprising several worms, the mythological application in this case, however, is apt.

Phylum Acanthocephala

Spiny-Headed Worms, *Macracanthorhynchus*

The adult *Macracanthorhynchus hirudinaceus* (mak-'ruh-kan-thuh-rink'us; Gr.*makros,* long, + *akantha,* thorn, + *rhynchos,* snout) (Figure 10-7) is parasitic in the small intestine of pigs, where it attaches to the intestinal lining and absorbs digested food of its host. Like tapeworms it has no digestive system at all.

The body is cylindrical and widest near the anterior end. A small, spiny proboscis on the anterior end bears six rows of recurved hooks for attachment to the intestinal wall. The proboscis is hollow and can be partially retracted into a proboscis sheath.

The worms are dioecious. Males are much smaller than females. Males have a genital bursa at the posterior end, which may be partly evaginated through the genital pore and is used in copulation. Eggs discharged by a female into a host feces may be eaten by white grubs (larvae of the beetle family *Scarabeidae*) in whom they develop. Pigs are infected by eating the grubs or the adult beetles.

Comparing Representatives of Three Phyla

Name _____

Date _____

Section _____

Features	Cnidaria Hydra	Platyhelminthes Planaria	Nematoda *Ascaris*
Symmetry			
Shape			
Germ layers			
Body covering			
Cephalization (present or absent)			
Coelomic cavity (if present, state what type)			

Features	Cnidaria Hydra	Platyhelminthes Planaria	Nematoda *Ascaris*
Musculature (layers present and how arranged)			
Digestive tract and digestion			
Excretion			
Nervous system			
Sense organs			
Reproduction, sexual			
Reproduction, asexual			

EXERCISE 16

The Echinoderms
Phylum Echinodermata
A Deuterostome Group

Echinoderms are an all-marine phylum comprising sea lilies, sea stars, brittle stars, sea urchins, sand dollars, and sea cucumbers. They are a strange group, strikingly different from any other animal phylum, a group that abandoned bilateral symmetry to become radial.

Echinoderms are deuterostomes, thus sharing with Hemichordata and Chordata several embryological features that set them apart from all the rest of the animal kingdom: anus developing from or near the blastopore and mouth developing elsewhere, enterocoelous coelom, radial and regulative cleavage, and mesoderm derived from enterocoelous pouches. Thus, all three phyla are presumably derived from a common ancestor.

It is an echinoderm's **dermal endoskeleton** of calcareous plates and spines, often fused into an investing armor, that provides the group with its name (L. *echinatus,* prickly, + *derma,* skin). They have a **water-vascular system** that powers a multitude of tiny tube feet used for locomotion and food gathering. Many

---

Classification
Phylum Echinodermata

EXERCISE 16A

Class Asteroidea—Sea Stars
Asterias

EXERCISE 16B

Class Ophiuroidea—Brittle Stars
Brittle stars

EXERCISE 16C

Class Echinoidea—Sea Urchins
Arbacia

EXERCISE 16D

Class Holothuroidea—Sea Cucumbers
Sea cucumbers

EXERCISE 16E

Class Crinoidea—Feather Stars and Sea Lilies
Feather stars

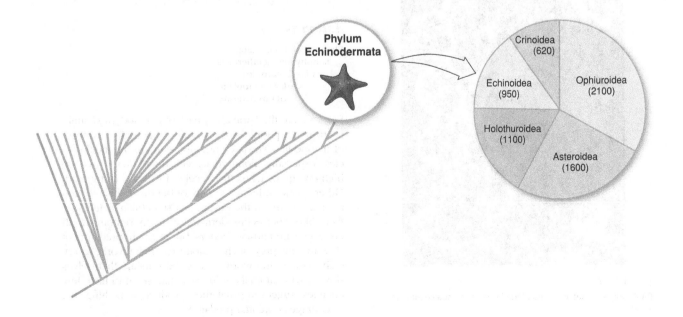

Phylum Echinodermata

Crinoidea (620)
Ophiuroidea (2100)
Echinoidea (950)
Holothuroidea (1100)
Asteroidea (1600)

are invested with pincerlike **pedicellariae** that snap at creatures that would settle on them. To breathe, many echinoderms rely on numerous **dermal branchiae** (skin gills) that project delicately through spaces in their skeletal armor. As if to emphasize their uniqueness, echinoderms lack a definite head, their nervous system and sense organs are poorly developed, locomotion is slow, and they lack segmentation. Of all their distinguishing features, however, none delineates the group more conspicuously than its **pentaradial symmetry:** body parts always arranged radially in five or multiples of five, no matter how the body plan has become adapted to different feeding strategies. This radial symmetry is, however, secondarily acquired because their larvae are unmistakably bilaterally symmetrical (Figure 16-1).

Classification

The following classification is abbreviated.

Phylum Echinodermata

Class Crinoidea (cry-noy´de-a) (Gr. *krinon,* lily, + *eidos,* form, + *ea,* characterized by). Sea lilies and feather stars. Aboral attachment stalk of dermal ossicles. Anus on oral surface; five branching arms with pinnules; ciliated ambulacral groove on oral surface with tentacle-like tube feet for food collecting; spines, madreporite, and pedicellariae absent. Examples: *Antedon, Florometra.*

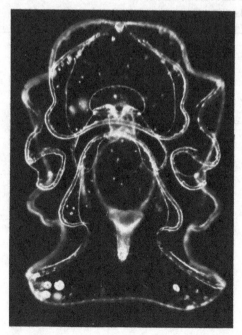

Figure 16-1
Bilaterally symmetrical auricularia larva of the sea cucumber, ×100.

Class Asteroidea (as´ter-oy´de-a) (Gr. *aster,* star, + *eidos,* form, + *ea,* characterized by). Sea stars. Star-shaped, with arms not sharply marked off from central disc; ambulacral grooves open, with tube feet on oral side; tube feet often with suckers; anus and madreporite aboral; pedicellariae present. Examples: *Asterias, Pisaster.*

Class Ophiuroidea (o´fe-u-roy´de-a) (Gr. *ophis,* snake, + *oura,* tail, + *eidos,* form). Brittle stars and basket stars. Star-shaped, with arms sharply marked off from central disc; ambulacral grooves closed, covered by ossicles; tube feet without suckers and not used for locomotion; pedicellariae absent. Examples: *Ophiura, Gorgonocephalus, Ophioderma.*

Class Echinoidea (ek´i-noy´de-a) (Gr. *echinos,* sea urchin, hedgehog, + *eidos,* form). Sea urchins, heart urchins, and sand dollars. More or less globular or disc-shaped, with no arms; compact skeleton, or test, with closely fitting plates; movable spines; ambulacral grooves closed and covered by ossicles; tube feet with suckers; pedicellariae present. Examples: *Arbacia, Strongylocentrotus, Lytechinus, Mellita.*

Class Holothuroidea (hol´o-thu-roy´de-a) (Gr. *holothourion,* sea cucumber, + *eidos,* form). Sea cucumbers. Cucumber-shaped; with no arms; spines absent; microscopic ossicles embedded in thick, muscular wall; anus present; ambulacral grooves closed; tube feet with suckers; circumoral tentacles (modified tube feet); pedicellariae absent; madreporite plate internal. Examples: *Thyone, Parastichopus, Cucumaria.*

EXERCISE 16A

Class Asteroidea—Sea Stars

Asterias

Phylum Echinodermata
  Subphylum Eleutherozoa
    Class Asteroidea
      Order Forcipulatida
        Genus *Asterias*

Sea stars are the "prima donnas" of echinoderms, familiar to many people as beautifully symmetrical symbols of marine life. Those commonly seen are intertidal species, especially along rocky coastlines. Many live on high-energy beaches that receive full force of the surf. Other species inhabit a variety of benthic habitats, often at great depths in the ocean. Sea stars (also called starfish), like other echinoderms, are strictly bottom dwellers. Some are particle feeders, but most are predators of slow-moving prey, such as molluscs (their favorite food), crabs, corals, and worms, since sea stars are themselves slow-moving animals. Adult sea stars seem to have few enemies, suggesting that they produce something that discourages potential predators.

Behavior

Examine a living sea star in a dish of seawater. Using the following suggestions, observe its behavior.*

Note the general body plan of the star with its **pentaradial** (Gr. *pente,* five, + L. *radius,* ray) symmetry; its five **arms,** or **rays;** its **oral-aboral flattening;** and its **mouth** on the underside. Lift up the dish and look at this oral surface. Notice the rows of **tube feet.** How are they used? _____ How are the ends of the tube feet shaped? _____ What is the sequence of action of a single tube foot as the animal is moving? _____ Tube feet are filled with fluid and are muscular, providing the necessary components for a hydraulic skeleton. When a foot contracts, water flows into a bulblike **ampulla** inside the arm. Tube feet and ampullae are parts of the **water-vascular system.**

Tilt the dish to one side (pour out a little water, if necessary) and watch the animal's reaction. Does it move up or down the inclined plane? _____

_____
Now tilt the dish in the opposite direction. Does the animal change direction? _____ Is it positively geotactic (moves toward the earth) or negatively geotactic? _____

Place a piece of fresh seafood (oyster, fish, or shrimp) near one of the arms. Is there any reaction? _____ Are the arms flexible? _____ If the sea star makes no move toward the food, touch the tip of an arm with it, or slip it under the end of an arm. Hold the dish up and look underneath. How is the food grasped? _____ How is it moved toward the mouth? _____ What position does the animal assume when feeding?

Examine the aboral surface with a hand lens or dissecting microscope. The **epidermis** is ciliated. Place a drop of carmine suspension (in seawater) on the exposed surface and note the direction of the ciliary currents. Notice the calcareous **spines** protruding through the skin (Figure 16-2). These are extensions of skeletal ossicles. Do the spines move? _____ Small, fingerlike bulges in the epidermis are **skin gills** (also called **dermal branchiae**) and **papulae** (sing. **papula;** L., pimple), concerned with gaseous exchange. Around the spines, you will see small **pedicellariae** (L. *pediculus,* little foot, + *aria,* like) (Figure 16-2). These calcareous, two-jawed pincers are modified spines concerned with capturing tiny prey and protecting the dermal branchiae from collecting sediment and small parasites. Touch with a small camel hair brush to observe the pincer action.

*Suggestions for demonstrations with living sea stars are found in Appendix A, pp. 408–409.

Look at the tip of each arm to see a small, red **eyespot** and elongate tube feet modified as **sensory tentacles** (Figure 16-2).

Written Report

Record your observations on separate paper.

External Structure

Place a preserved sea star in a dissecting pan and cover with water. If your observations of external structure are on a living sea star, place the animal in a clean pan or culture dish and cover with seawater.

The star-shaped body is composed of a **central disc** and five **arms** (rays). Are all the arms alike? _____ What would account for some of the arms being shorter than others? _____ Compare your specimen with those of your neighbors. Preserved specimens may seem rigid but live stars can bend their arms by means of muscles.

Aboral Surface. The central disc bears a small, porous **madreporite plate** (Fr. *madr pore,* reef-building coral, + *ite,* suffix for body part) composed of calcium carbonate (Figure 16-3). It allows seawater to seep into an intricate **water-vascular system,** which provides the means of locomotion. The arms on each side of

Figure 16-2
Distal portion of the ray of a living sea star (*Asterias*).

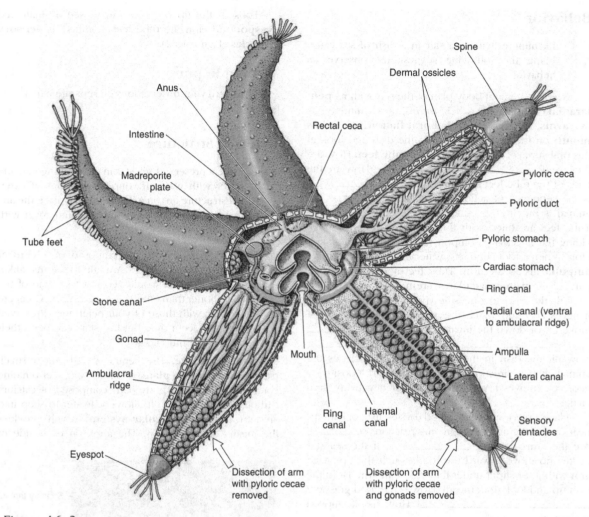

Figure 16-3
Anatomy of the sea star.

the madreporite are called the **bivium;** the other three are the **trivium.** The **anus** opens in the center of the central disc, but it is probably too small to see.

 Submerge one of the arms in water and examine the dorsal body wall under a dissecting microscope. Compare with a piece of dried body wall.

The body is covered with a thin, ciliated **epidermis,** through which white calcareous **spines** extend from the endoskeleton beneath. Are the spines movable? _____ Surrounding the base of each spine is a raised ring of skin bearing tiny, calcareous, pincerlike **pedicellariae.** Some are also found between the spines. Sometimes pedicellariae can be seen more easily on a dried piece of body wall. Some pedicellariae have straight jaws and others have curved jaws. They are moved by tiny muscles. What is the function of the pedicellariae? _____ Between the spines are

soft, transparent, fingerlike projections, the **skin gills,** or **dermal branchiae.** These are hollow evaginations of the coelomic cavity. What is the function of the dermal branchiae? _____

Drawings

 Sketch some pedicellariae in your notebook.

A small, pigmented **eyespot** is located at the tip of each arm.

Oral Surface. The **ambulacral** (L. *ambulare,* to walk) groove of each arm contains rows of **tube feet (podia).** The **ambulacral spines** bordering the groove are movable and can interlock when the groove is contracted to protect the tube feet. Note the size, shape, number, and arrangement of the tube feet. How many rows of tube feet are there?

Scrape away some tube feet and note arrangement of the pores through which they extend. If you are making observations on a living sea star, do not scrape off tube feet but instead brush them with a camel hair brush, noting the response of both tube feet and ambulacral ossicles.

Tube feet are a part of the water-vascular system. They are hollow, and their tips form suction discs for attachment (Figures 16-3 and 16-4). These are effective not only in locomotion but also in opening of bivalves for food.

The central **mouth** is surrounded by five pairs of movable spines. Push the spines outward, bend the arms back slightly, and note the thin **peristomial membrane,** which surrounds the mouth. Sometimes the mouth is filled with part of the everted **stomach.**

Endoskeleton

Echinoderms are the first invertebrates to have a meso-dermal endoskeleton. It is formed of calcareous plates, or **ossicles,** bound together by connective tissue.

 If you are studying a preserved sea star, cut off part of one of the arms of the bivium, remove the aboral wall from the severed piece, and study its inner surface. Compare with a piece of dried body wall, which is excellent for examining the arrangement of ossicles.

Note the skeletal network of irregular ossicles. Now look at the cut edge of the body wall and identify the outer layer of **epidermis;** the thicker layer of **dermis,** or connective tissue in which the ossicles are embedded; and the thin inner layer of ciliated **peritoneum.** Do sea stars have a true coelom? _____ The dermis and peritoneum are mesodermal in origin. Are the spines part of the endoskeleton? _____ Hold the piece up to the light. The thin places you see between the ossicles are where the dermal branchiae extend through the connective tissue.

Look at the oral surface of the severed arm. Note how the **tube feet** extend up between the **ambulacral ossicles,** emerging on the inside surface of the wall as bulblike **ampullae** (am-pool'ee; sing. **ampulla;** L., flask). Compress some of the ampullae and note the effect on the tube feet. Press on the tube feet and see the effect on the ampullae. Both are muscular and can regulate the water pressure by contraction. Scrape away some of the ampullae and tube feet and examine the shape of the ossicles in the ambulacral groove. How do they differ from ossicles elsewhere? _____ Note the alternating arrangement of **ambulacral pores,** through which the tube feet extend. Although the ambulacral ossicles form a groove on the oral surface of each arm, they form an **ambulacral ridge** on the inner surface.

Drawings

 In your notebook, sketch a series of ambulacral ossicles, showing the arrangement of the openings for the tube feet.

Internal Structure (Dissection)*

 Place the specimen aboral side up in a dissecting pan and cover with water. Select the three arms of the trivium and snip off their distal ends. Insert a scissors point under the body wall at the cut end of one of the arms. Carefully cut along the dorsolateral margins of each arm to the central disc. Lift up the loosened wall and carefully free any clinging organs. Uncover the central disc, but cut around the madreporite plate, leaving it in place. Be careful not to injure the delicate tissue underneath. The tissue around the anal opening in the center of the disc will cling. Cut the very short intestine close to the aboral wall before lifting off the body wall.

The **coelomic cavity** inside the arms and disc contains **coelomic fluid,** which bathes the visceral organs.

Digestive System. A pentagonal **pyloric stomach** (Gr. *pylōros,* gatekeeper) (Figure 16-3) lies in the central disc, and from it a **pyloric duct** extends into each arm, where it divides to connect with a pair of large, much-lobulated **pyloric ceca** (digestive glands) (Figure 16-3). A very short **intestine** leads up from the center of the stomach to the anus in the center of the disc. Attached to the intestine are two **rectal ceca,** small, branched sacs of uncertain function. Below (ventral to) the pyloric stomach is the larger, five-lobed **cardiac stomach,** which fills most of the central disc (Figure 16-3). Each lobe of the stomach is attached to the ambulacral ridge of an arm by a pair of **gastric ligaments,** which prevent too much eversion of the stomach.

When a sea star feeds on a bivalve, it folds itself around the animal, attaches its tube feet to the valves, and exerts enough pull to cause the shell to gape slightly. Then, by contracting its body walls to increase coelomic fluid pressure, it everts its stomach and inserts it into the slightly opened clam shell. There it digests the soft parts of the clam with digestive juices from the pyloric ceca. Partly digested material is drawn into the stomach and pyloric ceca, where digestion is completed. There is little waste fecal matter. When the sea star is finished feeding, the stomach withdraws into the coelom by contraction of the stomach muscles and relaxation of the body wall, which allows coelomic fluid to flow back into the arms.

---

*Directions for anesthetizing living stars for this study are given in Appendix A, p. 408.

Many stars feed on small bivalves by engulfing the entire animal, digesting its contents, then casting the shell out through the mouth.

Reproductive System. Sexes are separate (dioecious) in sea stars. Remove the pyloric ceca from one arm to find paired **gonads** attached to the sides of the ray where the ray joins the disc (Figure 16-3). During the breeding season, the gonads are much larger than at other times, when they may shrink to a small fraction of their breeding size. Each gonad opens aborally to the exterior at the point of attachment by a very small **reproductive duct** and **genital pore.** The sex can seldom be determined by simple inspection of the gonads, although the female gonads may be a little coarser in texture and more orange than the male gonads.

 Make a wet mount of a mashed bit of gonad and examine with a microscope.

In the ovary, eggs with large nuclei can be found; in the testes, many small sperm are to be found. In early summer, large streams of eggs and sperm are shed into the water, where fertilization occurs externally. Review Exercise 3B (pp. 37–42) for the development of a sea star.

Nervous System. The nervous system of a sea star consists of three interrelated systems. Foremost of these is the **oral** system, consisting of a **nerve ring** around the mouth in the peristomial membrane and a **radial nerve** to each arm running along the ambulacral groove to the eyespot.

 To find the nerve ring, remove the tube feet and movable spines around the mouth and expose the peristomial membrane.

The nerve ring is a whitish thickening on the outer margin of this membrane. To see one of the **radial nerves,** bend an arm aborally and look along the oral surface of the ambulacral groove for a whitish cord (Figure 16-4). Trace the nerve from the ring to its termination in the arm.

The other two systems are an aboral system lying near the upper surface of the sea star and a deep system positioned between the oral and aboral systems. You will be unable to see these. Freely connected to these three systems is the **epidermal nerve plexus.** This consists of a network of nerve cell bodies and their processes lying just beneath the epidermis that coordinate responses of the dermal branchiae to tactile stimulation.

Sense Organs. Chemoreceptors and cells sensitive to touch are found all over the surface.

Each pigmented **eyespot** consists of a number of light-sensitive ocelli.

Water-Vascular System. A water-vascular system is found only in echinoderms, which use it for locomotion and, in the case of sea stars, for opening of clam shells. If this system in your specimen has been injected with a colored injection medium, its features can be studied to greater advantage.

 Carefully remove the stomach from the central disc.

The **madreporite plate** (orange in life) on the aboral surface (Figure 16-3) contains ciliated grooves and pores. From it a somewhat curved **stone canal** (yellow in life and named for calcareous deposits in its wall) leads to a **ring canal** (Figure 16-3), which is found around the outer edge of the peristomial membrane next to the skeletal region of the central disc. The ring canal may be difficult to find if not injected.

Five **radial canals,** one in each arm, radiate out from the ring canal, running along the apex of the ambulacral groove just below the ambulacral ossicles and above the radial nerve. The position of the radial canal is best seen in a cross section of one of the arms (Figure 16-4). Short **lateral canals,** each with a valve, connect the radial canal with each tube foot. Now look on the inside of an arm and study the alternating arrangement of the ampullae. Note how each ampulla connects with a tube foot through a **pore** between the ambulacral plates.

The function of the madreporite plate has been a subject of controversy. The traditional view that the madreporite serves as a point of entry for seawater into the water-vascular system has been confirmed with the use of radioactive isotopes. Seawater entering the madreporite passes down the stone canal to the ring canals, from there to the radial canals, and finally through the lateral canals to the ampullae and tube feet.

Tube feet have longitudinal muscles; ampullae have circular muscles. When the tube feet are contracted, most of the water is held in the ampullae (Figure 16-4). When ampullae contract, water is forced into the elastic tube feet, which elongate because of the hydrostatic pressure within them. When the cuplike ends of the extended tube feet contact a hard surface, they attach with suction force and then contract, pushing water back into the ampullae and pulling the animal forward. Valves in the lateral canals prevent backflow of water into the radial canals. Although a single foot is not very strong, hundreds of them working together can move the animal along slowly and can create a tremendous pull on the shell of a bivalve mollusc. Suckers are of little use on a sandy surface, where the tube feet serve as tiny legs. Some species have no suckers but use the stiff podia like little legs to "walk." Sea stars can travel about 15 cm per minute.

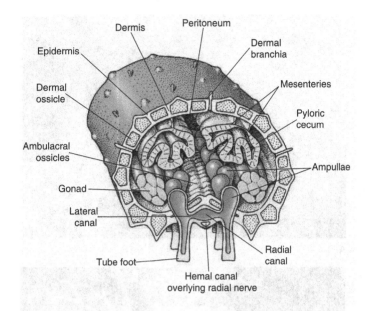

Figure 16-4
Cross section of a sea star arm.

Cross Section of an Arm of a Sea Star (Microslide)

Identify the **epidermis** covering the entire animal, **dermis** containing the **ossicles,** muscular tissue, **peritoneum,** and **coelomic cavity.** The spines have not yet erupted because these slides were prepared from young sea stars. Observe the **dermal branchiae** projecting from the coelom through the body wall. **Pyloric ceca** hang from the aboral wall by **mesenteries.** Notice the ampullae in the coelom and their connection to the **tube feet** and **lateral canals.** The canals may not always be seen. Why? _____ _____ Locate the **ambulacral ossicles** with the pores through which tube feet extend. Find the **radial canal,** a small tube under the **ambulacral groove,** and the **radial nerve** beneath the radial canal (Figure 16-4).

EXERCISE 16B

Class Ophiuroidea—Brittle Stars

Brittle Stars

Phylum Echinodermata
  Subphylum Eleutherozoa
    Class Ophiuroidea
      Order Ophiurida
        Available genera

Where Found

Brittle stars, the most agile of echinoderms, are widely distributed in all oceans and at all depths. In many habitats, they are also the most abundant echinoderms yet are seldom seen by casual observers. They are secretive animals that hide under and between intertidal and subtidal rocks by day to escape predation by fish. Even at night, they may extend only their arms from hiding places to feed. If a diver should expose them, they will quickly retreat to safety, using rowing movements of their arms. Should a fish (or a human) catch a brittle star by one arm, the animal usually will simply cast off the arm (autotomize), leaving the predator with a wiggling arm while its erstwhile owner scurries to safety beneath a nearby rock. It is common to find brittle stars with missing or partly regenerated arms.

External Features

General Body Form. Note that the arms of brittle stars are sharply marked off from the central disc—a characteristic of ophiuroids (Figure 16-5). The arms are more flexible than those of sea stars. Does their appearance give a clue as to why? _____ In both appearance and function, the arms resemble vertebral columns. In fact, internally they consist of a series of calcareous **vertebral ossicles,** each joined to the next by two pairs of muscles. Externally the arm is encased in a series of aboral, lateral, and oral **plates.**

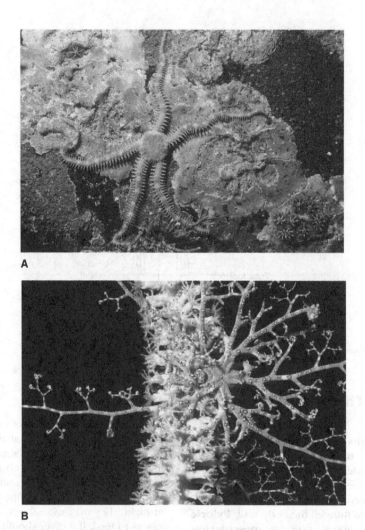

Figure 16-5

A, Brittle star *Ophiopholis aculeata* from the Gulf of Maine. **B,** Basket star, *Astrophyton muricatum,* on octocoral. Ophiuroids have sharply marked-off arms and are fragile.

Pull an arm off a preserved specimen and examine it in cross section. Locate the muscles and note the vertebral articulations.

Are there spines on the arms? _____ How do the spines compare with those of asteroids? _____ Do you find any pedicellariae or skin gills? _____

Oral Surface. On the oral side, note five triangular **jaws** around the mouth. Find the five **oral shields** (also called **buccal shields**), which are oval plates located on the interradial area between the rays (Figure 16-6). One of these is slightly modified as a **madreporite plate,** and its tiny pores connect with a madreporite canal inside. Compare the location of the madreporite plate in asteroids and ophiuroids.

Distal to the oral shields and close to each arm is a pair of grooves, representing the openings of the **bursae.** (In *Ophioderma* a second pair is located distal to the first.) The bursae, composed of 10 saclike cavities within the disc, are peculiar to ophiuroids. Water is pumped in and out of them for respiratory purposes, and the gonads discharge their products into them. In some species, they also serve as brood pouches, but in *Ophioderma* development is external.

The tube feet (podia) are small, do not have suckers, and project laterally between the skeletal plates. They are largely sensory in function but may also assist in locomotion. Examine the rough spines used in gripping the substrate. How do they compare with those of asteroids? _____

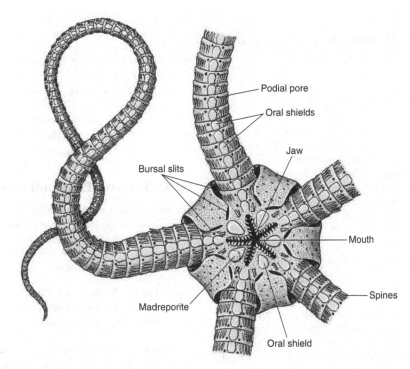

Figure 16-6
Oral view of central disc of a brittle star.

Behavior

Avoid rough handling of a brittle star because this may cause it to "freeze," becoming immobile, or even to cast off one or more of its arms.

Locomotion. Brittle stars "walk" by twisting, highly flexible arm movements. How are the arms used in locomotion? _____ Watch their movements carefully. What provides the actual force for forward movement? _____ Do the arms push or pull the brittle star? _____ Do the arms work in pairs? _____ How are the podia (tube feet) used—or are they used at all in locomotion? _____ Does one arm always lead or follow?_____ Note that locomotory patterns differ somewhat in different species of brittle stars.

Turn over the brittle star and watch its righting response. If placed on a sandy substrate, will the brittle star burrow? _____

Feeding. Most ophiuroids are either active predators or selective deposit feeders. Deposit feeders capture organic material with the podia that secrete copious amounts of mucus. Mucus and food are rolled into a ball by a podium, then transferred to a small scale that lies adjacent to the podium. The next podium picks up the food and transfers it to the next scale, and so on until the food ball reaches the mouth. Active predators, such

as species of the genus *Ophioderma,* capture benthic (bottom-dwelling) organisms by curling an arm around the prey and sweeping it into the mouth.

 Drop very small bits of fish or shrimp into the aquarium near (but not touching) some brittle stars to see the method of feeding.

Do the animals appear to sense the presence of food before touching it? _____ Is the species you are studying an active predator or a selective deposit feeder? _____ The digestive system is much reduced, compared with that of sea stars. The mouth leads by a short esophagus to a stomach, the site of digestion and absorption. There is no intestine, anus, or hepatic ceca.

Reactions to Other Stimuli. Note how the animal reacts to mechanical stimulation. Touch the tip of an arm. Does it retreat or advance toward the source of the stimulus? _____ Touch a more proximal part of the arm. Is the reaction the same or different? _____ Stimulate the base of an arm or the central disc. What happens? _____ Can you determine whether ophiuroids—at least the species you are studying—respond positively or negatively to light? _____ The water-vascular, hemal, and nervous systems are on a plan similar to that of asteroids.

Written Report

Record your behavioral observations on separate paper.

Table of Comparison

Complete a table of comparative characteristics of the external anatomy of the sea star and brittle star on p. 263. Include such items as symmetry, shape, integument, ambulacra, tube feet, skin gills, pedicellariae, skeleton, and digestive system. After you have observed the sea urchin and sea cucumber, add these to the table.

EXERCISE 16C
Class Echinoidea—Sea Urchins

Sea urchins, like sea stars, are familiar denizens of seashores. Lacking arms, and with the body enclosed within a globose shell, or test, of interlocking plates which bear movable spines, sea urchins have evolved a body design quite unlike that of sea stars and brittle stars. Nevertheless, they bear the typical pentamerous plan of all echinoderms, with a water-vascular system and other characteristics that set the strange echinoderms apart from any other animal phylum. Sea urchins and their kin, heart urchins and sand dollars, all bear a spiny armament suggesting *echinos,* the Greek word for hedgehog, from which the echinoids take their scientific name. Unlike the carnivorous sea stars and brittle stars, sea urchins are herbivores that scrape incrusting algae from rock surfaces, nibble on plants, or trap and eat drifting food. Sea urchins are "regular" echinoids: radially symmetrical, globose in shape, and armed with long spines. Other echinoids, such as sand dollars and heart urchins, are "irregular" echinoids: bilaterally symmetrical with bodies variably shaped, such as flattened sand dollars or heart-shaped heart urchins.

Arbacia

Phylum Echinodermata
 Subphylum Eleutherozoa
  Class Echinoidea
   Genus *Arbacia*
    Species *Arbacia punctulata*

Where Found

Like sea stars and brittle stars, echinoids are strictly marine, benthic animals widely distributed in all seas, from the intertidal to deep sea. Some favor rocky, high-energy coastlines with pounding surf, but most echinoids are subtidal, grazing in turtle-grass buds or on coral reefs or (especially the irregular echinoids)

burying themselves in sandy bottoms, where they feed on microscopic organic matter. *Arbacia punctulata* (Gr. *Arbaces,* first king of Media*), the purple sea urchin on the East Coast, is found from Cape Cod to Florida and Cuba. Other common species include *Strongylocentrotus drobachiensis* (Gr. *strongylos,* round, + *kentron,* spine), the green sea urchin of both East and West Coasts of North America; *Strongylocentrotus purpuratus,* purple urchin of the West Coast; and species of *Lytechinus* (Gr. *lytos,* broken, + *echinos,* urchin) (Figure 16-7) on both coasts.

Behavior and External Structure

External features of a sea urchin are best observed in a living animal. However, if living forms are not available, submerge a preserved specimen in a bowl of water and use the following account, directed toward live urchins, to identify the external structures.

Place a living sea urchin on a glass plate, submerge in a bowl of seawater, and observe under a dissecting microscope.

Spines. Examine the long, movable **spines,** each attached at a ball-and-socket joint by two sets of ring muscles. Remove a spine (instructor's option) and note that its socket fits over a rounded **tubercle** on the test (Figure 16-8). An inner ring of **cog muscles** holds the spine erect. Hold the tip of a spine and try to move it. Do you feel the locking mechanism of the cog muscles? _____ Of what advantage is such a locking mechanism? _____ Now, with a probe, touch the epidermis near a spine. Does the spine move? _____ In which direction? _____ The outer ring of muscles is responsible for directional movement. Are all the spines the same length? _____ Are they all pointed on the distal ends? _____

Tube Feet. Notice that the tube feet all originate from rows of perforations in the five **ambulacral regions.** The podia can be extended beyond the ends of the spines. Do any possess suckers? Are any suckerless? _____ Do they move? What happens when you touch one? _____ When you jar the bowl? _____

Mouth and Peristome. Examine the oral side of the urchin and find the **mouth,** with its five converging **teeth** and collarlike **lip** (Figure 16-8). The teeth are part of a complex chewing mechanism called **Aristotle's lantern,** which is operated internally by several sets

---

*The name of the genus *Arbacia,* bestowed by British zoologist John Edward Gray in 1835, is an example of a "nonsense" name that lacks any descriptive value. Gray apparently chose the name after reading Lord Byron's poem *Sardanapalus,* concerning Arbaces, who, according to legend, founded the Median empire (now part of northern Iran) about 830 B.C.

Figure 16-7

The green sea urchin *Strongylocentrotus drobachiensis.* Note the slender, suckered tube feet. Urchins often attach bits of shell, marine algae, and other debris to themselves for camouflage. Small, stalked, white-tipped pedicellariae can be seen surrounding the bases of spines near the center of the photograph.

of muscles.* The lip contains circular, or "purse-string," muscles.

The membranous **peristome** surrounding the mouth is perforated by five pairs of large oral tube feet called **buccal podia.** Do these podia have suckers? _____ They are probably sensitive to chemical stimuli. The peristome also bears some small spines.

Pedicellariae. Notice on the peristome a number of three-jawed **pedicellariae** on the ends of long, slender stalks. Smaller but more active pedicellariae are located among the spines. Stimulate some of them by touching gently with a camel hair brush. You may want to pinch off some of the pedicellariae to examine more closely on a slide, particularly if you are using a preserved specimen. Their functions are to discourage intruders and to help keep the skin clean.

Locomotion. Note how the urchin uses its spines and tube feet in locomotion. Carefully, so as not to injure its tube feet, turn the urchin over (oral side up). Does it use its spines or tube feet to right itself? _____ Notice which ambulacra turn first and mark that row by removing some of its spines or by marking some of the spines with thread; then turn the animal over again and see if the same ambulacra turn first. Repeat once more.

---

*The curious name for the protrusible chewing mechanism of sea urchins derives from a passage in the writings of Aristotle (384–322 B.C), where he compared the chewing apparatus to the frame of a lantern.

Tilt the glass plate to determine if the urchin moves up or down. Tilt in the opposite direction and see what happens. Is it positively or negatively geotactic? _____

Some sea urchins are adapted for burrowing into rock or other hard material by using both their spines and chewing mechanisms. *Strongylocentrotus purpuratus,* common on the North American Pacific Coast, excavates cup-shaped depressions in stone.

Most echinoids have tiny modified spines called **sphaeridia** (Gr. *sphaira,* sphere, + *idion,* dim. suffix), believed to be organs of equilibrium. In *Arbacia* these are minute, glassy bodies located one in each ambulacrum close to the peristome. Try to find and remove the sphaeridia to see whether their removal affects the urchin's righting reaction or its geotactic responses.

Direct a beam of bright light toward an urchin. How does it react?_____

Epidermis. The test, podia, pedicellariae, and spines are covered with **ciliated epidermis,** although the epidermis may have become worn off from the exposed spines. Drop a little carmine suspension on various parts of the sea urchin and note the direction of the ciliary currents. Of what advantage are such currents to the urchin? _____

Gills. At the outer edge of the peristome, between the ambulacra, find five pairs of branching peristomial **gills,** which open into the coelomic cavity.

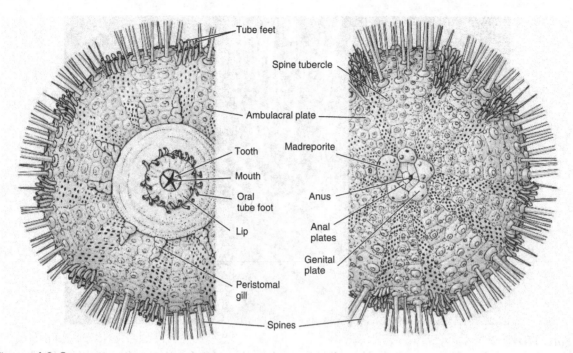

Figure 16-8

External structure of a sea urchin. Oral *(left)* and aboral *(right)* surfaces are shown with spines partly removed.

Written Report

Record your observations on sea urchin behavior on separate paper.

Test (Endoskeleton).

Examine a dried sea urchin test from which the spines have been removed and a dried sand dollar and/or heart urchin.

The test, or endoskeleton, is composed of calcareous plates (ossicles) symmetrically arranged and interlocked or fused so as to be immovable. Note the tubercles to which the spines were attached. Note the arrangement of the plates into 10 meridional double columns—five double rows of **ambulacral plates** alternating with double rows of interambulacral plates. What is the function of the perforations in the ambulacral plates? _____ In asteroids the tube feet were extended between the plates rather than through them.

Examine the test of a sand dollar, a heart urchin, or both. Can you find perforations in them similar to those of the urchin? _____ Do they have ambulacra, and is their arrangement pentamerous? _____ The ambulacra in echinoids are homologous to the ambulacra of asteroids and ophiuroids.

On the aboral surface, note the area that is free from spines, the **periproct.** The **anus** is centrally located, surrounded by four (sometimes five) valvelike **anal plates** (Figure 16-8). Around the anal plates are five **genital plates,** so-called because each bears a **genital pore.** Note that one of the genital plates is larger than the others and has many minute pores. This is the **madreporite plate,** which has the same function in sea urchins as it does in sea stars, for the echinoids have a **water-vascular system** in common with all echinoderms.

The test grows both by the growth of plates and by the production of new plates in the ambulacral area near the periproct.

Table of Comparison

Complete a table of the comparative characteristics of the external anatomy of the sea star, brittle star, and sea urchin on p. 263. Include such items as symmetry, shape, integument, ambulacra, tube feet, skin gills, pedicellariae, skeleton, and digestive system. After you have observed the sea cucumber, add that to the table.

EXERCISE 16D
Class Holothuroidea—Sea Cucumbers

Sea Cucumbers

Phylum Echinodermata
  Subphylum Eleutherozoa
    Class Holothuroidea
      Order Dendrochirotida
        Genus *Cucumaria* (or *Thyone*)
          or
      Order Aspidochirotida
        Genus *Parastichopus*

Where Found

Sea cucumbers, perhaps the oddest members of a phylum distinguished by strange animals, look remarkably like their vegetable namesake. They are characterized by an elongate body, a leathery body wall with warty surface, an absence of arms, and a mouth and an anus located at opposite poles of the animal. They are benthic (bottom-dwelling), slow-moving animals found in all marine habitats. Two common genera on the East Coast of the United States are *Thyone* and *Cucumaria; Parastichopus* is a familiar genus on the West Coast (Figure 16-9).

Behavior and External Structure

 If possible, study living specimens in an aquarium or in a bowl of seawater containing a generous layer of sand, and then examine a preserved specimen. Sea cucumbers are slow to react. They should be left undisturbed for some time before the laboratory period if you are to see them relaxed and feeding.

Note that a holothurian, unlike other echinoderms, is orally-aborally elongated and has a cylindrical body, with the **mouth** encircled by **tentacles** at one end and **anus** at the other.

A more detailed description and behavior of the animal will depend somewhat on the species you are observing. Notice the tentacles. Are they branched and extensible (as in *Cucumaria* and *Thyone*), short and shield-shaped (as in *Parastichopus*), or of some other type? _____ The tentacles, which are modified tube feet, are hollow and a part of the **water-vascular system;** they are connected internally with the radial canals. The type of tentacle structure is related to feeding habits. *Cucumaria* and *Thyone* are suspension feeders that stretch their mucus-covered tentacles into the

water or over the substrate until they are covered with tiny food organisms; then they thrust the tentacles into the mouth, one by one, to lick off the food. Can you observe these actions? *Parastichopus* and some others are deposit feeders that simply shovel mud and sand into the mouth, digest out organic particles, and void the remainder.

Have you noticed any rhythmic opening and closing of the anus? _____ This is a respiratory movement coordinated with the pumping action of the cloaca, which pumps water into and out of the **respiratory trees** (internal respiratory organs).

Does the animal try to burrow into the sand? _____ Does it cover itself completely or leave the ends exposed? _____ *Thyone* may take 2 to 4 hours to bury its middle by alternate circular and

A

B

Figure 16-9

Two sea cucumbers from the Pacific Coast of North America. **A,** *Parastichopus californicus* is a deposit feeder that grazes the bottom with its tentacles. **B,** *Cucumaria miniata* is a suspension feeder that traps planktonic organisms on its extended, mucus-coated tentacles. When loaded, the tentacles are pushed one by one into the mouth and the food is ingested.

longitudinal muscle contractions. It is likely to be more active in the late afternoon and night than in the morning. If you are watching *Parastichopus* move, what does its muscular action remind you of? _____ Are there waves of contraction? _____

Does the sea cucumber react to mechanical stimulus? _____ Try touching a tentacle. Does one or more than one tentacle react? _____ Touch several tentacles. What happens when you stroke the body or gently pick up the animal? Does it expel water when you pick it up? _____ Having observed its movement and reactions, can you see the advantages of the hydraulic skeleton? What other phyla used the hydraulic skeleton to advantage? _____

Note the **podia.** Are they scattered all over the body or arranged in ambulacral rows? _____ This pattern differs among different species. Are the podia all alike? That is, are ventral podia any different from dorsal podia? _____ Are any of them suckered? _____ If the pentamerous arrangement of ambulacra is evident in your specimen, how many rows make up the ventral **sole?** ____ How many are on the dorsal surface? ____ If you place the animal on a solid surface, do the podia attach themselves? _____ Can the animal right itself if turned over? _____ Are the podia involved in the righting action? _____ Are muscles involved? _____

Does the animal show any geotactic reaction if placed on a vertical or sloping surface? ____ Some burrowing forms are positively geotactic and move downward; other species are negatively geotactic and climb upward. *Thyone* gives no geotactic response.

Do you find any pedicellariae or skin gills? _____ Do you feel the presence of a test under the epidermis? _____ That is because the skeleton of the holothurian is usually limited to microscopic ossicles embedded in the tough, leathery body wall.

Written Report

Record your observations on sea cucumber behavior on separate paper.

Internal Structure

Locate the five longitudinal ambulacral areas of a preserved sea cucumber. The sole (the ventral side applied to the substrate) has three ambulacra with well-developed podia. The dorsal side has two ambulacra with smaller podia (in some species, podia are absent on the dorsal surface). With scissors, open the body by making a longitudinal

incision on the ventral (sole) side of the animal, between the central and right ambulacra. Pin down the walls and cover with water.

Digestive System. Note the large **coelomic cavity.** Just behind the mouth is the **pharynx,** supported by a ring of calcareous plates (Figure 16-10). It is followed by a short, muscular **stomach** and a long, convoluted **intestine,** held in place by mesenteries and expanding somewhat at the end to form a **cloaca,** which empties at the **anus.**

Respiratory System. Two branched **respiratory trees** are attached to the cloaca; they serve as both respiratory and excretory organs. They are aerated by a rhythmic pumping of the cloaca. Several inspirations 1 minute or more apart are followed by a vigorous expiration that expels all the water.

Note the muscles between the cloaca and the body wall. Long **retractile muscles** (how many? _____) run from the pharynx to join the longitudinal **muscle bands** in the body wall.

Water-Vascular System. A **ring canal** surrounds the pharynx. One or more rounded or elongated sacs called **polian vesicles** hang from the ring canal into the coelom and open into the ring canal by a narrow neck. Polian vesicles are believed to function as expansion chambers in maintaining pressure within the water-vascular system. One or more **stone canals** also open into the ring canal from the body cavity. In adult sea cucumbers, the water-vascular system has usually lost contact with the seawater outside. Coelomic fluid, rather than seawater, enters and leaves the system.

Five **radial canals** extend from the ring canal forward along the walls of the pharynx to give off branches to the tentacles, which are actually modified tube feet. From there the radial canals run back along the inner surface of the ambulacra, where each gives off **lateral canals** to the **podia** and **ampullae.** Valves in the lateral canals prevent backflow. Note the ampullae along the ambulacra in the inner body wall.

Reproductive System. The **gonad** consists of numerous tubules united into one or two tufts on the side of the dorsal mesentery. These become quite large at sexual maturity. (Your specimen may have a much enlarged gonad.) A **gonoduct** passes anteriorly in the mesentery to the **genital pore.** The sexes are separate, and fertilization is external.

Endoskeleton. The **endoskeleton** consists largely of tiny, calcareous ossicles scattered in the dermis. These can be seen on a prepared slide.

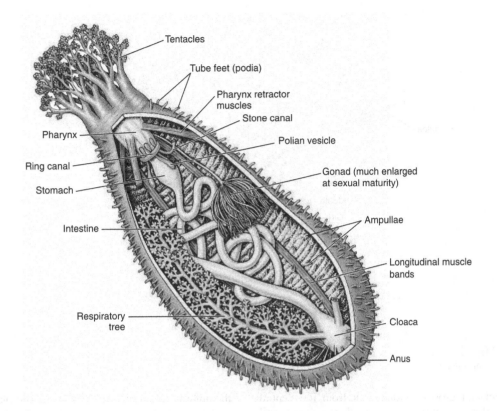

Figure 16-10
Internal anatomy of a sea cucumber.

Table of Comparison

Complete the comparative table (p. 263) of the likenesses and differences between the external anatomy of the sea star, brittle star, sea urchin, and sea cucumber, mentioning such things as shape, ambulacra, tube feet, skin gills, skeleton, and integument.

EXERCISE 16E
Class Crinoidea—Feather Stars and Sea Lilies

Feather Stars

Phylum Echinodermata
  Subphylum Pelmatozoa
    Class Crinoidea
      Order Articulata
        Genus *Antedon*

Where Found

Crinoids are found in all seas except the Baltic and Black seas. Most are subtidal, although some are littoral, and some are found as deep as 5000 meters. The free-living feather stars (Figure 16-11) prefer rocky bottoms and are most abundant in shallow tropical lagoons. The sea lilies (about one-eighth of the species) are stalked and sessile and prefer muddy sea bottoms and deep waters.

General Structure

A feather star passes through a stalked stage but is free-moving as an adult (Figure 16-11). It is made up of the following three general regions: (1) 10 long, jointed **arms,** bearing jointed **pinnules;** (2) the **calyx,** containing the digestive and other organs; and (3) a circlet of short-jointed **cirri,** on which the animal can rest or move about. The calyx and arms together are called the **crown.** The leathery skin covering the calyx is called the **tegmen** (L., covering).

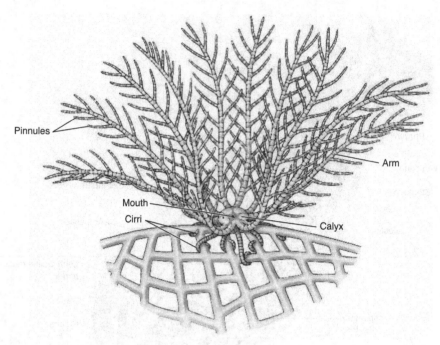

Figure 16-11
Feather star, *Antedon*.

Ambulacral grooves radiate out from the central mouth to the anus and pinnules, so that each arm and pinnule has a ciliated food groove. Tube feet are located along the food grooves in the pinnules.

Crinoids are suspension feeders, using a mucus-ciliary method of capture and food movement. Small organisms are caught in mucous nets and moved along the ambulacral grooves to the mouth. The pinnules can secrete a narcotizing toxin for quieting the prey.

Feather stars can crawl by holding onto objects with the adhesive ends of their pinnules and pulling themselves along by bending their arms. They can also swim by raising and lowering alternate sets of arms.

Comparative Table of Echinoderm Characteristics

Name _____

Date _____

Section _____

Characteristic	Sea Star	Brittle Star	Sea Urchin	Sea Cucumber

NOTES

Phylum Chordata
A Deuterostome Group
Protochordates
Subphylum Urochordata
Subphylum Cephalochordata

What Defines a Chordate?

Chordates show a remarkable diversity of form and function, ranging from **protochordates** to humans. Most chordates are vertebrates, but the phylum also includes a few invertebrate groups. All animals that belong to phylum Chordata must have at some time in their life cycle the following characteristics.

1. **Notochord.** The notochord (Gr. *nōton*, back, + L. *chorda*, cord) (Figure 17-1) is a slender rod of cartilage-like connective tissue lying near the dorsal side and extending most of the length of the animal. It is regarded as an early endoskeleton and has the functions of such. In most vertebrates, it is found only in the embryo.

2. **Pharyngeal pouches and slits.** The pharyngeal pouches and slits are a series of paired slits in the

---

What Defines a Chordate?
Classification
Phylum Chordata

EXERCISE 17A
Subphylum Urochordata—*Ciona*, an Ascidian
Ciona

EXERCISE 17B
Subphylum Cephalochordata—*Amphioxus*
Amphioxus

---

pharynx, serving as passageways for water to the gills. In some vertebrates, they appear only in the embryonic stages.

3. **Dorsal tubular nerve cord.** A dorsal tubular nerve cord, with its modification, the brain, forms

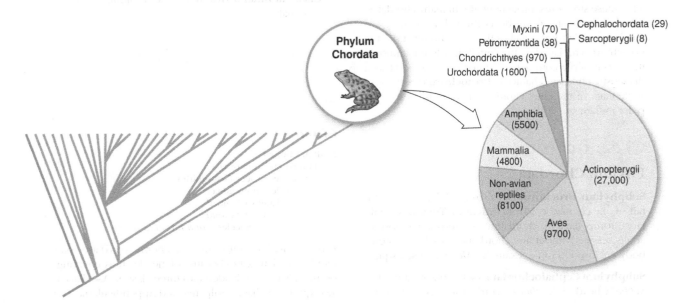

Phylum Chordata

Myxini (70)
Petromyzontida (38)
Chondrichthyes (970)
Urochordata (1600)
Cephalochordata (29)
Sarcopterygii (8)

Amphibia (5500)
Mammalia (4800)
Non-avian reptiles (8100)
Aves (9700)
Actinopterygii (27,000)

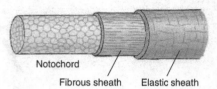

Figure 17-1
Structure of the notochord and surrounding sheaths. Cells of the notochord proper are thick-walled, pressed together loosely, and filled with semifluid. Stiffness is caused mainly by turgidity of fluid-filled cells and surrounding connective tissue sheaths. The primitive type of endoskeleton is characteristic of all chordates at some stage of the life cycle. The notochord provides longitudinal stiffening of the main body axis, a base for trunk muscles, and an axis around which the vertebral column develops.

the central nervous system. It lies dorsal to the alimentary tract and has a fluid-filled cavity, in contrast to the invertebrate nerve cord, which is ventral and solid.

4. **Endostyle or thyroid gland.** The endostyle or its derivative, the thyroid gland, is found in all chordates, but in no other animals. The endostyle secretes mucus and traps small food particles for protochordates and lamprey larvae. Some cells in the endostyle are homologous with cells of the thyroid gland found in the remainder of vertebrates.

5. **Postanal tail.** A postanal tail projects beyond the anus at some stage and serves as a means of propulsion in water. It may or may not persist in the adult. Along with body muscles and stiffened notochord, it provides motility for a free-swimming existence.

These features vary in chordates. Some chordates have all of these structures throughout life. In many chordates, the pharyngeal slits never break through from the pharynx but merely form pouches that have no function, the notochord is replaced by the vertebral column, and only the dorsal nerve cord actually persists in the adult as a diagnostic chordate character. **Protochordates** demonstrate each of the chief chordate characteristics at some point in their life cycle.

Classification

Phylum Chordata

Subphylum Urochordata (u'ro-kor-da'ta) (Gr. *oura*, tail, + L. *chorda*, cord). **(Tunicata.)** Tunicates. Only larval forms have all chordate characteristics; almost all adults sessile, without notochord and dorsal nerve cord; body enclosed in tunic. Example: *Molgula*, a sea squirt.

Subphylum Cephalochordata (sef'a-lo-kor-da'ta) (Gr. *kephalē*, head, + L. *chorda*, cord). Lancelet. Notochord

and nerve cord persist throughout life; lance-shaped. Example: *Branchiostoma* (amphioxus).

Subphylum Vertebrata (ver'te-bra'ta) (L. *vertebratus*, backboned). **(Craniata.)** Vertebrates. Enlarged brain enclosed in cranium; nerve cord surrounded by bony or cartilaginous vertebrae; notochord in all embryonic stages and persists in adults of some fishes; typical structures include two pairs of appendages and body plan of head, trunk, and postanal tail.

Superclass Agnatha (ag'na-tha) (Gr. *a*, without, + *gnathos*, jaw). Hagfishes, lampreys. No jaws or ventral fins; notochord persistent.

  Class Petromyzontida (pet'trō-mī-zon'ti-də) (Gr. *petros*, stone, + *myzon*, sucking). Lampreys.
  Class Myxini (mik-sy'ny). Hagfishes.

Superclass Gnathostomata (na'tho-sto'ma-ta) (Gr. *gnathos*, jaw, + *stoma*, mouth). Jawed fishes, all tetrapods. Jaws present; usually paired limbs; notochord persistent or replaced by vertebral centra.

  Class Chondrichthyes (kon-drik'thee-eez) (Gr. *chondros*, cartilage, + *ichthys*, a fish). Sharks, skates, rays, and chimaeras.
  Classes Actinopterygii (ak'ti-nop-te-rij'ee-i) and **Sarcopterygii** (sar-cop-te-rij'ee-i), formerly grouped within class Osteichthyes (os'te-ik'thee-eez) (Gr. *osteon*, bone, + *ichthys*, a fish). Bony fishes.
  Class Amphibia (am-fib'e-a) (Gr. *amphi*, both or double, + *bios*, life). Amphibians. Frogs, toads, and salamanders.
  Class Reptilia (rep-til'e-a) (L. *repere*, to creep). Reptiles. Non-avian reptiles: snakes, lizards, turtles, crocodiles, and others.
    Subclass Aves (ay'veez) (L. pl. of *avis*, bird). Birds.
  Class Mammalia (ma-may'lee-a) (L. *mamma*, breast). Mammals.

EXERCISE 17A
Subphylum Urochordata—*Ciona*, an Ascidian

Ciona

Phylum Chordata
  Subphylum Urochordata
    Class Ascidiacea (sea squirts)
      Order Enterogona
        Family Cionidae
          Genus *Ciona*
            Species *Ciona intestinalis*

Urochordata (Gr. *oura*, tail, + L. *chorda*, cord) are commonly called tunicates because of their leathery covering, or tunic. They are divided into three classes: Ascidiacea, sea squirts; Thaliacea, salpians; and Appendicularia. The largest group is the ascidians (Gr. *askidion,* leather bag or bottle), which are also the most generalized. They are called sea squirts because of their habit, when handled, of squirting water from the excurrent siphon. Any of the small, translucent ascidians may be used for this exercise. Adult tunicates are sessile, whereas the larvae undergo a brief free-swimming existence.

Where Found

Tunicates are found in all seas and at all depths. Most of them are sessile as adults, although some are pelagic (found in the open ocean). *Ciona intestinalis* (Gr. *Chionē,* demigoddess of mythology) is a cosmopolitan species common in shallow water on wharf pilings, on anchored and submerged objects, and on eelgrass. It grows to 15 cm in its largest dimension. Although sea squirts (ascidians of class Ascidiacea) are common, they also are commonly overlooked in the marine environment. Nearly all shallow-water sea squirts are found attached to almost any available rigid surface: wharf pilings, rocks, shells, and ship bottoms. One of the best places to see sea squirts is on pilings, where they may cover the surface.

External Features and Behavior

Sea squirts are fairly hardy in a marine aquarium.

 Examine, in a finger bowl of seawater, a living solitary tunicate, such as *Ciona* or *Molgula,* or a portion of a colony of *Perophora* or other ascidians as available.

Observe the use of the two openings, or **siphons.** When fully submerged and undisturbed, the siphons are open, and respiratory water, kept moving by ciliary action, enters the more terminal siphon (called the **incurrent, or oral, siphon**) at the mouth, circulates through a large pharynx, and leaves through the **excurrent, or atrial, siphon** on one side (the dorsal side) (Figures 17-2 and 17-3).

 Release a little carmine suspension near the animal to verify this.

The outer covering of a tunicate is called the **tunic,** or **test** (Figure 17-3). It is secreted by the **mantle,** which lies just inside it, and it contains cellulose—an uncommon substance in animals. The mantle contains muscle fibers, by which the body can contract. If the tunic is translucent enough and the light is properly adjusted, you may be able to see some of the internal structure.

Neuromuscular System. The tunicate nervous system is reduced and not well understood. There is a cerebral ganglion (closely associated with a sub-neural gland of uncertain function) located between the siphons. The

Figure 17-2

Ciona intestinalis, a solitary tunicate, showing its siphons in use. It remains anchored throughout life to one spot on the seafloor. Its free-swimming larva bears all the chordate hallmarks: notochord, pharyngeal slits, dorsal tubular nerve cord, and postanal tail.

tunic probably has no sensory nerves, but pressure on the tunic may be transmitted to nerves in the mantle. Both direct and crossed reflexes have been observed in some ascidians and can be tested in a living *Ciona* or other tunicate by touching selected areas with the tip of a glass, rod, or dissecting needle.

Direct reflexes result from mechanical stimulation of the *outer* surface of the siphons or tunic.

 Gently stimulate various areas of the tunic and note the response. Gently touch the outer surface of one of the siphons, note the response, and then stimulate the other siphon.

What areas of the body are most sensitive? **Crossed reflexes** result from mechanical stimulation of the *inner* surface of the siphons. The normal response is to close the *other* siphon and then contract the body.

Gently touch the inner surface of the oral siphon. What happens? _____ Try a stronger stimulus of the same siphon. Do you get the same response? _____ How do these responses differ from those in which the outer surface was stimulated? _____ Repeat with the atrial siphon.

Of what protective value would these reflexes be to the animal? _____

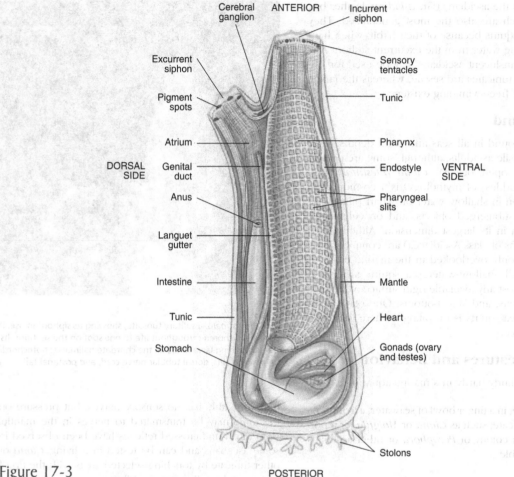

Figure 17-3
Structure of a solitary sea squirt, *Ciona*.

ANTERIOR

Cerebral ganglion

Incurrent siphon

Excurrent siphon

Sensory tentacles

Pigment spots

Tunic

Atrium

Pharynx

DORSAL SIDE

Genital duct

Endostyle   VENTRAL SIDE

Anus

Pharyngeal slits

Languet gutter

Intestine

Mantle

Tunic

Heart

Stomach

Gonads (ovary and testes)

Stolons

POSTERIOR

Internal Structure

 Internal structure can be observed on either a living or a preserved specimen. Use fine scissors to slit the tunic longitudinally, beginning at the incurrent siphon and continuing the cut to the base of the pharynx. Be *very* careful to cut *only* the tunic and not the mantle beneath it. Slip the animal out of its tunic; then return the animal to the bowl of seawater and study with a dissecting microscope.

Respiratory System. The **branchial sac,** or **pharynx,** is the largest internal structure, and the space between it and the mantle is the **atrium** (Figure 17-3). The pharyngeal wall is perforated with many pharyngeal slits, through which water passes into the atrium to be discharged through the excurrent siphon. The vascular wall of the pharynx serves as a gill for gaseous exchange.

Circulatory System. In a living specimen, with test removed and a light properly adjusted, you should be able to see the beating of the **heart,** located near the posterior end on the right side. The tubular heart empties into two vessels, one at each end. Its peristaltic waves are of unusual interest, because they send the blood in one direction for a while and then reverse direction and pump the blood in the opposite direction. Apparently there are two pacemakers that initiate contractions, one at each end of the heart, and they alternate in dominance over each other. The tunicate vascular system is an open type of system. Blood cells are numerous and colorful. There are no respiratory pigments.

Digestive System. At the junction of the **mouth** and **pharynx** is a circlet of **tentacles** that form a grid, which screens the incurrent water. By dropping a grain of sand into the incurrent siphon of a living tunicate, you may be able to observe the ejection reflex.

Inside the pharynx along the midventral wall is the **endostyle,** a ciliated groove that secretes a great deal of mucus. Cilia on the walls of the pharynx distribute the mucus. Food particles become tangled in the mucus and are propelled by cilia to a dorsal gutter (Figure 17-3), in which the mucus with its trapped food becomes rolled

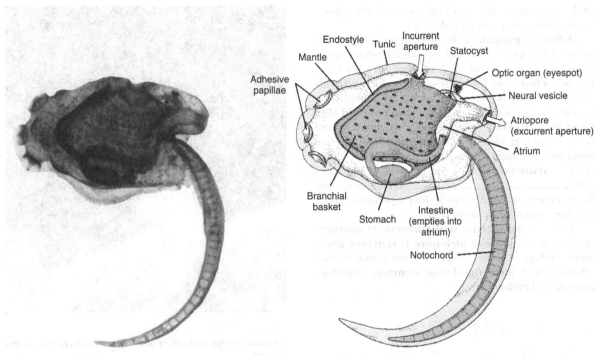

Figure 17-4
Tadpole larva of a tunicate, photographed from a stained slide specimen.

into a compact cord. (In *Ciona* and a few other tunicates, the gutter is lined with a row of curved, ciliated, fingerlike processes called *languets* [F. *languette,* small tongue].) The cord is propelled posteriorly to the esophagus and stomach.

 If living ascidians are available, examine one that has been submerged for some time in a suspension of carmine particles in seawater. Open the pharynx by cutting through the incurrent siphon and downward, a little to one side of the midventral line. Then cut around the base and lay the animal open in a pan of water. You should be able to see a concentration of carmine particles in the middorsal area. Cut out a small piece of the pharyngeal wall (free from the tunic and mantle) and mount on a slide to observe pharyngeal slits and beating cilia.

It may be difficult to differentiate among **esophagus, stomach,** and **intestine.** The **anus** empties into the atrium near the excurrent siphon.

Excretion. A ductless structure near the intestine is assumed to be a type of nephridium and to be excretory in function.

Reproduction. *Ciona,* like most tunicates, is hermaphroditic and has a single ovary and testis, each with a gonoduct that opens into the atrium.

Some tunicates are colonial. In some colonial tunicates zooids (distinct individuals) are separate and attached by a stolon, as in *Perophora*. In others, zooids are regularly arranged and partly united at the base by a common tunic; all incurrent siphons are at one side and excurrent siphons at the other. Another type has a system of zooids that share a common atrial (excurrent) chamber. Colonies are formed asexually by budding.

Solitary tunicates generally shed their eggs from the excurrent siphon, and development occurs in the sea. Colonial species usually brood their eggs in the atrium, and the microscopic larvae leave by the excurrent siphon. For a very brief period, the larvae are nonfeeding and live a planktonic, free-swimming existence; then they settle down, attach to the substrate, and metamorphose.

Ascidian Larvae (Study of Stained Slides)*

Ascidian larvae are free-swimming (Figure 17-4). Why are the larvae often called "tadpole" larvae? _____ They do not look like sessile adult sea squirts and are actually more characteristic of the chordates than are the adults. They possess not only pharyngeal slits but also a notochord, dorsal tubular nerve cord, and tail, structures that have been lost in the

_____
*Slides suitable for this exercise are available from Carolina Biological. See Appendix B, p. 419.

adult. You may be able to identify some of the following structures on a stained slide.

Adhesive papillae at the anterior end of the larva are used to attach to some object during metamorphosis, which occurs within a short time after hatching. The **notochord** can be identified in the long tail. This character, which is lost in the adult, gives subphylum Urochordata ("tail-cord") its name. A **nerve cord** dorsal to the notochord enlarges anteriorly into a neural vesicle. Can you identify a pigmented, photoreceptive **eyespot?** A smaller, pigmented area anterior to the eye is a **statocyst.** What is the function of the statocyst? _____ At metamorphosis these portions of the nervous system degenerate, and a ganglion serves as the nerve center.

Look for the anterior **oral (incurrent) aperture** and the more posterior **atriopore (excurrent aperture).** Perhaps you can identify the **branchial basket** (pharynx) with **pharyngeal slits, stomach, intestine, atrium,** and **endostyle.**

EXERCISE 17B
Subphylum Cephalochordata— *Amphioxus*

Amphioxus

Phylum Chordata
   Subphylum Cephalochordata
      Genus *Branchiostoma* (= *Amphioxus*)
         Species *Branchiostoma lanceolatus*

The little lancelet, *Branchiostoma* (Gr. *branchia*, gills, + *stoma*, mouth), commonly called amphioxus, illustrates basic chordate structure and is considered similar to the ancestor of the vertebrates. Besides the basic characteristics—**notochord, pharyngeal slits, dorsal hollow nerve cord,** and **postanal tail**—it also possesses the beginning of a **ventral heart** and a **metameric arrangement** of muscles and nerves. There are only two genera of cephalochordates—*Asymmetron* (Gr. *asymmetros*, ill-proportioned) and *Branchiostoma*.

Where Found

Branchiostoma is common along the southern California and southern Atlantic coasts of the United States, as well as the coasts of China and the Mediterranean Sea. On sandy bottoms, it dives in headfirst, then twists upward so that the tail remains buried in sand and the anterior end is thrust upward into the water (Figure 17-5).

External Structure

 Place a preserved mature specimen in a watch glass and cover with water. Do not dissect or mutilate the specimen.

Figure 17-5
Amphioxus in typical feeding position, with oral aperture facing upward.

How long is it? _____ Why is it called a lancelet? _____ Does it have a distinctive head? _____ Observe the **dorsal fin,** which broadens in the tail region **(caudal fin)** and continues around the end of the tail to become the **ventral fin.**

The anterior tip is the **rostrum** (Figure 17-6). With a hand lens, find the opening of the **oral hood,** which is fringed by a number of slender oral tentacles, also called buccal cirri, which strain out large particles of sand and are sensory in function.

On the flattened ventral surface are two **metapleural folds** of skin, extending like sled runners to the ventral fin. Find the **atriopore,** which is anterior to the ventral fin. The atriopore is the opening of the atrium (L., entrance hall), a large cavity surrounding the pharynx. The **anus** opens slightly to the left of the posterior end of the ventral fin.

In mature specimens, little, blocklike **gonads** (testes or ovaries) lie in the atrium anterior to the atriopore and just above the metapleural folds on each side. They can be seen through the thin body wall.

Study of the Whole Mount

 Examine with low power a stained and cleared whole mount of an immature specimen.

Chevronlike **myotomes** (Gr. *mys*, muscle, + *tomos*, slice) along the sides of the animal are segmentally arranged muscles. Does the myotome of an amphioxus

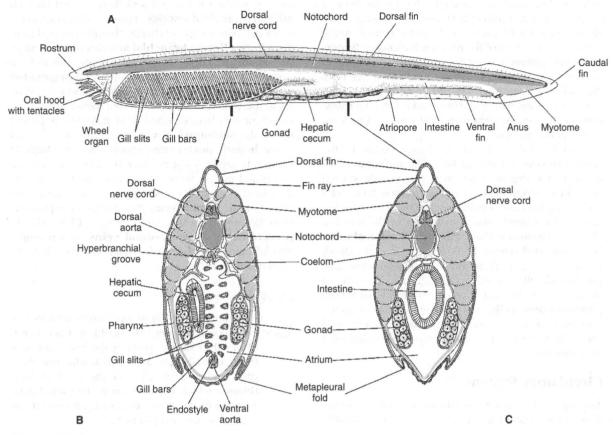

Figure 17-6

Structure of amphioxus, showing **A,** external structure and **B, C,** transverse sections through the pharynx and intestine.

zigzag more or less than the myomere of a bony fish? _____ How might the differences in musculature help us predict whether amphioxus or the fish would be the better swimmer? _____ Identify the various parts of the **fin** and note its skeletal support, the transparent **fin rays.** You may have to reduce the light to see the fin rays.

Beneath the rostrum is a large chamber called the **buccal cavity,** which is bounded laterally by fleshy, curtainlike folds and is open ventrally. The rostrum and lateral folds together make up the **oral hood** (Figure 17-6). The roof of the oral hood bears the notochord, which may have a supporting function in spreading the hood open. Each of the oral tentacles is stiffened by a skeletal rod of fibrous connective tissue. Behind the buccal cavity is an almost perpendicular membrane, the **velum** (L., veil), pierced ventrally by a small opening, the true **mouth,** which is always open and leads into the **pharynx.** On the walls of the buccal cavity, projecting forward from the base of the velum, are several fingerlike, ciliated patches that compose the **wheel organ.** The rotating effect of its cilia helps maintain a current of

water flowing into the mouth. Around the mouth, projecting posteriorly from the velum, are about a dozen delicate **velar tentacles,** also ciliated. Both oral tentacles and velar tentacles have chemoreceptor cells for monitoring incurrent water.

The large **pharynx** narrows into a straight **intestine** extending to the **anus** (Figure 17-6). The sidewalls of the pharynx are composed of a series of parallel, oblique **gill bars,** between which are **pharyngeal slits.** Just posterior to the pharynx is a diverticulum of the intestine called the **hepatic cecum,** or liver, which extends forward along one side of the pharynx. Surrounding the pharynx is the **atrium,** a large cavity that extends to the **atriopore.** Water entering the mouth filters through gill slits into the atrium and then out the atriopore.

Cephalochordates, like sponges, clams, and tunicates, are filter feeders. They use a mucus-ciliary method, feeding on minute organisms. As the animal rests with its head out of the sand, the ciliated tentacles, wheel organ, and gills draw in a steady current of food-laden water, from which the cirri and velar tentacles strain out large and unwanted particles. On the floor of the pharynx is an **endostyle** (Figure 17-6) consisting of alternating rows of ciliated cells and mucus-secreting cells, and in the roof of the pharynx is a ciliated **hyperbranchial groove** (= epipharyngeal groove). Particles of food entangled in the stream of mucus secreted by the endostyle are carried upward by cilia on the inner surface of the gill bars, then backward toward the **intestine** by cilia in the hyperbranchial groove. Digestion occurs in the intestine.

Oxygen–carbon dioxide exchange occurs in the epithelium covering the gill bars. The **notochord** just dorsal to the digestive system is transversely striated and is best seen in the head and tail regions. It provides skeletal support and a point of attachment for muscles. Note that it extends almost to the tip of the rostrum. Above and parallel to the notochord is the **dorsal tubular nerve cord** (Figure 17-6). How far does it extend? _____ Is there any sign of a structure that you would call a brain? _____ The row of black spots in the nerve cord consists of pigmented **photoreceptor cells.** Chemoreceptors are scattered over the body but are particularly abundant on the oral and velar tentacles. Touch receptors are located over the entire body.

Circulatory System

Amphioxus does not have a heart; peristaltic contractions of the **ventral aorta** keep the colorless blood in motion, sending it forward and then upward through **afferent branchial arteries** (Figure 17-7) to capillaries in the gill bars for gas exchange. Blood is carried from the gills by **efferent branchial arteries** up to a pair of **dorsal aortas.** These join posterior to the gills to form a **median dorsal aorta,** which gives off **segmented arteries** to capillaries of the myotomes and to capillaries in the wall of the intestine. From the intestinal wall, blood, now rich in digested food nutrients, is picked up by the **subintestinal vein** and is carried forward to the **hepatic portal vein,** which enters the **hepatic cecum.** In capillaries of the liver, nutrients are removed and stored in liver tissue or processed and returned to the blood as needed. Blood returns to the ventral aorta by way of the **hepatic vein.** Blood with waste products from the muscular walls returns by way of left and right **precardinal** and **postcardinal veins,** which empty into left and right **ducts of Cuvier** and then into the ventral aorta.

Oral Report

Compare circulation in amphioxus with that in earthworms and crayfish. Be able to trace a drop of blood to various parts of the body and back to the ventral aorta, and explain what the blood gains and loses in each of the capillary beds through which it passes on its journey. Locate as many of the main vessels as you can on any transverse sections you have.

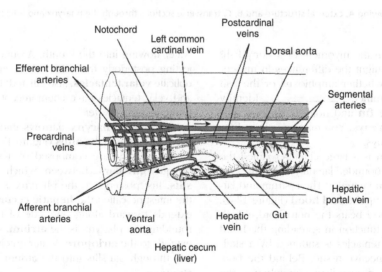

Figure 17-7

Major circulatory vessels of amphioxus. The ventral aorta pumps the blood forward and then upward to the gill capillaries via what arteries? _____ What arteries come from the dorsal aorta and feed the capillaries of the myotomes and intestinal wall? _____ Blood from the intestine, now rich in digested food nutrients, is carried forward to the hepatic cecum via what vein? _____ Blood returns to the ventral aorta by way of what vein? _____

Cross Section—Stained Slide

 Look at a cross section through the pharynx with an unaided eye and understand how the section is cut with reference to the whole animal. Note the **dorsal fin,** its supporting **fin ray,** and the ventral **metapleural folds** (see Figure 17-6). With a microscope, examine the **epidermis,** a single layer of columnar epithelial cells, and **dermis,** a gelatinous connective tissue layer. Large **myotomes,** or muscles, are paired, but members of a pair are not opposite each other. Myotomes are separated by connective tissue, myosepta.

The **nerve cord,** enclosed within the **neural canal,** has in its center a small **central canal,** which is prolonged dorsally into a slit. In some sections, dorsal **sensory nerves** or ventral **motor nerves** may be seen. These are given off alternately from the cord to the myotomes. The large, oval **notochord** with vacuolated cells is surrounded by a **notochordal sheath.**

The cavity of the **pharynx** is bounded by a ring of triangular **gill bars** separated by **pharyngeal slits** that open into the surrounding **atrium** (see Figure 17-6B). From your study of the whole mount, why do you think the cross section shows the gill bars as a succession of cut surfaces? _____ The somewhat rigid gill bars contain blood vessels and are covered by ciliated **respiratory epithelium,** where gaseous exchange is made. On the dorsal side of the pharynx, find the ciliated **hyperbranchial groove;** on the ventral side, the **endostyle.** The latter secretes mucus, in which food particles are caught. What is the function of the cilia in the grooves? _____

Gonads (ovaries or testes) lie on each side of the atrial cavity. The reduced **coelom** consists of spaces, usually paired, on each side of the notochord and hyperbranchial groove, as well as on each side of the gonads and below the endostyle. In favorable specimens, little **nephridial** tubules may be found in the dorsal coelomic cavities (see Figure 17-6). What is their function? _____

Ventral to the notochord are paired **dorsal aortas.** The **ventral aorta** lies ventral to the endostyle.

Drawings

 On separate paper, make drawings of such sections of amphioxus as your instructor requests.

NOTES

EXERCISE 18

The Fishes—Lampreys, Sharks, and Bony Fishes

EXERCISE 18A
Class Petromyzontida—Lampreys (Ammocoete Larva and Adult)

Lampreys

Phylum Chordata
  Subphylum Vertebrata
    Superclass Agnatha
      Class Petromyzontida
        Genus *Petromyzon*
          Species *Petromyzon marinus*

Hagfishes and lampreys are the only living descendants of the earliest known vertebrates, a group of Paleozoic jawless fishes collectively called ostracoderms. Hagfishes and lampreys are conventionally grouped together in superclass Agnatha ("without jaws") and share certain characteristics, including the absence of jaws, internal ossification, scales, and paired fins. In other respects, however, hagfishes and lampreys are radically different from each other.

Lampreys have a worldwide distribution and most are **anadromous** (an-ad'ruh-mus; Gr. *anadromos,* running upward), meaning that they ascend rivers and streams to spawn. The species *Petromyzon marinus* (Gr. *petros,* stone, + *myzon,* sucking, referring to its habit of holding its position in a current by grasping a stone with its mouth) is the sea lamprey that lives in the Atlantic drainages of Canada, the United States, Iceland, and Europe and is landlocked in the Great Lakes. It grows to be 1 m long and can live both in fresh water and in the sea. It is a marine species that migrates up freshwater streams to spawn. Young larvae, known as **ammocoetes** (sing. **ammocoete;** Gr. *ammos,* sand, + *koitē,* bed, Fr.*keisthai,* to lie, referring to the preferred larval habitat), live in sand for 3 to 5 years as filter feeders. Then they metamorphose rapidly into adults and become parasites of fishes. Attaching themselves with their suckerlike mouth, they rasp away the fish's flesh with their horny teeth and suck out blood and body fluids. Adults grow rapidly for a year, spawn in winter or spring, and soon die. After invading the Great Lakes in the nineteenth century, sea lampreys devastated the

EXERCISE 18A
Class Petromyzontida—Lampreys (Ammocoete Larva and Adult)
Lampreys
Ammocoete Larvae
Adult Lampreys

EXERCISE 18B
Class Chondrichthyes—Cartilaginous Fishes
Squalus, dogfish sharks
Demonstrations

EXERCISE 18C
Class Actinopterygii—Bony Fishes
Perca, yellow perch

EXPERIMENTING IN ZOOLOGY
Aggression in Paradise Fish, *Macropodus opercularis*

EXPERIMENTING IN ZOOLOGY
Analysis of the Multiple Hemoglobin System in *Carassius auratus,* Common Goldfish

important commercial fisheries there. Wounding rates of fishes are lower now, but sea lampreys remain a threat to the commercial fishing trade.

Freshwater lampreys, known as brook or river lampreys, belong to genera *Lampetra* (L. *lambo,* to lick or lap up) and *Ichthyomyzon* (Gr. *ichthyos,* fish, + *myzon,* sucking), of which there are about 33 species. They have larval habits similar to those of the marine form, but adults in about half the species are not parasitic. Nonparasitic forms do not eat as adults and live only a month or so after emerging from the sand to spawn.

Ammocoete Larvae

Although ammocoete larvae resemble amphioxus in appearance and behavior, they bear several characteristics that anticipate the vertebrate body plan that are lacking in amphioxus. For example, how is blood propelled in amphioxus? _____

The ammocoete has a two-chambered heart; two median

eyes, each with lens and receptor cells; a three-part brain; thyroid and pituitary glands; and a pronephric kidney. Instead of the numerous pharyngeal slits found in the amphioxus, an ammocoete larva has only seven pairs.

 Examine a preserved ammocoete larva as well as a stained whole mount of a small specimen.

Study of the Preserved Larva

 Cover the preserved larva with water in a water glass. Use a hand lens or dissecting microscope.

List two physical differences between the preserved specimen and a mature amphioxus. _____ _____ Note **myotomes** (segmental muscles) appearing faintly on the surface (Figure 18-1). Do myotomes have the same arrangement as those of amphioxus? _____ Note the **oral hood** with **oral papillae** attached to the roof and sides of the hood. They are used, as in amphioxus, for filter feeding. The **lateral groove** on each side contains seven small **gill slits.** The anus, or **cloacal opening,** is just anterior to the **caudal fin.** Are the **caudal** and **dorsal fins** continuous? _____ Note **chromatophores** scattered over the body.

Study of the Stained Whole Mount

 With low power, examine a stained whole mount of an ammocoete larva.

On a whole mount, find the darkly stained, dorsal, hollow **nerve cord,** enlarged anteriorly to form the **brain.** Immediately below it is the lighter **notochord** (Figure 18-1).

The oral hood encloses a **buccal cavity,** to the back and sides of which are attached oral papillae. Posterior to the buccal cavity is the **velum,** a large pair of flaps that create water currents. The large **pharynx** has **internal gill slits,** which open into **gill pouches.**

Gill pouches open to the outside by small **external gill slits.** How many pairs of gill slits are there in the ammocoete? _____ Using low power, focus upward onto the outer surface of the animal to see a row of small external gill slits. Between the internal gill slits are cartilaginous rods, **gill bars,** which strengthen the pharynx walls. Note **gill lamellae** on the pharynx walls. They are rich in capillaries, in which the blood gives up its carbon dioxide and takes up its oxygen from the water.

The ammocoete is a filter feeder. Is amphioxus also a filter feeder? _____ Water is kept moving through the pharynx by muscular action of both the velum and whole branchial basket. This contrasts with amphioxus, in which water is moved by ciliary action.

The **endostyle** (subpharyngeal gland) in the floor of the pharynx is a closed tube the length of four gill slits. It secretes mucus by a duct into the pharynx. Food particles brought in by water currents are trapped in the mucus and carried by ciliary action to the **esophagus.** During metamorphosis of the larva, a portion of the endostyle becomes a part of the adult's thyroid gland.

The narrow esophagus widens to become the **intestine,** the posterior end of which, called the **cloaca,** also receives the kidney ducts. The **anus** opens to the outside a short distance in front of the postanal tail.

The **liver** lies under the posterior end of the esophagus, and embedded in it is the **gallbladder,** which appears as a clear, round vesicle. A two-chambered **heart** lies under the forepart of the esophagus.

Over the heart and around the esophagus is the **pronephric kidney,** consisting of a number of small tubules that empty into the cloaca by pronephric ducts (not easily distinguished on the whole mounts). Later a mesonephric kidney will develop above the intestine, using the same ducts, and the pronephros will degenerate.

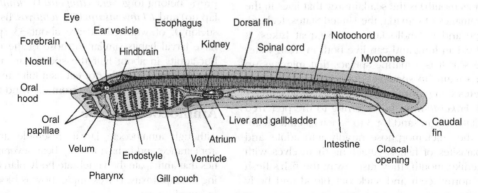

Figure 18-1
Ammocoete larva, sagittal section.

The tubular dorsal **nerve cord** enlarges anteriorly into a three-lobed **brain,** visible in most slides. How does the nerve cord differ in location from that of the flatworms? _____ How does the nerve cord differ from those of annelids and arthropods? _____ The **forebrain** contains the **olfactory lobe.** In front of the forebrain is the **nasohypophyseal canal,** opening dorsally to the outside by a median **nostril.** The darkly pigmented **eyes** connect with each side of the **midbrain.** At this stage, the eyes are covered with skin and muscle and have little sensitivity to light; however, the ammocoete larva does have photoreceptors in the tail. Find the **hindbrain** and, with careful focusing, try to see one of the clear, oval **ear vesicles** that flank each side of it. Which lobe of the brain is chiefly concerned with the sense of smell? _____ Of sight? _____ Of hearing and equilibrium? _____ How is the nervous system of this agnathan advanced over that of the cephalochordate amphioxus? _____

Circulation in Ammocoetes

The circulatory system is similar to that of amphioxus, but blood is driven by a **two-chambered heart.** The circulatory pattern is basically that of all fishes. It is a single-circuit system with two sets of capillaries: capillary beds of the gills and capillaries of the body. The **ventral aorta** carries deoxygenated blood forward from the heart, bifurcating at about the fourth gill pouch and giving off eight pairs of **afferent** (L. *ad,* toward, + *ferre,* to carry) **branchial arteries** to the gills' capillary beds, where the blood is oxygenated. Eight pairs of **efferent** (L. *ex,* out, + *ferre,* to carry) **branchial arteries** direct oxygenated blood to the **dorsal aorta,** which sends a pair of arteries forward to the brain and head. Most of the dorsal aorta blood, however, runs posteriorly, giving off **segmental arteries** to capillaries of the body walls and one large **intestinal artery** to capillary beds in the intestinal wall. The **hepatic portal vein** carries blood from the intestine to the liver capillaries; the **hepatic vein** carries blood from the liver capillaries to a thin-walled sac, the **sinus venosus,** at the back of the heart. Blood from the body wall and myotomes is picked up by cardinal veins. On each side, an **anterior cardinal vein,** lateral to the notochord, and a **posterior cardinal vein,** lateral to the dorsal aorta, unite to form a **duct of Cuvier,** which, with its mate from the other side, enters the sinus venosus. The sinus venosus is connected to the thin-walled **atrium** of the heart by valves that prevent backflow. Valves also guard the opening from the atrium to the thicker, more muscular **ventricle,** which pumps blood through valves into the ventral aorta. How does the ammocoete circulatory system differ from that of an earthworm? _____

Transverse Sections of Ammocoetes

 Your slide may contain four typical sections—one each through the brain, pharynx, intestine, and postanal tail. Or it may contain 15 to 20 sections through the body, arranged in sequence. As you study each section, refer to the whole mount again to interpret relationships. Use the low power of the microscope.

Sections Anterior to the Pharynx. Sections through the **forebrain** may include the **oral papilla** and **oral hood.** Sections through the **midbrain** may include **eyes, buccal chamber,** and portions of **velar flaps.** Sections through the **hindbrain** may include **ear (otic) vesicles** and buccal chamber (Figure 18-2A) or the forepart of the pharynx. Compare the size of the brain with that of the spinal cord in more posterior sections. Do you find a **notochord** lying just below the brain in any of the sections? _____ Why is the notochord considered a primitive type of endoskeleton? _____

Sections Posterior to the Pharynx. Choose a section through the trunk posterior to the pharynx and identify the following (Figure 18-2C): **epidermis; myotomes** (lateral masses of muscles); **nerve cord** surrounded by the **neural canal** and containing a cavity, the **neurocoel; notochord,** with large, vacuolated cells; **dorsal aorta** (probably contains blood cells); and **posterior cardinal veins,** one on each side of the aorta (blood cells are usually present). You may find the cardinals joining to form the duct of Cuvier. The **coelomic cavity,** lined with peritoneum, contains the visceral organs. What distinguishes a true coloem from other cavities in the body? _____

Visceral contents of the coelomic cavity will vary according to the location of the section.

1. Just behind the pharynx, you will find the **esophagus,** of columnar epithelium; the paired **pronephric kidneys,** appearing as sections of small tubules; and chambers of the **heart.**

2. Sections cut posterior to the heart will show the dark **liver** and possibly the hollow **gallbladder** ventral, or lateral, to the esophagus, with sections of pronephric kidneys or their ducts located under the posterior cardinals.

3. Sections through the intestine will reveal it as a large tube of columnar epithelium with a conspicuous infolding, the **typhlosole,** carrying the **subintestinal artery** (Figure 18-2C). Above the intestine, you may find the **mesonephric kidneys,** with their tubules, and a small **gonad**

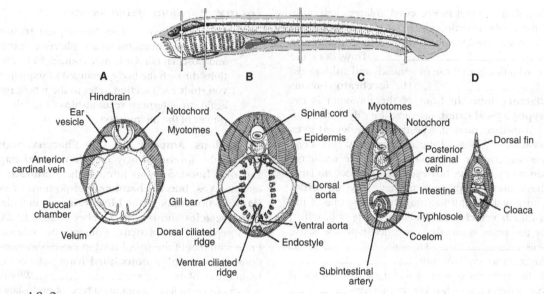

Figure 18-2

Transverse sections of ammocoete larva. **A,** Posterior part of buccal chamber. **B,** Pharynx. **C,** Intestine. **D,** Cloaca.

between the kidneys. The **cloaca** is located farther back (Figure 18-2D).

4. In sections posterior to the anus (postanal tail), identify the caudal fins. What other structures can you identify? _____

Sections through the Pharynx. The body wall, nerve cord, and notochord will be similar to the preceding sections. The central part of the section is taken up by the large pharynx, on whose walls are the **gills,** with their platelike **gill lamellae,** extending into the pharynx or into the **gill pouch,** depending on how the section has been cut. Each lamella has lateral ridges. Some sections, such as that in Figure 18-2B, may show only gill bars without the feathery lamellae. The gills are liberally supplied with blood vessels. Outside the gill chambers, you will find sections through cartilage rods that give support to the branchial basket.

In the middorsal and midventral regions of the pharynx are **ciliated ridges** bearing grooves. The cilia are concerned with the movement toward the esophagus of mucous strands, in which food particles are caught. Below the pharynx in certain sections is the bilobed **subpharyngeal gland,** whose function is probably the secretion of mucus. Later, certain portions of this gland are incorporated into the adult thyroid gland. Between the ventral ciliated ridge and the subpharyngeal gland is the single or paired **ventral aorta.** Note the **gill pouches** lateral to the pharynx, the **lateral groove,** and in some sections **external gill slits** to the outside. Locate the **anterior cardinal veins** on each side of the notochord and the **dorsal aorta** beneath it.

Drawings

 On separate paper, draw such transverse sections as are required by your instructor. Label fully. How many features of the amphioxus adult do you find repeated in the ammocoete, the larval form of a vertebrate? _____ Do you think this might be interpreted as an example of homology? _____ Keep in mind the structure of these early chordate forms and be able to compare them with those of the fish, amphibian, and mammal forms that you will study later.

Adult Lampreys

External Structure

 Examine a preserved specimen of an adult lamprey.

It will be immediately evident that the adult lamprey differs in many anatomical details from the ammocoete, in addition to the obvious difference in their size. During the dramatic metamorphosis from larva to adult, the body becomes rounder and shorter, the pharynx becomes divided longitudinally, the larval hood is replaced by an oral disc with teeth, the eyes enlarge, and the nostril shifts to the top of the head. These changes are essential to the shift from a larval life habit of filter feeding to an adult existence as a parasite of fish.

Note the eel-like shape of the lamprey and its tough, scaleless skin. Among the epithelial cells are numerous gland cells that produce a protective slime. Identify the two **dorsal fins** and **caudal fin** (Figure 18-3A). There

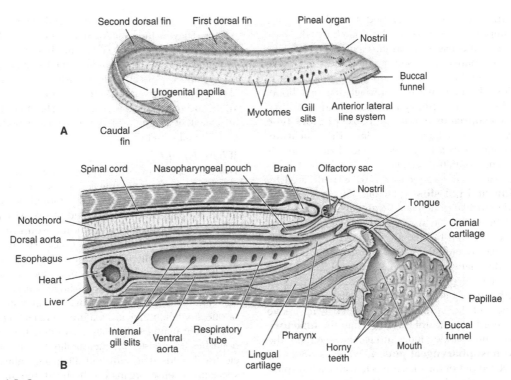

Figure 18-3
Adult lamprey. **A,** External structure. **B,** Sagittal section.

are no paired appendages. What does a lack of paired fins tell you about how a lamprey might swim, as compared with a bony fish? _____

_____

Examine the hood-shaped **buccal funnel** supported by a cartilaginous ring that serves as a sucking disc for attachment to a host. The opening is fringed by numerous fingerlike sensory papillae, and the interior of the funnel bears horny "teeth"; these are actually epidermal thickenings and not homologous to true vertebrate teeth, which are derived from mesoderm. Locate the **mouth** at the back of the buccal funnel and dorsal to the **tongue.** The tongue also bears sharp, horny teeth used for rasping.

A single **nostril** located middorsally on top of the head opens into an olfactory sac (the latter visible in the sagittal section, below). Just behind the nostril is a small, oval area marking the position of the so-called third eye, the **pineal organ.** It is not an eye in the true sense, but it does contain photoreceptors that detect changes in illumination and adjust internal activities of the lamprey. The pineal organ is present in most fishes but is better developed in lampreys than in any other living vertebrate except certain reptiles. Note the functional, lidless **eyes** and seven **external gill slits** just behind the eye on each side of the head.

The **lateral line system,** characteristic of nearly all fishes, consists of specialized receptors located in small

patches on the head and trunk of the lamprey. They can be located as groups of pores extending below and caudally from the eye on each side of the head. These receptor cells are sensitive to currents and water movement. How would they be useful to the lamprey? _____ In the lamprey, the receptors are open to the exterior and not protected within canals as they are in bony fishes.

Find the **urogenital* sinus,** with its projecting urogenital papilla and the ventral juncture of the trunk and the tail. There is an **anal opening** in front of the urogenital sinus.

How do the structures of the myotomes compare with those of amphioxus? _____

_____

Internal Structure

 Examine a sagittal section of the anterior portion of the lamprey body (Figure 18-3B).

Identify the **notochord,** a rodlike mass of vacuolated cells enclosed by a tough, fibrous sheath. As in amphioxus, the firm yet flexible notochord prevents the body from shortening when the muscles contract. The

_____

*Urogenital = urinogenital. The stem **uro** as used in "urogenital" derives from the Greek *ouron,* meaning urine. Unfortunately, the stem is used in other terms to mean "tail" (Gr. *oura,* tail), as in *Urodela, urostyle,* and *uropod.*

notochord remains well developed throughout the life of the lamprey. In addition to the notochord, the lamprey's skeleton consists of various elements of cartilage and fibrous connective tissue. Some skeletal elements can be seen in the sagittal section.

Follow the digestive tract through the oral hood, mouth, tongue, and **pharynx,** which leads into two tubes: the **esophagus** dorsally and a **respiratory tube** ventrally. The esophagus leads into the **intestine,** which continues as a long tube to the cloaca. There is no stomach, a primitive feature.

The wall of the respiratory tube is perforated by seven **internal gill slits.** Each gill slit leads into an enlarged branchial pouch lined with gill lamellae (these may not be visible on the sagittal section). Bony fish pass water through the mouth and then over the gills before it exits behind the gills. Why is this not possible for a feeding lamprey? _____ How might it solve the problem? _____

The **brain,** a bilobed structure similar to the brain of sharks, and the **spinal cord** are seen lying above the notochord. The nostril leads first into the **olfactory sac** with a much-folded inner surface and then into the elongate **nasopharyngeal pouch.** Water is drawn in and squeezed out of the olfactory sac with each respiratory movement of the pharynx. The pineal organ may be visible just behind the nostril.

The **heart** lies within the **pericardial cavity,** a division of the coelom. Venous drainage from the body is received by the **sinus venosus,** which empties into the **atrium** on the left side of the pericardial cavity. Blood from the atrium passes into the **ventricle** on the right side of the pericardial cavity and is then pumped into the **ventral aorta.** The ventral aorta gives off eight pairs of afferent branchial arteries that lead to gill capillaries, where the blood is oxygenated, then collected by the **dorsal aorta** lying just ventral to the notochord. The dorsal aorta continues caudally, supplying blood to the viscera and body musculature. Usually these major blood vessels are difficult to see in a sagittal section.

EXERCISE 18B

Class Chondrichthyes—Cartilaginous Fishes

Squalus, Dogfish Sharks

Subphylum Vertebrata
  Superclass Gnathostomata
    Class Chondrichthyes
      Subclass Elasmobranchii
        Order Squaliformes
          Genus *Squalus*

Cartilaginous fishes are a compact, ancient assemblage of about 970 species characterized by cartilaginous

skeletons, powerful jaws, and well-developed sense organs. They include sharks, skates, rays, and chimaeras. Subclass Elasmobranchii (e-laz′-mo-bran′kee-i; Gr. *elasmos,* metal plate, + *branchia,* gills) embraces sharks, skates, and rays—cartilaginous fishes with exposed gill slits opening separately to the outside. Most are carnivores and many are top predators. The dogfish shark is an excellent example of the generalized body plan of early jawed vertebrates.

Where Found

Dogfish sharks are small marine sharks that grow to about 1 m in length (females are slightly larger than males). Two species commonly studied belong to the genus *Squalus* (L. *squalus,* a kind of sea fish), the spiny dogfishes: *Squalus acanthias* of the North Atlantic and *Squalus suckleyi* of the Pacific Coast. The two species are morphologically similar. Spiny dogfishes are distinguished by a spine on the anterior edge of both dorsal fins. Spiny dogfishes gather in huge schools of up to 1000 individuals of both sexes when immature, but only of one sex when they are mature. In detecting and capturing their main foods, bottom-dwelling fish and crabs, dogfishes are assisted by their ability to sense the weak electrical fields that surround all living animals, using specialized sense organs on the head, the ampullae of Lorenzini. Spiny dogfishes are ovoviviparous (L. *ovum,* egg, + *vivus,* living, + *parere,* to bring forth); that is, they give birth to living young without dependence on placental nourishment. Embryos develop in an egg capsule in the oviduct until they hatch in the mother just before birth.

External Structure

 Examine an intact, preserved dogfish to identify the following features.

The body is divided into the **head** (to the first gill slit), **trunk** (to the cloacal opening), and **tail.** The **fins** include a pair of **pectoral fins** (anterior), which control changes in direction during swimming; a pair of **pelvic fins,** which serve as stabilizers and which in males are modified to form claspers used in copulation; two medium **dorsal fins,** which also serve as stabilizers; and a **caudal fin,** which is **heterocercal** (asymmetric dorsoventrally) (Figure 18-4).

Identify the **mouth** with its rows of **teeth** (modified placoid scales), which are adapted for cutting and shearing; two ventral **nostrils,** which lead to olfactory sacs and are equipped with folds of skin that allow continual in-and-out movement of water; and lateral **eyes,** which lack movable eyelids but have folds of skin that can cover the eyeballs. The part of the head anterior to the eyes is called the **rostrum** (snout).

A pair of dorsal **spiracles** posterior to the eyes are modified gill slits that open into the pharynx. They can be closed by folds of skin during part of the respiratory

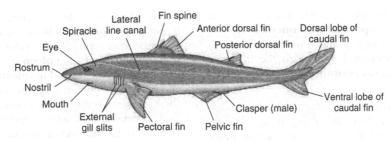

Figure 18-4

External anatomy of a dogfish shark, *Squalus* sp.

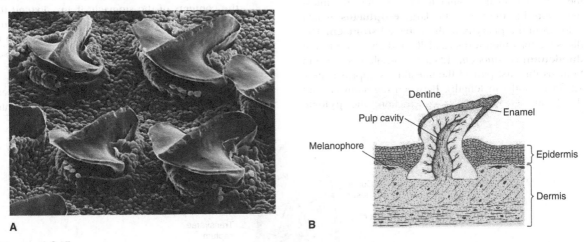

A   **B**

Figure 18-5

A, Surface view of shark skin, showing dermal denticles, or placoid scales, SEM, ×195. **B,** Lateral section of a single denticle.

cycle to prevent the escape of water. Spiracles serve for water intake when a shark is feeding. Five pairs of **gill slits** are the external openings of the gill chambers.

 Insert a probe into one of the slits and notice the angle of the gill chamber.

The **pharynx** is the region in back of the mouth into which the gill slits and spiracles open. A **lateral line,** appearing as a white line on each side of the trunk, represents a row of minute, mucus-filled sensory pores used to detect differences in velocity of surrounding water currents and thus to detect the presence of other animals, even in the dark. Note the **cloacal opening** between the pelvic fins.

The leathery skin consists of an outer layer of epidermis covering a much thicker layer of dermis densely packed with fibrous connective tissue. Draw your finger lightly over the shark's skin to feel the spines of the **placoid scales** (Gr. *placos,* tablet, plate) (Figure 18-5). Each scale is anchored in the dermis and is built much like a tooth (the shark's teeth are, in fact, modified placoid scales). The scale contains a pulp cavity and a thick layer of dentine, both derived from the dermis, and is covered with hard enamel, derived from the epidermis.

Spiny scales help reduce friction-producing turbulence as a shark swims, thus lessening drag.

With its dark dorsal and light ventral surfaces **(countershading),** the animal's coloration is protective, whether viewed from above or below.

Internal Structure

If a dissection is not to be made, examine longitudinal and transverse sections of the shark. Note the cartilaginous skull and vertebral column. With the help of Figure 18-6, identify as many of the internal structures as possible.

Dissection of a Shark

 Open the coelomic cavity by extending a midventral incision posteriorly from the pectoral girdle through the pelvic girdle and then around one side of the cloacal opening to a point just posterior to it. On each side, make a short transverse cut just posterior to the pectoral fins and another one just anterior to the pelvic fins. Rinse out the body cavity.

The shiny membrane lining the body cavity and its organs is the **peritoneum** (Gr. *peritonaios,* stretched around). The peritoneum lining the inner surface of the body wall is called **parietal peritoneum,** and that covering the visceral organs and forming the double-membraned **mesenteries** that suspend the digestive organs is called **visceral peritoneum.**

Digestive System

Identify the large **liver** (Figure 18-6). It has two large lobes and a small median lobe. Lying along the right margin of the median lobe of the liver is a thin, tubular sac, the **gallbladder.** Bile from the liver is concentrated in the gallbladder and then discharged during meals by way of the common bile duct into the intestine. Dorsal to the liver is the large **esophagus,** which leads from the pharynx to the J-shaped **stomach.** The digestive tract then turns caudally and gives rise to the **duodenum** (L. *duodeni,* 12 each, so-called because in humans this first part of the intestine is approximately 12 fingerwidths in length). Between the stomach and duodenum is a muscular constriction, the **pyloric**

valve, which regulates the entrance of food into the intestine. The **pancreas** lies close to the ventral side of the duodenum, with a slender dorsal portion extending posteriorly to the large **spleen** (not a part of the digestive system). The **valvular intestine** (ileum) is short and wide and contains a **spiral "valve,"** or **ridge.** The short, narrow **rectum** has extending from its dorsal wall a **rectal gland,** which regulates ion balance. The cloaca receives the rectum and urogenital ducts.

 Make a longitudinal incision in the ventral wall of the esophagus and stomach. Remove and save the contents of the stomach, if any. Extend the longitudinal incision along the wall of the ileum (taking care not to destroy the blood vessels) to expose the **spiral valve.** Rinse out the exposed digestive tract.

Examine contents from the stomach and compare with those of others being dissected. What do you infer

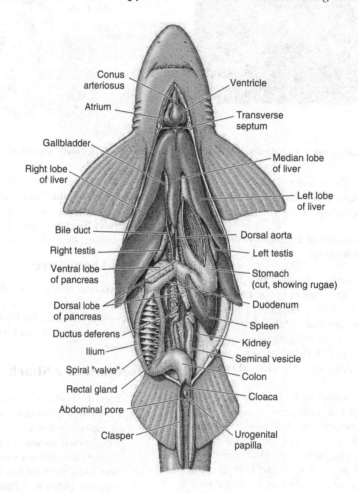

Figure 18-6

Internal anatomy of a dogfish shark, ventral view. What large organ likely assists in keeping the shark buoyant? _____ What structure slows the passage of food through the gut? _____ What organ is formed around the posterior end of the J-shaped stomach? _____ What gland is specific to the cartilaginous fishes and helps regulate the fishes' salt imbalance? _____ What organ functions as the primary source of red blood cell production? _____

about the shark's eating habits? Examine the inner surface of the digestive tract. The walls of the esophagus bear large papillae, whereas the walls of the stomach are thrown into longitudinal folds called **rugae** (roog′ee; L. *ruga,* wrinkle). Note the structure of the pyloric valve. Observe the cone-shaped folds of the **spiral valve** and see if you can determine how materials pass through. The spiral valve, not really a "valve" but a fold of tissue that spirals down the ileum much like a spiral staircase, slows the passage of food through the gut. Why might slowing the passage of food be beneficial for the digestive process?

_____

 If the intestine has been everted into the cloacal region, carefully pull it back into the body cavity.

Urogenital System
Although the excretory and reproductive systems have quite different functions, they are closely associated structurally and so are studied together (Figure 18-7).

Male. Soft, elongated **testes** lie along the dorsal body wall, one on each side of the esophagus (Figure 18-7). They are held in place by a mesentery called the **mesorchium** (Gr. *mesos,* middle, + *orchis,* testicle). A number of very fine tubules (vasa efferentia) in the mesentery run

from each testis to a much convoluted **mesonephric duct** (also called Wolffian duct or ductus deferens). The **kidneys** (also called opisthonephroi) are long and narrow and lie behind the peritoneum on each side of the dorsal aorta. They extend from the pectoral girdle to the **cloaca.** The sperm ducts, which serve as both urinary ducts and sperm ducts, take a twisting course along the length of the kidneys to the cloaca and collect wastes from the kidneys by many fine tubules. The sperm ducts widen posteriorly into **seminal vesicles,** which dilate terminally into **sperm sacs** before entering the cloaca. The cloaca is a common vestibule into which both the rectum and the urogenital ducts empty. In the center of the cloaca, dorsal and posterior to the rectum, is a projection called the **urogenital papilla,** which is larger in males than in females. Seminal vesicles empty into the urogenital papilla, which empties into the cloaca.

 Slit open the cloaca to see the urogenital papilla.

A groove along the inner edge of each **clasper** is used in transferring spermatozoa to a female at copulation.

Female. A pair of **ovaries** lie against the dorsal body wall, one on each side of the esophagus (Figure 18-7). Enlarged ova may form several rounded projections on

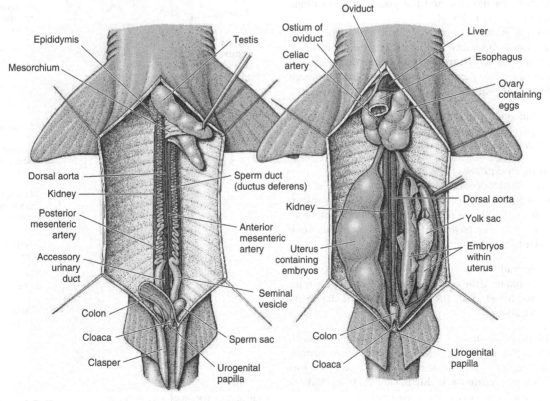

Figure 18-7
Urogenital system of a dogfish shark. **Left,** Male. **Right,** Female.

the surface of the ovaries. A pair of **oviducts** (Müllerian ducts) run along the dorsal abdominal mesentery. The anterior ends join to form a common opening into the abdominal cavity, called the **ostium tubae.** The oviducts are anteroventral to the liver but may be difficult to find except in large females. Ripened ova leave the ruptured wall of the ovary and enter the abdominal cavity. They are drawn through the ostium into the oviducts, where fertilization may occur. An expanded area of each oviduct dorsal to the ovary is a **shell gland (oviducal gland),** which in *Squalus* secretes a thin membrane around several eggs at a time. The posterior end of each oviduct enlarges into a **uterus,** the caudal end of which opens into the **cloaca.** In immature dogfishes both the shell gland and uterus may not be apparent.

One to seven eggs, depending on the species, may develop in each uterus. Vascularized villi on the wall of the uterus come in contact with the yolk sac of the embryo in a placenta-like manner. As mentioned earlier, spiny dogfishes are ovoviviparous because the embryo does not depend on placental nourishment. However, other sharks include some that are dependent on the mother for nourishment through the placental connection (**viviparous;** L. *vivus,* living, + *parere,* to bring forth) and still other sharks that lay shelled eggs containing a large amount of yolk (**oviparous;** L. *ovum,* egg, + *parere,* to bring forth). Gestation periods vary from 16 to 24 months, and the young at birth range from 12 to 30 cm in length.

Slender **kidneys** (opisthonephroi) extend the length of the dorsal abdominal wall, dorsal to the peritoneum. A very slender **Wolffian duct** embedded on the ventral surface of each kidney empties into the cloaca through a **urogenital papilla.**

 Slit open the cloaca and identify the urogenital papilla, the entrance of the rectum, and, on the dorsal side, openings from the uteri.

Circulatory System

Because sharks do not have bone marrow, the spleen is the location of red blood cell production. The spleen also filters blood much as does the lymph system of other animals. The basic plan of circulation in the shark is similar to that in the ammocoete larva.

 Spread the ventral body wall to reveal the cavity containing the heart (**pericardial cavity).** Lift up the **heart** to see the thin-walled, triangular **sinus venosus.**

Blood passes from the sinus venosus to the **atrium,** which surrounds the dorsal side of the muscular **ventricle;** it then flows into the ventricle, which pumps it forward into the **conus arteriosus** (Figure 18-8). **Valves** prevent backflow between compartments.

Venous System.

 Slit open the sinus venosus transversely, extending the cut somewhat to the left; wash out its contents.

Look for openings into the sinus venosus of one of each of the following paired veins: (1) **common cardinal** (L. *cardinalis,* chief, principal) **veins (ducts of Cuvier)** (Figure 18-8), which extend laterally and into which empty large **anterior cardinal sinuses, posterior cardinal sinuses,** and **subclavian veins** (L.*sub,* under, + *clavus,* key); (2) **inferior jugular veins** (L. *jugulum,* collarbone) from the floor of the mouth and gill cavities (these veins are not shown in Figure 18-8); and (3) **hepatic veins,** which empty near the middle of the posterior wall of the sinus venosus and bring blood from the liver.

The **hepatic portal vein** (Figure 18-8) gathers blood chiefly from the digestive system through a system

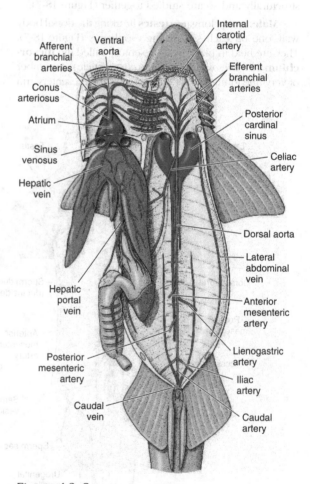

Figure 18-8
Circulatory system of a dogfish shark.

of gastric, pancreatic, and intestinal veins. The hepatic portal vein enters the right lobe of the liver and divides into several small **portal veins** (trace some of these subdivisions); it then divides into a system of capillaries, from which some of the carbohydrates brought from the intestine may be stored in liver cells as glycogen (animal starch) until needed. Blood from capillaries flows into the **hepatic veins** and from there into the sinus venosus.

Renal portal veins arise from the **caudal vein** in the tail and carry blood to capillaries of the kidneys. Many small renal veins carry blood from the kidneys to the posterior cardinal sinuses and from there to the sinus venosus.

Arterial System. The arterial system includes (1) the afferent and efferent branchial arterial system and (2) the dorsal aorta and its branches.

From the conus arteriosus, trace the **ventral aorta** forward, removing most of the muscular tissue to the lower jaw. The ventral aorta gives off three paired branches, which give rise to **five pairs of afferent branchial arteries** (Figure 18-8). In injected specimens, you can follow these arteries into the interbranchial septa, where each gives off tiny arteries to the gill lamellae.

 The **efferent branchial arteries** are more difficult to dissect. With scissors, cut through the left corner of the shark's mouth and backward through the centers of the left gill slits, continuing as far as the transverse cut you made earlier at the base of the pectoral fins. Now cut transversely across the floor of the pharynx straight through the sinus venosus, and turn the lower jaw to one side to expose gill slits and the roof of the pharynx. Locate the spiracle internally. It represents the degenerated first gill slit. Dissect the mucous membrane lining from the roof of the mouth and pharynx to expose four pairs of **efferent branchial arteries,** which carry oxygen-rich blood from the gill filaments and unite to form the **dorsal aorta.** By cutting the cartilages under which they pass, trace these arteries back to the gills.

The dorsal aorta extends posteriorly along the length of the body ventral to the vertebral column. It gives rise to **subclavian arteries,** which connect to the pectoral region, a **celiac artery** (Gr. *koilia,* belly) (Figure 18-8), which gives off branches to the intestinal tract and gonads, numerous **parietal arteries** to body walls, **mesenteric arteries** to the intestine and rectum, **renal arteries** to the kidneys, and **iliac arteries** (L. *ilia,* flanks) to the pelvic fins. The aorta continues to the tip of the tail as the **caudal artery.**

Respiratory System

In sharks, water taken in through both mouth and spiracles is forced laterally through five pairs of gills and leaves through five pairs of external gill slits (some elasmobranchs have a different number of gills).

 On the shark's right (intact) side, separate the gill units by cutting dorsally and ventrally from the corners of each gill slit. Now you can examine the structure of the intact gills on this side and observe the gills in cross section on the other side.

The area between the **external gill slits** and **internal gill slits** comprises the **gill chambers** (**gill pouches** and **branchial chambers**). The incomplete rings of heavy cartilage supporting the gills and protecting the afferent and efferent branchial arteries are called **gill arches.** Short, spikelike projections extending medially from the gill arches are **gill rakers.** What might be the function of gill rakers? _____ Cartilaginous **gill rays** fan out laterally from the gill arches to support the gill tissues.

 Remove an intact half of a gill arch, along with its gill tissue. Examine with a hand lens. Float a small piece of gill in water and examine with a dissecting microscope.

Primary lamellae (gill filaments) are small, platelike sheets of epithelial folds arranged in rows along the lateral face of each gill. Under a microscope, primary lamellae are seen to be made up of rows of tiny plates, called **secondary lamellae,** which are the actual sites of gas exchange. Blood capillaries in secondary lamellae are arranged to carry blood inward, or in the opposite direction of seawater, which is flowing outward. This countercurrent flow encourages gas exchange between the blood and water. Gill lamellae are arranged in half-gills, or **demibranchs,** on each side of the branchial arch. The two demibranchs together form the gill unit, or **holobranch.** The spiracles are believed to be remnants of the first gill slit. They are usually larger in the slow-moving, bottom-dwelling sharks than in fast-swimming sharks, in which, because of their motion, there is a more massive flow of water through the mouth.

Oral Report

 Be able to identify both external and internal features of the shark and give the functions of each organ or structure.

Be able to trace the flow of blood from the heart to any part of the body (such as the pectoral region, the kidneys, and the tail) and back to the heart.

Demonstrations

1. *Dogfish uterus with developing pups or dogfish embryos with attached yolk sac*

2. *Various sharks, skates, and rays*

3. *Preparation of the skull and/or skeleton of a shark*

4. *Corrosion preparation of the arterial system*

5. *Shark teeth*

6. *Microslides of shark skin*

EXERCISE 18C

Class Actinopterygii—Bony Fishes

Perca, Yellow Perch

Subphylum Vertebrata
    Class Actinopterygii
        Superorder Teleostei
            Order Perciformes
                Genus *Perca*
                    Species *Perca flavescens*

Where Found

The yellow perch is a common freshwater fish widely distributed through the lakes of the American Midwest and parts of Canada. A closely related species is found in Europe and Asia.

Characteristics

Actinopterygii (bony fishes) represents the largest group of vertebrates, both in number of species (more than 23,600) and in number of individuals. There are an amazing variety of forms and structures. They flourish in fresh water and seawater and in both deep and shallow water. Their chief characteristics usually are **dermal scales, operculum over the gill chamber** of each side, **bony skeleton, terminal mouth, swim bladder, homocercal tail,** and both **median** and **paired fins.**

External Structure

 Obtain a preserved fish and, after you have studied its external anatomy, compare it with living fishes in the aquarium. What can their structure tell you of their living habits? _____

The body of the perch is fusiform, or torpedo-shaped. Is it compressed in any of its planes? _____ Identify the **head,** which extends to the posterior edge of the **operculum; trunk,** which extends to the anus; and **tail** (Figure 18-9). Identify the **pectoral, pelvic, anal, dorsal,** and **caudal fins.** How many of each are there? _____ Which of the fins are paired? _____ Note the **fin rays,** which support the thin membrane of each fin. Some of the rays are soft and some are spiny. How would you expect these spiny rays to look when the fish is threatened by a predator? _____ The caudal fin is **homocercal** (Gr. *homos,* same, + *kerkos,* tail), meaning that the upper and lower halves are equal.

The terminal **mouth** is adapted for overtaking prey while swimming. Fishes with superior mouths (those facing upward) are usually surface feeders, whereas those with inferior mouths (facing downward) are usually bottom feeders. Do the **eyes** have lids? _____ Could the perch have binocular vision? Why? _____ _____On each side in front of the eye, a pair of **nostrils** open into an olfactory sac. Water enters the sac

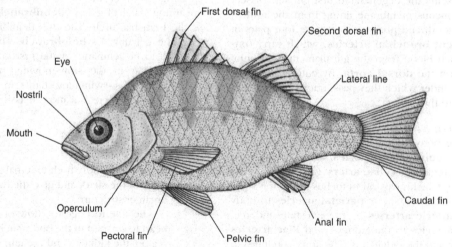

Figure 18-9
Yellow perch, external features.

through the anterior aperture, which is provided with a flaplike valve, and leaves through the posterior aperture. The **ears** are located behind the eyes, but they are not visible externally. A **lateral line** along the side of the body is a row of small pores or tubules connecting with a long, tubular canal bearing sensory organs. These are sensitive to pressure and temperature changes and are responsive to water currents. Many microscopic sense organs are found in the skin.

Lift a gill cover, or **operculum** (L., cover), and study its structure. Along the ventral margin of the operculum, find a membrane supported by bony rays. This membrane fits snugly against the body to close the branchial cavity during certain respiratory movements. With your probe, examine the **gills** beneath the operculum.

Find the **anus** near the base of the anal fin and the small, slitlike **urogenital opening** just posterior to the anus.

Note the arrangement of the **scales.**

 Remove a scale from the lateral line region, mount in water on a slide, and examine with low power.

The anterior, or embedded, side of the perch scale has radiating grooves. The posterior, or free, edge has very fine teeth. These are **ctenoid scales** (ten′oid; Gr. *kteis, ktenos,* comb). Note the fine, concentric lines of growth. The scales are covered with a very thin epidermis, which secretes mucus over the scales. This reduces friction in swimming and makes capture by a predator more difficult. Ctenoid scales are usually found on fishes with spiny rays in the fins, whereas soft-rayed fishes usually have cycloid scales, which lack marginal teeth.

Skeletal System

 Examine the mounted specimen of a perch.

The skeletal system of a bony fish has three main components: a **vertebral column,** a **skull,** and an **appendicular skeleton** (Figure 18-10). We focus on the skeleton of a perch, an actinopterygian (teleost).

Vertebral Column. The vertebral column typically has one vertebra per body segment. Like amphioxus, fish trunk muscles are arranged as zigzagging myotomes. The alternating side-to-side contractions of these muscles is what produces the undulating body movement that propels a fish through water. The vertebral column of bony fishes is well suited to withstand the forces placed on it during the contraction of these trunk muscles during swimming. Fishes have a pair of **ribs** for every vertebra; they serve as stiffening elements in the connective tissue septa that separate the muscle segments and thus improve the effectiveness of muscle contractions. Many fishes have both dorsal and ventral ribs, and some have numerous, riblike intermuscular bones as well.

Skull. The skull of bony fishes is highly variable. Bones that may be present in one group of bony fishes may be completely absent in another group. It is convenient to divide the skull into the bones related to the jaws, the **neurocranium** and **operculum.** The jaw bones have undergone significant changes in bony fishes to allow the diversity of feeding types. The upper jaw now consists of both the **maxilla** and **premaxilla.** The lower teeth-bearing jaw bone is the **dentary.**

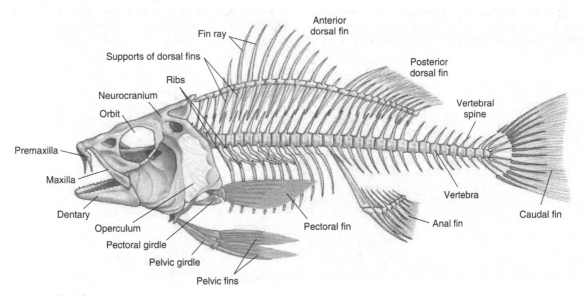

Figure 18-10
Skeleton of a perch.

The neurocranium is the most solid part of the skull and protects the brain. This portion of the skull is made up of many bones, and the exact number varies from one type of bony fish to another. The operculum bones are fairly consistent in form and function across bony fishes, and they protect the gills.

Appendicular Skeleton. This part of the bony fish skeleton consists primarily of support for the various fins. The **dorsal fins** consist of **fin rays** and **supports for the fin rays.** Depending on the species of bony fish, it may have both an anterior and a posterior dorsal fin or just one dorsal fin. The **caudal fin** and **anal fin** have similar bony supports. Most prominently on the appendicular skeleton are the **pelvic girdle** and **pectoral girdle.** The pectoral girdle consists of a series of small bones that support the pectoral fins and allow each fin to articulate independently. The pelvic girdle is simpler and usually consists of a bone on each side. In some bony fishes, the pelvic girdle is connected to the pectoral girdle. What do you think are the primary functions of each fin as they relate to fish swimming? Caudal fin? _____ Dorsal fins? _____ Anal fin? _____ Pectoral fins? _____ Pelvic fins? _____

Muscular System

Although the muscles of a perch are less complex than those of land vertebrates, they make up a much larger mass in relation to body size. Tetrapod locomotion results largely from direct action of muscles on bones of the limbs, but fish locomotion results from indirect action of the segmental muscles—**myomeres**—on the vertebral column, a method by which a large muscle mass produces a relatively small amount of action. This type of movement is efficient in a water medium, but it would be less effective on land. Myomeres (derived from embryonic myotomes) consist of blocks of longitudinal muscle fibers placed on each side of a central axis, the vertebral column. Their contraction, therefore, bends the body, and the action passes in waves down the body, alternating on each side.

 After cutting off the sharp dorsal and ventral spines, skin one side of the body and note the shape of the myomeres.

They resemble Ws that are turned on their sides and stacked together. A horizontal septum of connective tissue divides the muscles into dorsal **epaxial muscles** (Gr. *epi,* upon, + *axis,* axle, meaning above the axis, or vertebral column) and ventral **hypaxial muscles** (Gr. *hypo,* under, + *axis,* axle, meaning below the vertebral column) (Figure 18-11). Posteriorly both epaxial and hypaxial muscles are active in locomotion, but anteriorly hypaxial muscles serve more for support of body viscera than for locomotion. Try to separate the myomeres. Observe the direction of the muscle fibers. Do they run zigzag, as the myomeres seem to? Or are they all directed horizontally—or vertically?

 Now watch the swimming motions of fishes in the aquarium and visualize the use of the body muscles in locomotion. What part do fins play in locomotion?

Dissection of individual muscles in the fish is difficult and will not be attempted here. Muscles operating the jaws, opercula, and fins are often named according to their function and, as in other vertebrates, include adductors, abductors, dilators, levators, and so on (see Exercise 22).

Mouth Cavity, Pharynx, and Respiratory System

Before starting the dissection, it is good, if you have not already done so, to cut off the sharp dorsal and ventral fins to protect the hands.

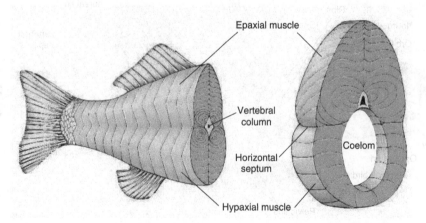

Epaxial muscle

Vertebral column

Horizontal septum

Hypaxial muscle

Coelom

Figure 18-11
Diagram of the skeletal musculature of a teleost fish.

Cut away the operculum from the left side, exposing the gill-bearing bars, or arches. How many arches are there? _____

Cut one gill arch, place in water, and examine with a hand lens or dissecting microscope.

If injected, branchial arteries will be colored. Note **gill filaments** borne on the posterior, or aboral, side of the arch (Figure 18-12A). Are the filaments arranged in a single or double row? _____
It is in these filaments, containing capillaries from the branchial arteries, that exchange of gases takes place. **Gill rakers** on the oral surface of each gill bar strain out food organisms and offer some protection to the gill filaments from food passing through the pharynx.

 Cut through the angle of the left jaw, continuing the cut through the middle of the left gill arches to expose the mouth cavity and pharynx.

Open the mouth wide and note **gill slits** in the pharynx. In the mouth, locate the fine **teeth.** What would be the main function of these teeth? _____ Just

behind the teeth, across the front of both the upper and lower jaw, find the **oral valves.** These are transverse membranes that prevent the outflow of water during respiration. An inflexible **tongue** is supported by the hyoid bone. Explore the **spacious** pharynx, noting the size and arrangement of gill bars and gill slits. Gills separate the **oral cavity** from the **opercular cavity.**

The mechanics of water movement across the gills involve the combined pumping action of both the oral and opercular cavities—a "double-pump" system. The volume of the **oral pump** (mouth cavity) can be changed by raising and lowering the jaw and floor of the mouth. The volume of the **opercular pump** (opercular cavity) can be enlarged and decreased by muscles that swing the operculum in and out. Valves guard the opercular clefts, preventing the backflow of water. The action of the two pumps creates a pressure differential, which maintains a smooth flow of water across the gills throughout nearly the entire breathing cycle.

 Now watch fishes in the aquarium, observing their respiratory movements until you understand the sequence.

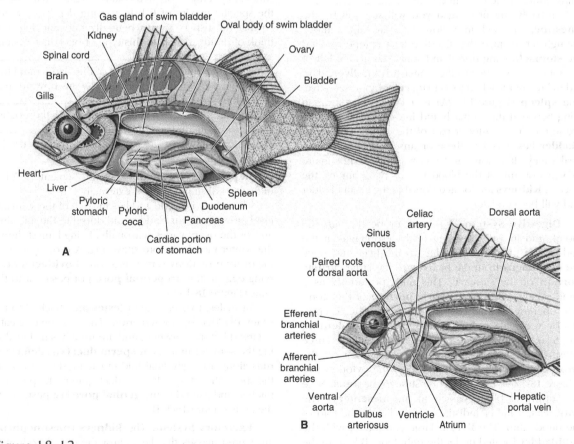

Figure 18-12

Yellow perch. **A,** Internal anatomy. **B,** Principal vessels of the circulatory system.

Water movement across the gills is actually much smoother and less pulsatile than it appears from watching a fish respire. The reason is that the pressure in the opercular cavity is maintained *lower* than the pressure in the mouth cavity for about 90% of the respiratory cycle, and this provides the pressure that drives water across the gills.

Abdominal Cavity

 Starting near the anus and being careful not to injure the internal organs, cut anteriorly on the midventral line to a region anterior to the pelvic fins. Now, on the animal's left body wall, make a transverse cut, extending dorsally from the anal region; make another cut dorsally between the pectoral and pelvic fins; then remove the left body wall by cutting between these two incisions. On the right side, make similar transverse cuts, so that the right wall can be laid back, but do not remove it.

You have now exposed the abdominal cavity. This, together with the **pericardial cavity,** which contains the heart, makes up the **coelomic cavity.** What is the shiny lining of the coelom called? _____

Probably the first organ you will see will be the **intestine,** encased in yellow fat. Carefully remove enough fat to trace the digestive tract anteriorly. Find the **stomach,** lying dorsal and somewhat to the left of the intestine. Anterior to the stomach is the **liver,** dark red in life but bleached to a cream color by preservative. The **spleen** (Figure 18-12A) is a dark, slender organ lying between the stomach and intestine. The **gonads** are in the dorsoposterior part of the cavity. The **swim bladder** lies dorsal to these organs and to the peritoneal cavity. It is long and thin-walled. Do not injure its walls or any of the blood vessels lying among the viscera. **Kidneys** are located dorsal to the swim bladder and will be seen later.

Digestive System. Run your probe through the mouth and into the opening of the esophagus at the end of the pharynx. Now lift up the liver and trace the **esophagus** from the pharynx to the large **cardiac portion** of the stomach. This ends posteriorly as a blind pouch. The short **pyloric portion** of the stomach, opening off the side of the cardiac pouch, empties by way of a **pyloric valve** into the **duodenum,** the S-shaped proximal part of the intestine. Three intestinal diverticula, the **pyloric ceca,** open off the proximal end of the duodenum near the pyloric valve (Figure 18-12A). Follow the intestine to the **anus.** Note the supply of blood vessels in the **mesentery.** The **pancreas,** a rather indistinct organ, lies in the fold of the duodenum. The **liver** is large and lobed, with the **gallbladder** located under the right lobe. Bile from the liver is drained by tubules into the gallbladder, which in turn opens by several ducts into the duodenum posterior to the pyloric ceca.

Cut open the stomach and place its contents in a glass dish with water. Compare with your neighbor's findings. Examine the stomach lining. How is its surface increased? _____ Cut open and examine the pyloric valve. Open a piece of the intestine, wash it, and examine the lining with a dissecting microscope. What type of muscle would you expect to find in the intestine?_____

Swim Bladder. The swim bladder is a long, shiny, thin, but tough-walled sac that fills most of the body cavity dorsal to the visceral organs. In some fishes (not perch), it connects with the alimentary canal. Cut a slit in it and observe its internal structure. In its anterior ventral wall, look for the **gas gland,** which contains a network of capillaries, and the **rete mirabile** (rē′tē muh-rab′uh-lē; L., wonderful net), which assists in secretion of gases, especially oxygen, into the bladder at high pressure. Another capillary bed, the **oval,** lies in the dorsal body wall. Gases are resorbed from the swim bladder in this area. The swim bladder is a "buoyancy tank," or hydrostatic organ, that adjusts the specific gravity of fish to varying depths of water, so that the fish is always neutrally buoyant. Can you think of disadvantages to this type of buoyancy system?

_____

What will happen to the volume of the bladder and to a perch's specific gravity if the perch swims upward from some depth toward the surface? _____ _____When you dissected the dogfish shark, did you find a swim bladder? _____ _____What does a shark use for buoyancy? _____

Reproductive System. Sexes are separate, but it is difficult to distinguish them externally.

The **ovary** is single and lies in back of the stomach, just below the swim bladder and dorsal to the intestine. Size of the ovary varies seasonally, being largest during the winter months before spawning. A prolongation of the ovary posteriorly serves as a sort of **oviduct** for carrying eggs to the **urogenital pore** just posterior to the anus (Figure 18-13A).

In males, two elongated **testes** are attached to the swim bladder by mesenteries. They become greatly enlarged before spawning and are usually smallest during the summer months. A **sperm duct (vas deferens)** runs along a longitudinal fold in each testis adjacent to the spermatic artery. The two ducts join in the posterior midline and extend to the **genital pore** just posterior to the anus (Figure 18-13B).

Excretory System. The **kidneys (mesonephroi)** are paired masses that lie against the dorsal body wall and extend the whole length of the abdomen above the swim bladder. They are often fused posteriorly, but the anterior parts are usually separated by the dorsal aorta. The anterior ends consist largely of blood sinuses and have lost their renal function. In the posterior end, they follow the body wall ventrally. Here the posterior ends of the **mesonephric ducts** (Wolffian ducts) may be seen extending the short distance from the kidneys to a small **urinary bladder,** which lies posteriorly between the gonad and swim bladder. In females the urinary bladder joins the oviduct to form a **urogenital sinus,** emptying through the **urogenital pore.** In males the bladder empties separately through a **urinary pore,** around which there may be a small, external projection of the bladder called the **urinary papilla.** The male urinary and genital pores lie close together posterior to the anus.

Circulatory System

 Extend the midventral incision to the jaw to expose the heart. Enlarge the opening by removing a triangular piece of body wall on each side of the cut.

Heart. The **pericardial cavity** is separated from the abdominal cavity by a **transverse septum.** The septum is not homologous to the diaphragm of mammals.

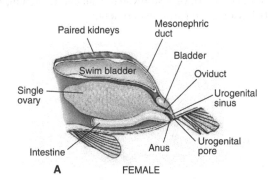

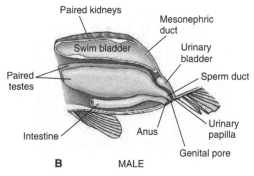

Figure 18-13
Urogenital system. **A,** Female. **B,** Male.

The fish heart is often referred to as a two-chambered heart—a thin-walled **atrium** and muscular **ventricle**—but it actually consists of four chambers in series (see Figure 18-12B). The first chamber is the **sinus venosus,** the thin-walled sac adjoining the atrium posteriorly. The sinus venosus serves as a receiving chamber for venous blood returning from the body, and it helps assure a smooth flow of blood into the second chamber in the series, the atrium. Blood is pumped from the atrium to the ventricle, which, with each contraction (called the **systolic** period of the heartbeat), ejects blood into the final chamber, the **bulbus arteriosus.** When the ventricle contracts, blood pressure rises and is transmitted to the bulbus arteriosus. Then, as the ventricle relaxes (the **diastolic** period of the heartbeat), the high pressure persists in the bulbus arteriosus and maintains an even flow of blood into the ventral aorta. Valves between the bulbus and ventricle prevent backflow of the blood during the diastolic period.

Arterial System. From the bulbus arteriosus, blood flows into the short **ventral aorta** (see Figure 18-12B).

 Remove the operculum and trace the aorta forward.

The ventral aorta gives off four pairs of **afferent branchial arteries** to the branchial arches. From capillaries in the gills, the oxygenated blood is collected by **efferent branchial arteries** and is emptied into two roots of the **dorsal aorta** above. These roots join immediately to form the dorsal aorta.

The dorsal aorta is the major distributing vessel of fish circulation. Branches of the dorsal aorta supply arterial blood to the head, body musculature, swim bladder, and internal organs, such as gut, liver, gonads, and kidney. Note that fish circulation is a **single-circuit** system. All blood leaving the heart passes through at least two sets of capillaries: capillaries of the gills and of the body organs. With the evolution of lungs in tetrapod vertebrates, blood circulation became drastically altered into a **double-circuit** system, with separate pulmonary and systemic circuits.

 Examine fish blood on a slide; note oval **erythrocytes** and various types of **leukocytes.** Do the red cells have nuclei? _____

Oral Report

 Be able to identify the organs and external structures of a perch and give their functions.

Make a comparison between various body systems of a perch and those of an ammocoete larva. Compare with those of a dogfish shark.

EXPERIMENTING IN ZOOLOGY

Aggression in Paradise Fish,
Macropodus opercularis

Many organisms compete for resources that are limited in the environment. These resources can be food, shelter, or mates. Males of many species of animals compete for females. Competition for females often leads to aggressive encounters between conspecific males, and these encounters can escalate into fights that involve physical contact. Thus, natural selection has favored aggressive behavior in males of some species, so much that their aggression is innate (instinctive). Males in these species interact aggressively even when females are not present. Scientists who have observed aggressive interactions between males have suggested that the intensity of encounters can depend on how closely matched the males are in size and strength. Small males can become injured when fighting larger males and may choose not to fight. However, when males are closely matched in size and strength, aggressive encounters tend to be intense as each male attempts to establish its dominance and ultimately its access to the resource (females, in this case).

Paradise fish, *Macropodus opercularis* (Figure 18-14), are tropical fish from Southeast Asia. They have organs in their mouth that allow them to breathe air as well as use their gills. Males are more colorful than females and have red and blue bars running vertically down their body. Several paradise fish can be kept together in a single tank; however, when two males are isolated from the other fish, they begin to display aggressive interactions.

Getting Ready

Work with a partner for this exercise. Try to work in a room that can be darkened. You should have access to a fish tank (approximately 10 to 40 liters) that has an overhead tank light. If an overhead light is not available, illuminate the tank from the side with a small desk lamp. Turning off the room light will minimize the ability of the fish to see you and will minimize their distractions. Have a stopwatch available for timing fish behavior during your experiment.

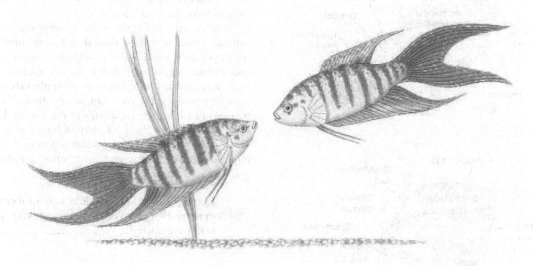

Figure 18-14
Two male paradise fish interacting.

How to Proceed

From a communal tank, select two male paradise fish that appear similar in size and other physical traits. Make sure to add the male fish to the experimental tank at exactly the same time. For the next 15 minutes, quantify the interactions between the males. The easiest way to measure aggressive interactions is to record the amount of time the two males stay very close to each other. You might elect to record all time that the fish spend within one body length of one another. If the two males display aggression to each other, you will notice several different types of behaviors. For example, males might chase each other, raise their dorsal fins, swim parallel very closely together, or even come side to side and vibrate, thereby sending mechanical waves toward each other. If you decide to use categories of behaviors as well as total time spent near each other, you might want to consider observing two "practice" males before starting your experiment, so that you can become familiar enough with the various behaviors to be able to count them during the experiment.

After recording your observations and data from the two males that are closely matched in size, select two new males. This time, however, choose two males that differ conspicuously in size (although make sure you have two males and are not placing a male and female together). Repeat the experiment, keeping track of time the males spend together and the number of aggressive behaviors displayed.

Compile data from the entire class and calculate overall mean times males spend together in closely matched contests versus contests in which males differ in size.

Do males that are closely matched in size interact more than males that differ in size? _____
Do the closely matched males have encounters that escalate into more aggressive behaviors (e.g., biting, nipping) than males that differ in size? _____

Questions for Independent Investigations

1. Keeping the fish matched in size, how might light levels affect aggressive interactions? _____
2. Scientists who study fish aggression have found that individuals that are tank residents are more aggressive than fish that have been recently added to a tank. How could you test this with paradise fish? _____
3. Many kinds of fish have chemical alarm pheromones that are released when a fish is injured. Gently remove a couple of scales from a paradise fish and rinse its body with filtered water. This rinse water may now contain alarm pheromones. Add these chemicals to a tank with two interacting males. How might these chemicals affect the aggression levels of the males? _____ Why? _____
4. What might happen to aggressive interactions if paradise fish are exposed to a potential predator? _____

References

Csanyi, V., J. Haller, and A. Miklosi. 1995. The influence of opponent-related and outcome-related memory on repeated aggressive encounters in paradise fish. Bio. Bull. **188**:83–86.

Francis, R. C. 1983. Experiential effects on agonistic behavior in the paradise fish, *Macropodus opercularis*. Behaviour **85**:292–313.

Gerlai, R. 1993. Can paradise fish recognize a natural predator? An ethological analysis. Ethology **94**:127–136.

Jakobsson, S., O. Brick, and C. Kullberg. 1995. Escalated fighting behaviour incurs increased predation risk. Animal Behav. **49**:235–249.

EXPERIMENTING IN ZOOLOGY
Analysis of the Multiple Hemoglobin System in *Carassius auratus,* Common Goldfish

Carassius, Goldfish

Subphylum Vertebrata
   Class Actinopterygii
      Order Cypriniformes
         Family Cyprinidae (carps and minnows)
            Genus *Carassius*
               Species *Carassius auratus*

Cells require oxygen to utilize aerobic pathways in the production of ATP. For large, multicellular animals, diffusion of oxygen from the environment into the animal is insufficient to supply their metabolic needs. This problem led to the development of complex oxygen exchange surfaces and organs in animals and to the development of oxygen transport molecules within circulatory systems. In vertebrates most oxygen is transported in the blood bound to hemoglobin within red blood cells. Oxygen is picked up by hemoglobin in the gills or lungs at the exchange surfaces and delivered to tissues by circulation of the blood. The hemoglobin molecule in vertebrates consists of four noncovalently linked subunits that form a tetrameric molecule. Typically this tetramer is assembled from two α (alpha) polypeptide chains and two β (beta) polypeptide chains. Each polypeptide subunit of hemoglobin binds a heme group containing a ferrous iron responsible for binding the oxygen molecule (Figure 18-15).

Oxygen availability is relatively constant in the terrestrial environment; however, in the aquatic environment, oxygen availability is highly variable because oxygen solubility in water is dependent upon temperature, ionic concentration, pH, and amount of biomatter consuming or producing oxygen. Cyprinid fishes, which include carp, minnows, and goldfish, often inhabit shallow ponds in which temperature may vary by as much as 10° or 20° C each day. Typically, as the temperature of water increases, oxygen solubility decreases. A change in water temperature from 0° C to 40° C drops dissolved oxygen to about one-half. An additional confounding factor is that animal tissue metabolism increases as temperature increases.

The decrease in oxygen availability, combined with increased oxygen demand as water temperature increases, poses a problem for maintaining aerobic respiration in fishes. One adaptation fish have evolved to deal with variable oxygen availability is to produce multiple forms of hemoglobin. These multiple forms of hemoglobin in fishes may be distinguished electrophoretically (di Prisco and Tamburrini, 1992; Riggs, 1970) and may differ in physiological properties. The differences in physiological properties may allow for enhanced oxygen transport when oxygen availability is low in the environment. Trout are known to have up to nine distinctly different hemoglobin forms (I–IX), whereas goldfish exhibit three different hemoglobin forms, called G_1, G_2, and G_3. These three forms in goldfish vary in concentration as temperature varies, presumably brought about by rapid changes in aggregation of different subunits (Houston and Cyr, 1974; Houston and Rupert, 1976; Houston et al., 1976).

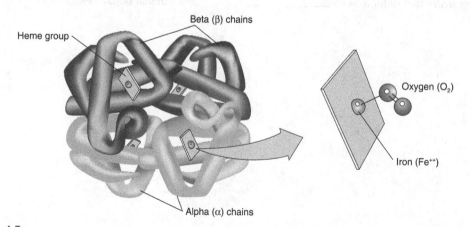

Figure 18-15
Human hemoglobin molecule, showing the four polypeptide chains (two α and two β), each associated with a heme group to which an oxygen molecule will bind.

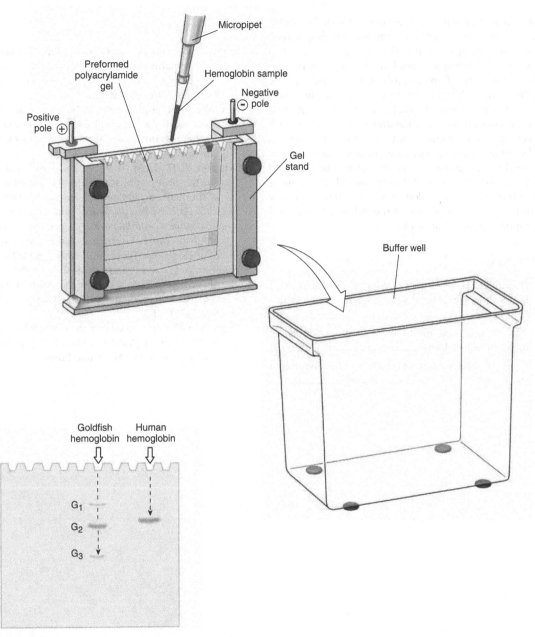

Figure 18-16
Diagram outlining the preparation, loading, and electrophoresis of a vertical polyacrylamide gel to separate the isoforms (G_1, G_2, and G_3) of hemoglobin from goldfish.

How to Proceed*

We can visualize the multiple hemoglobin systems found in common goldfish using simple native polyacrylamide gel electrophoresis. In this procedure, we will remove red blood cells from goldfish that have been maintained in the laboratory at about 20° C to 25° C using a heparinized syringe. (Heparin is a compound that prevents

coagulation of blood removed from the circulatory system.) The cells will be washed in isotonic saline (0.9% NaCl) to remove serum proteins and lysed in distilled water to release the hemoglobins. (Distilled water is hypotonic to the red blood cells; therefore, the cells will swell and burst, releasing hemoglobin and other cellular components.) The hemoglobin lysate will be mixed 1:1 with a loading buffer and a 20 μl sample applied to a well on an 8% native polyacrylamide gel (Figure 18-16). A sample of human hemoglobin

*Additional suggestions for implementation of this exercise are found in Appendix A, p. 412–413.

prepared in the same way as the goldfish hemoglobin will serve as a marker on the gel. Electrophoretic separation will proceed for 30 to 45 minutes at 80 to 90 volts. Following electrophoresis, you should be able to see three faint reddish-orange bands in the goldfish lane indicating the presence of the three isoforms of hemoglobin. Typically the G_2 band (middle band) predominates, whereas the G_1 (upper) and G_3 (lower) bands are fainter. Only one band will appear in the human hemoglobin lane. To assist in visualization of the hemoglobin bands, the gel will be removed from its case, stained with Coomassie Blue dye for a few minutes and then destained to remove dye not bound to protein. A picture of the gel may be taken if appropriate equipment is available.

Questions for Thought

1. How might possession of multiple hemoglobin isoforms allow for adaptation to different environments? _____

2. Why do you think trout have so many different forms of hemoglobin? _____

3. Can you suggest any other species of fish that might show multiple forms of hemoglobin? _____

References

di Prisco, G., and M. Tamburrini. 1992. The hemoglobins of marine and freshwater fish: the search for correlations with physiological adaptation. Comp. Biochem. Physiol. **102B:**661–671.

Houston, A. H., and D. Cyr. 1974. Thermoacclimatory variation in the haemoglobin systems of goldfish *(Carassius auratus)* and rainbow trout *(Salmo gairdneri).* J. Exp. Biol. **61:**455–461.

Houston, A. H., K. M. Mearow, and J. S. Smeda. 1976. Further observations upon the hemoglobin systems of thermally acclimated freshwater teleosts: pumpkinseed *(Lepomis gibbosus),* white sucher *(Catostomus commersoni),* carp *(Cyprinus carpio),* goldfish *(Carassius auratus)* and carp-goldfish hybrids. Comp. Biochem. Physiol. **54A:**267–273.

Houston, A. H., and R. Rupert. 1976. Immediate response of the hemoglobin system of the goldfish, *Carassius auratus,* to temperature change. Can. J. Zool. **54:**1737–1741.

Riggs, A. 1970. Properties of fish hemoglobins. In Hoar, W. S., and D. J. Randall, (eds.). Fish physiology. Vol. 4. New York, Academic Press.

EXERCISE **19**

The Amphibians
Frogs

Amphibians are a transition group between aquatic and the strictly land vertebrates. They have the soft, moist epidermis of aquatic forms and therefore cannot stray far from water or moist surroundings. Amphibian eggs lack the tough protective shell and specialized extra embryonic membranes characteristic of eggs of terrestrial vertebrates and so remain adapted to an aquatic habitat. Many amphibians have developed lungs for air breathing but still have aquatic larvae with external gills. A moist skin serves also as a respiratory organ. Evolution of lungs has brought a change in circulation that includes a pulmonary circuit as well as a systemic circuit. Amphibians have a three-chambered heart (two atria and one ventricle). They are usually four-limbed for walking or jumping but many have webbed feet for swimming.

Frogs and toads belong to order Anura (Gr. *an,* without, + *oura,* tail), the largest and most diverse group of living amphibians. Anurans differ from salamanders (order Urodela) and tropical caecilians (order Gymnophiona) in several distinctive ways that are associated with a specialized jumping mode of locomotion. A frog's body is extremely shortened and virtually fused with the head, an adaptation that provides rigidity to the skeletal framework. It lacks true ribs. Caudal vertebrae (which would normally form the tail) are fused into a single, pillarlike bone, the urostyle. The hindlegs are much larger and more powerful than the forelegs. Anurans are the most diverse of the amphibians and are commonly used in the general zoology laboratory because of their availability. The large bullfrog, *Rana catesbeiana,* and the small leopard frog, *Rana pipiens,* are commonly used for dissection.

Frogs

Phylum Chordata
    Subphylum Vertebrata
        Class Amphibia
            Order Anura (= Salientia)
                Family Ranidae
                    Genus *Rana*

EXERCISE 19A
Behavior and Adaptations
Frogs

EXERCISE 19B
Skeleton

EXERCISE 19C
Skeletal Muscles
Directions for study of frog muscles

EXERCISE 19D
Digestive, Respiratory, and Urogenital Systems
Mouthparts
Dissection of a frog

EXERCISE 19E
Circulatory System

EXERCISE 19F
Nervous System
Demonstrations

Where Found

Ranid frogs (family Ranidae) are almost worldwide in distribution. Favorite habitats are swamps, low meadows, brooks, and ponds, where they feed on flies and other insects. Their young, tadpoles, develop in water and are herbivorous. It should be noted that ranids, like many groups of frogs, appear to be declining in number around the world. It is not entirely known what might be causing the decline, but many scientists are now investigating the conservation biology of amphibians.

EXERCISE 19A
Behavior and Adaptations

 Place a live frog on a piece of wet paper towel in a jar large enough not to cramp it. Do not let its skin become dry. Do not excite it unnecessarily.

Observe its adaptations. Make notes of your observations. Have a mounted frog skeleton at your table for comparison.

Is the skin smooth or rough? Moist or dry? Examine the frog's feet. How are they adapted for jumping? For swimming? For landing on a slippery rock or log? Note the sitting position and compare with the mounted skeleton. In what ways is the body form of a frog adapted as a lever system that can catapult the animal into the air? _____

Compare the color of the dorsal and ventral sides. Imagine a predator approaching a swimming frog from above or from below. What is the protective advantage in this dorsal-ventral difference in coloration? _____

Knowing that a frog captures prey by striking at it with its protrusable tongue, how is the position of the eyes advantageous to the animal? _____ _____ How do the eyes close? _____ Examine the skeleton and see how this is possible. Note the transparent nictitating membrane. How is it used? _____

Feeding Reactions. Place live fruit flies or mealworms in the jar with the frog. If the frog is hungry and is not excited, it may feed. Describe how it seizes prey.

Breathing. Observe movement of the throat and nostrils. Air is drawn into the mouth; then the nostrils close and throat muscles contract to force the air into the lungs. This form of breathing is called positive pressure breathing. The nostrils (nares) can be opened or closed at will. Record the number of movements per minute of the throat and then of the nostrils. _____ Do their rates coincide? _____ Do the sides of the body move in breathing? _____ Excite the animal by prodding; then, as soon as it becomes quiescent, count the rate of breathing again.

Righting Reaction. Place the frog on its back, release it, and note how it rights itself. Repeat this experiment, but hold the frog down gently with your hand until it ceases to struggle. When you release it, the frog may remain in this so-called hypnotic state for some time.

Locomotion. Observe a frog in an aquarium. What is the floating position? How does it use its limbs in swimming? How does it dive from a floating position? Note how it jumps.

Written Report

Record your observations on p. 300.

External Structure

Study a preserved frog and compare it with a live frog and a mounted skeleton.

Note the **head** and **trunk.** Note the **sacral hump** produced by the protrusion of the pelvic girdle. Find this hump on the mounted skeleton. The **cloacal opening** is at the posterior end of the body.

On the **forelimbs,** identify the arm, forearm, wrist, hand, and digits. On the **hindlimbs,** find the thigh, shank, ankle, foot, and digits. How does the number of digits compare with your own? _____ Can you find the rudimentary thumb (prepollux) and the rudimentary sixth toe (prehallux)? During breeding season, the inner (thumb) digit of males is enlarged into a nuptial pad for clasping a female. Observe the **webbed** toes of the hindfoot. How is a long ankle advantageous to a frog? _____

The **eyes** are protected by **eyelids** and by a transparent **nictitating membrane** (L. *nictare,* to wink). Look in the corner of your neighbor's eye for a vestige of this membrane, the semilunar fold.

The **tympanic membrane** (eardrum) is a circular region of tightly drawn skin just back of the eye. The frog has no external ear—only the middle and internal ears.

Identification

Label the external parts of the frog in the drawing on p. 299.

Class _____

Order _____

Genus _____

Name _____

Date _____

Section _____

External Anatomy of Leopard Frog

LAB REPORT

Observations on Behavior of a Frog

Feeding reaction _____

_____

_____

_____

Breathing _____

_____

_____

_____

Reaction to touch _____

_____

_____

_____

Righting reaction _____

_____

_____

_____

Locomotion _____

_____

_____

_____

Other observations _____

_____

_____

_____

_____

_____

EXERCISE 19B
Skeleton

Shaping the Body for Life on Land

In amphibians, as in fishes, a well-developed skeleton provides a framework for the muscles in movement and protection for the viscera and nervous systems. Movement onto land and the development of tetrapod legs capable of supporting the body's weight introduced a new set of stress and leverage problems. These changes are most noticeable in frogs and toads, where the entire musculoskeletal system is specialized for jumping and swimming by simultaneous extensor thrusts of the hindlimbs. Frogs no longer move in the typical sinuous, or fishlike, motion of their aquatic ancestors. Consequently the vertebral column has lost its flexibility and, together with the enlarged pelvic girdle, has become a rigid frame for transmitting force from the hindlimbs to the body.

 Prepared skeletons are brittle and delicate. Handle them with care and do not deface the bones in any way. Use a probe or dissecting needle, not a pencil, in pointing.

The **axial** (L., axis) **skeleton** includes the skull, vertebral column, and sternum. The **appendicular** (L. *ad,* to, + *pendare,* to hang) **skeleton** includes the pectoral and pelvic girdles, forelimbs, and hindlimbs.

For a discussion of the structure and growth of bones and their articulations, see Exercise 22A.

Axial Skeleton

Skull. The skull and jaws of a frog serve as protection for the brain and special sense organs. As with the rest of the frog skeleton, it is vastly altered as compared with early amphibian ancestors. It is much lighter in weight, is more flattened in profile, and contains fewer bones and less ossification. The front part of the skull, with locations for the eyes, nose, and brain, is better developed, whereas the back of the skull, which in fishes contains gill apparatus, is much reduced. A lighter skull was essential to mobility on land, and the other changes fitted the frog for its improved senses and means of feeding and breathing.

The skull (Figure 19-1) includes the **cranium,** or braincase; **visceral skeleton,** made up of bones and cartilage of the jaws; hyoid apparatus; and little bones of the ears. All these elements of the visceral skeleton*

are derived from the jaws and gill apparatus of fish ancestors. The **orbital fossae** and **nasal fossae** are dorsal openings where the eyes and external nares are located.

Locate on the dorsal side of the skull the **nasal** bones; the single **sphenethmoid** (Gr. *sphēn,* wedge, + *ēthmos,* sieve, + *eidos,* form); the long **frontoparietals,** which cover much of the brain; the **prootics** (pro'ah-ticks; Gr. *pro,* before, + *ous,* ear), which enclose the inner ears; the **exoccipitals** (L. *ex,* without, + *occiput,* back of the head), which surround the hindpart of the brain; and the **foramen magnum,** the opening for the spinal cord.

The jaws of a frog combine lightness and strength with large mouth size for eating insects and other prey. (Some tropical frogs resemble walking mouths!) The upper jaw is formed by the **premaxillae, maxillae** (L., jaw), and **quadratojugals** (L. *quadratus,* squared, + *jugam,* yolk). Which bones bear teeth? _____ The **squamosal** (L. *squama,* scale) supports the cartilaginous **auditory capsule.** The three-pronged **pterygoid** (ter'uh-goid; Gr. *pteryx,* wing, + *eidos,* form) articulates with the maxillary, prootic, and quadratojugal (Figure 19-1).

On the ventral surface of the skull, find the wing-shaped **vomers** (L., ploughshare) (**vomerine teeth** are projections of these bones); slender **palatines** (L. *palatum,* palate); and dagger-shaped **parasphenoid** (Gr. *para,* beside, + *sphēn,* wedge, + *eidos,* form), which forms the floor of the braincase. Cartilages form the sides of the braincase.

The lower jaw **(mandible)** consists of small **mentomeckelians** (L. *mentum,* chin, + J. F. Meckel, German anatomist), long **dentary** bones, and **angulosplenials** (L. *angulus,* corner, + *splenium,* patch).

The **hyoid** (Gr. *hyoeidēs,* Y-shaped) **apparatus,** the much reduced and transformed remnants of gill arches, lies in the floor of the mouth. It may be missing in prepared skeletons, or it may be mounted separately. It is cartilaginous and supports the tongue and larynx.

In some preparations, the **columella,** a small bone used in the transmission of sound, is found in the auditory capsule.

Vertebral Column. The backbone of a frog consists of only nine vertebrae and a **urostyle** (Gr. *oura,* tail, + *stylos,* pillar), the latter representing fusion of several caudal vertebrae. The first vertebra, the **atlas** (Gr. *Atlas,* a Titan of Greek mythology, who bore the heavens on his shoulders), articulates with the skull. The ninth, or **sacral*** (L. *sacer,* sacred), vertebra has transverse processes for articulation with the ilia of the pelvic girdle.

---

*The term "visceral" (from the Latin *viscera,* bowels) refers to elements and structures of the body associated with the gut tube. The visceral skeleton represents specialized parts of the primitive gut of jawed vertebrates.

*The origin of the term "sacrum," meaning holy bone, is unknown. It is speculated that the curved appearance of the human sacrum suggested to Renaissance anatomists a resemblance to an obsidian knife used in ancient sacrifice.

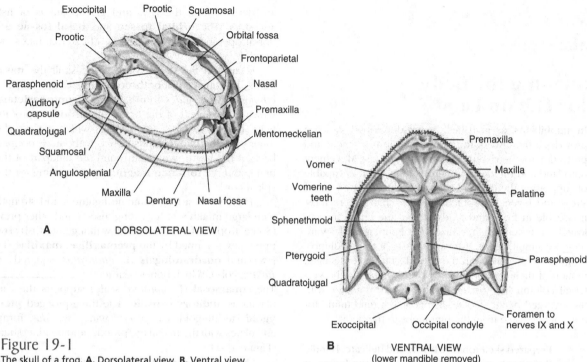

A   DORSOLATERAL VIEW

B   VENTRAL VIEW
(lower mandible removed)

Figure 19-1
The skull of a frog. **A,** Dorsolateral view. **B,** Ventral view.

 With the help of Figure 19-2, identify the parts of a vertebra.

No frogs of the large family Ranidae have ribs either as larvae or adults; ribs do appear, however, in two other frog families.

The sternum (L., breastbone) provides ventral protection for the heart and lungs and a center for muscular attachment. Its four parts, beginning at the anterior end, are the **episternum** (Gr. *epi*, upon), a cartilaginous, rounded end often not seen in prepared skeletons; **omosternum** (Gr. *omos*, shoulder); **mesosternum** (Gr. *mesos*, middle), the section located posterior of the coracoid bone of the pectoral girdle; and **xiphisternum** (Gr. *xiphos*, sword), a cartilaginous, heart-shaped end often not present on prepared skeletons. The episternum and omosternum are not visible in Figure 19-3.

Appendicular Skeleton

Pectoral Girdle and Forelimbs. The pectoral girdle serves as support for the forelimbs, which, in frogs, are used mainly to absorb the shock of landing after a jump. The pectoral girdle articulates with the sternum ventrally. Each half of the girdle includes a suprascapula and scapula (L., shoulder blade) and a clavicle (collar bone) (L. *clavicula*, small key) lying anterior to the coracoid (Gr. *korax*, crow, + *eidos*, form). Consult Figure 19-3 for the bones of the forelimb.

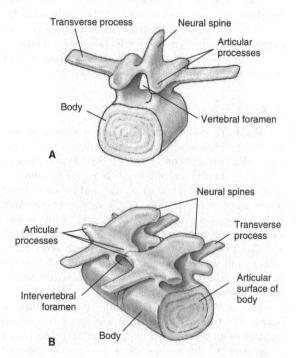

Figure 19-2
Frog vertebrae. **A,** Anterior view. **B,** Two vertebrae, posterior lateral view showing articulations.

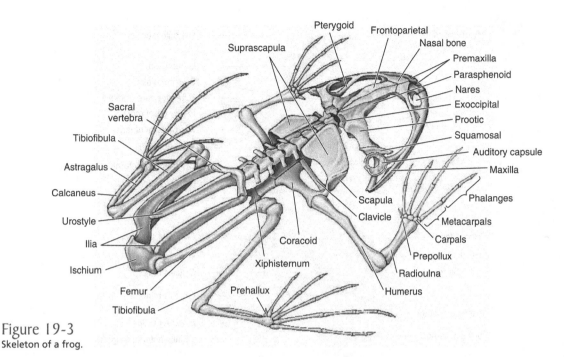

Figure 19-3
Skeleton of a frog.

Pelvic Girdle and Hindlimbs. The pelvic girdle supports the hindlimbs. Each half is made up of a long **ilium** (L., flank), an anterior **pubis** (L. *pubes,* mature), and a posterior **ischium** (Gr. *ischion,* hip). Consult Figure 19-3 for the bones of the hindlimb.

Oral Report

 Be familiar with the parts of the skeleton and the purpose served by each part.

EXERCISE 19C
Skeletal Muscles

A frog has hundreds of muscles, but this exercise describes only the most important ones (more correctly, the most conspicuous ones, since they are all important to a frog).

If you learn a few of the Greek and Latin roots of some of the muscle names, they will give you clues to their orientation or action. For example, **rectus** means straight, so the fibers of rectus muscles generally run along the long axis of the body. **Gracilis** means slender. **Triceps** means three heads, and this muscle has three tendons of origin; the **biceps** has two heads of origin. Long muscles are called **longus** and short muscles are called **brevis**; large muscles are termed **magnus** or **major. Anticus** means anterior. Other muscles are named for specific movements. The **sartorius** is derived from the Latin word for tailor and is homologous to a human muscle of the same name that is active in crossing the legs (tailors, before the days of sewing machines, sat on the floor with crossed legs). The **gastrocnemius** (Gr. *gaster,* stomach, + *kneme,* tibia) is named for its fat "belly."

NOTE: You will also need some familiarity with the terminology relating to muscle connections and their actions. Refer to the general discussion of skeletal muscles in Exercise 22B.

Directions for Study of Frog Muscles

 To skin the frog, slit the skin midventrally from anal region to chin, keeping the scissors point up to prevent injuring the underlying muscles. Make a transverse cut completely around the body just above the hindlegs and another one anterior to the forelegs. A middorsal cut the length of the back will divide the skin into portions that can be peeled off easily. Loosen the skin with a blunt instrument and carefully pull off over a leg. Be careful not to tear thin muscle attached to the skin. The skin can be pulled over the head and eyes in the same way.

The large spaces between skin and muscle where the skin is not attached are **subcutaneous lymph sacs.**

 In separating muscles from each other, first observe the direction of the muscle fibers and the extent of the muscle; then use your fingers, a blunt probe,

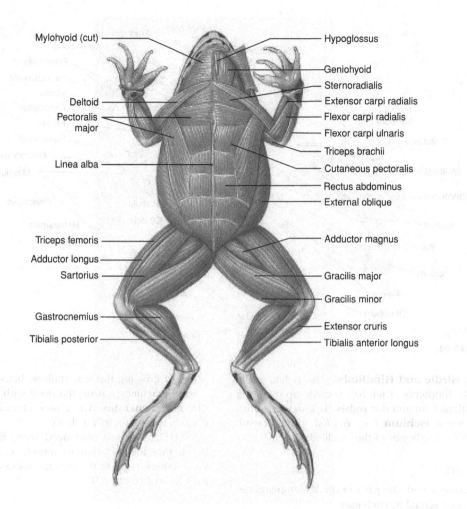

Mylohyoid (cut)

Hypoglossus

Geniohyoid

Sternoradialis

Extensor carpi radialis

Flexor carpi radialis

Flexor carpi ulnaris

Triceps brachii

Deltoid

Pectoralis
major

Cutaneous pectoralis

Linea alba

Rectus abdominus

External oblique

Triceps femoris

Adductor magnus

Adductor longus

Sartorius

Gracilis major

Gracilis minor

Gastrocnemius

Extensor cruris

Tibialis posterior

Tibialis anterior longus

Figure 19-4
Muscles of a frog, ventral view.

or the *handle* of a scalpel to loosen the tissues. *Never use scissors, a scalpel blade, or a needle for dissecting muscles.* Never cut a muscle unless instructed to do so. If it is necessary to cut superficial muscles to find deep muscles, cut squarely across the belly (middle fleshy portion) of the muscle, leaving the origin and insertion in place.

Trunk Muscles

The trunk muscles of a frog, no longer required to produce the lateral flexion movements of the amphibians' swimming ancestors, have been modified to brace the back and to support the viscera in air. The ventral trunk muscles (Table 19-1) are arranged in layers that run in different directions. The **rectus abdominis** runs longitudinally, forming a sling from pubis to sternum (Figure 19-4). In the midventral line is a thin but tough band of connective tissue, the **linea alba** (literally, "white line"). Inserting on the linea alba are

two oblique muscle bands, the **external oblique** and the **transversus,** the latter lying beneath the external oblique and rectus abdominis. (The transversus is not shown in Figure 19-4 or 19-5.) These assist the rectus abdominis in supporting the viscera.

Thigh Muscles

A frog's limb muscles are derived from muscles that raised and lowered the fins of fishes, now much modified to brace and move the limbs for walking and thrust-swimming. Not surprisingly limb muscles are complex because they perform several actions. Nevertheless, we can recognize two major groups of muscles on any limb: an anterior and ventral group that pulls the limb forward (protraction) and toward the midline (adduction) and a second set of posterior and dorsal muscles that draws the limb back (retraction) and away from the body (abduction). Only the more conspicuous thigh muscles are included in this study (Table 19-1).

TABLE 19.1

Major Trunk and Leg Muscles of Frogs

Muscle	Origin	Insertion	Action
Ventral Trunk Muscles			
Pectoralis	Sternum and fascia of body wall	Humerus	Flexes, adducts, and rotates arm
Rectus abdominis	Pubic border	Sternum	Supports abdominal viscera
External oblique	Dorsal fascia of vertebrae, also ilium	Sternum, linea alba	Constricts abdomen and supports viscera
Transversus	Ilium and vertebrae	Linea alba	Helps support abdominal viscera
Ventral Thigh Muscles			
Sartorius	Pubis	Tibiofibula	Flexes shank and adducts thigh
Adductor magnus	Pubic and ischial symphysis	Distal end of femur	Adducts and flexes thigh
Gracilis major	Ischium	Tibiofibula	Adducts thigh and flexes or extends shank, according to its position
Gracilis minor	Ischium	Tibiofibula	Same as gracilis major
Adductor longus	Ilium	Femur	Adducts thigh
Dorsal Thigh Muscles			
Triceps femoris	Three divisions: one head on acetabulum, two on ilium	Tibiofibula	Abducts thigh and extends lower leg
Biceps femoris	Ilium	Tibiofibula	Flexes shank
Semimembranosus	Ischium	Tibiofibula	Adducts thigh and flexes or extends shank, according to its position
Gluteus	Ilium	Femur	Rotates thigh forward
Shank Muscles			
Gastrocnemius	Two heads: distal end of femur and tendon from triceps femoris	By Achilles tendon to sole of foot	Flexes shank and extends ankle and foot
Peroneus	Femur	Distal end of tibiofibula; head of calcaneus	Extends shank; when foot is extended, extends it farther; when flexed, flexes it farther
Tibialis anterior longus	Femur; divides into two bellies	By two tendons on ankle bones	Extends shank; flexes ankle
Extensor cruris	Femur	Ventral surface of tibiofibula	Extends shank
Tibialis posterior	Side of tibiofibula	Ankle	Extends foot when flexed; flexes foot when fully extended

In the first group (protractors and adductors) are the **sartorius, adductor magnus, gracilis major, adductor longus** (visible on the ventral surface, Figure 19-4), **biceps femoris,** and **gracilis minor** (visible on dorsal surface, Figure 19-5). All of these draw the limb forward and toward the midline or flex more distal parts of the limb. In the second group (retractors and abductors) is the **triceps femoris,** a large muscle of three divisions, all of which abduct the thigh and extend the lower leg (Figure 19-5).

Shank Muscles

The most conspicuous shank muscle is the **gastrocnemius,** which extends from the femur to the foot and inserts by the Achilles tendon; it extends the ankle during jumping and swimming. Because the gastrocnemius is easily dissected out together with the sciatic nerve that innervates it, it is commonly used in physiological studies of skeletal muscle. The ankle is flexed by the **tibialis anticus longus** and other muscles not shown

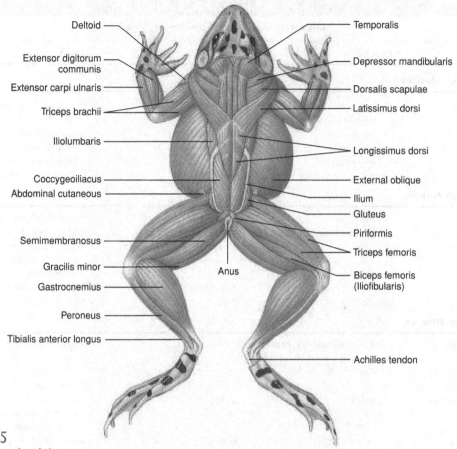

Deltoid

Extensor digitorum communis

Extensor carpi ulnaris

Triceps brachii

Iliolumbaris

Coccygeoiliacus

Abdominal cutaneous

Semimembranosus

Gracilis minor

Gastrocnemius

Peroneus

Tibialis anterior longus

Temporalis

Depressor mandibularis

Dorsalis scapulae

Latissimus dorsi

Longissimus dorsi

External oblique

Ilium

Gluteus

Piriformis

Triceps femoris

Biceps femoris (Iliofibularis)

Anus

Achilles tendon

Figure 19-5
Muscles of a frog, dorsal view.

in Figure 19-5. The major action of the **peroneus** is to flex the ankle joint and extend the shank.

If the frog you are dissecting is in the *Rana* group, it likely has well-developed leg muscles for swimming and jumping. Toads, another large group of frogs, are toxic and have less developed hindlimb muscles. Why might a toxic animal have less developed leg muscles?

_____

_____

Other Muscles

With the help of Figures 19-4 and 19-5, you can identify many of the muscles of the back, shoulder, head, and arm.

How the Muscles Act

A muscle has only one function—to contract. For effective action, muscles must be arranged in antagonistic pairs. The gastrocnemius and tibialis anticus longus represent such an antagonistic pair. Loosen the body of each of these muscles, pull on the gastrocnemius,

and see what happens. Now pull on the tibialis anticus longus. Which of these muscles would be used in jumping or diving? _____ Which in sitting? _____ See whether you can locate other antagonistic pairs.

For most movements, groups of muscles rather than single muscles are required. By varying the combination of these groups, many complicated movements are possible.

Oral Report

 Be able to demonstrate a careful dissection of the muscles and to name the muscles and their actions.

Written Report

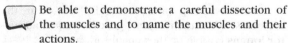 On separate paper, tell (1) what principal muscles of the hindleg are involved when a frog leaps and (2) when the frog resumes a sitting position, what principal muscles contract.

Name _____

Date _____

Section _____

Principal Leg Muscles Involved in Leaping

Principal Leg Muscles Involved in Sitting

EXERCISE 19D
Digestive, Respiratory, and Urogenital Systems

Mouthparts

 Pry open the mouth, cutting the angle of the jaw if necessary, and wash in running water.

The posterior portion of the mouth cavity is the **pharynx**, which connects with the **esophagus.** Feel the **maxillary teeth** along the upper jaw and the **vomerine teeth** in the roof of the mouth (Figure 19-6). Are these better adapted for biting and chewing or for holding prey to prevent escape? _____
Find the **internal nares** (sing. **naris**) in the roof of the mouth and note how they connect with the external nares. Note how the ridge on the lower jaw fits into a groove in the upper jaw to make the mouth closure airtight. This is important for a frog's respiratory movements.

Eustachian tubes, which connect with and equalize air pressure in the middle ear, open near the angle of the jaws. In male frogs, openings on the floor of the mouth slightly anterior to the eustachian tubes lead to **vocal sacs,** which, when inflated, serve as resonators to intensify the mating call. Examine the **tongue** and note where it is attached. Which end of the tongue is flipped out to catch insects? _____ Feel the **sensory papillae** on the tongue surface. The free end of the tongue is highly glandular and produces a sticky secretion that adheres to the prey. Behind the tongue is a slight elevation in the floor of the mouth, containing the **glottis,** a slitlike opening into the **larynx.**

Dissection of a Frog

 Make an incision through the abdominal wall from the junction of the hindlegs to the lower jaw, cutting through the bones of the pectoral girdle as you go. Make transverse cuts anterior to the hindlegs and posterior to the forelegs, and pin back the flaps of muscular tissue.

Note the three layers of the body wall: **skin, muscles** (with enclosed skeleton in some places), and **peritoneum,** which lines the large **coelom.**
In mature females, the ovaries, with their dark masses of eggs, may fill much of the coelomic cavity. In this case, remove the left ovary and its white, convoluted oviduct.
Note the **heart** enclosed in its **pericardial sac** and surrounded by lobes of the **liver.** Lift up the heart to find the **lungs.**

Digestive System

The digestive tract is relatively short in adult amphibians, a characteristic of most carnivores. The larval (tadpole) stages of frogs, however, are herbivorous, feeding on pond algae and other vegetation. They have a relatively long digestive tract because their bulky food must be submitted to time-consuming fermentation before useful products can be absorbed.
You have seen the **mouth** and **pharynx.** Lift the heart, liver, and lungs to see where the **esophagus** empties into the stomach (Figure 19-7). A **pyloric valve** controls movements of food into the **small intestine.** Note the blood vessels in the mesentery, which holds the stomach and small intestine in place. Why must the digestive tract be so well supplied with blood?

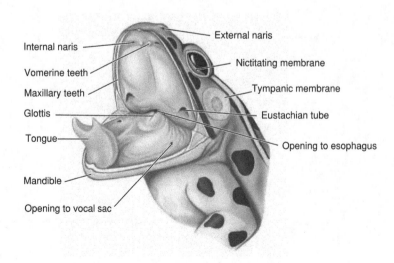

Figure 19-6
Mouthparts of a frog.

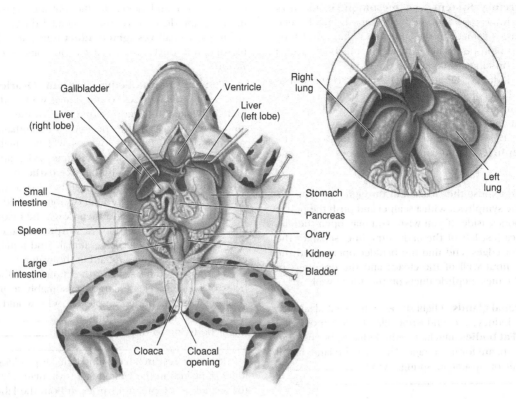

Figure 19-7
Abdominal cavity of a frog, ventral view. **Right,** the liver has been lifted up and turned back to expose the lungs.

The **liver,** the largest gland in the body, secretes bile, which is carried by a small duct to the **gallbladder** for storage. Find the gallbladder between the right and median lobes of the liver. The **pancreas** is thin and inconspicuous, lying in the mesentery between the stomach and duodenum.

The **large intestine** narrows down in the pelvic region to form the **cloaca,** which also receives urine from the kidneys and products from the reproductive organs. It empties through the **cloacal opening.** Not all vertebrate animals have cloacas; mammals do not.

Respiratory System

Amphibians breathe through their skin **(cutaneous respiration)** as well as with their lungs (although some adult amphibians do not have lungs and rely primarily on gas exchange through the skin). Some respiration also occurs through the lining of the mouth, which is highly vascular. Cutaneous respiration is very important for a frog, especially in winter, when it burrows into the bottom mud of ponds and ceases all lung breathing.

A frog has no diaphragm. Thus, it draws air into its mouth cavity through nares by closing the **glottis** (opening into the windpipe) and depressing the floor

of its mouth. Then, by closing the nares and raising the floor of its mouth cavity, it forces air from the mouth through the glottis into the lungs (positive pressure breathing). Air is expelled from the lungs by contraction of the muscles of the body wall and elastic recoil of the stretched lung.

 Probe through the **glottis** into the **larynx.** Find the short **bronchus,** connecting each **lung** to the larynx. Slit open a lung and observe its internal structure.

Note the little pockets, or **alveoli** (sing. **alveolus**), in the lining. What is the purpose of this arrangement? Did you find any parasites in the lungs of your specimen? _____ Can you identify them (refer to page 150)? _____

Urogenital System

Functionally the urogenital system is two systems—the **urinary,** or **excretory system,** and the **reproductive system.** However, because some structures function in both systems, they are usually considered together.

Be careful not to injure blood vessels as you study this system.

Excretory System. The **mesonephric kidneys** separate urine from blood. They rid the body of metabolic wastes (aided by the lungs and skin), and they maintain a proper water balance in the body and a general constancy of content in the blood.

The kidneys (Figure 19-8) lie close to the dorsal body wall, separated from the coelom by a thin peritoneum. The **urinary bladder,** when collapsed, appears as a soft mass of thin tissue just ventral to the large intestine. It is bilobed and empties into the cloaca. The **mesonephric ducts** connect the kidneys with the cloaca.

 To expose the cloaca, cut through the ischiopubic symphysis with a scalpel and push the pelvic bones aside. If you wish, you may open the cloaca just left of the midventral line, separate the cut edges, and find the bladder opening on the ventral wall of the cloaca and the openings of the mesonephric ducts on the dorsal wall.

Adrenal glands, a light stripe on the ventral surface of each kidney, are endocrine glands, not urogenital organs. **Fat bodies** attached to the kidneys, but lying in the coelom, are for fat storage. They may be large in fall and small or absent in spring. Why? _____

_____

Male Reproductive System. A small, pale **testis** lies on the ventral side of each kidney (Figure 19-8). Sperm pass from the testis into some of the kidney tubules and then are carried by the mesonephric ducts

to the cloaca and hence to the outside. Thus, male mesonephric ducts serve also as genital ducts. In leopard frogs, a small **vestigial oviduct** runs parallel to the mesonephric ducts (this is absent in some species of *Rana*).

Female Reproductive System. Ovaries are attached by mesenteries to the dorsal wall of the coelom. In winter and early spring, the ovaries are distended with eggs. If the specimen was euthanized in summer or early fall, the ovaries will be small, pale, and fan-shaped. Convoluted **oviducts** widen anteriorly (dorsal to the lungs) into funnel-like **ostia** and posteriorly into **uteri,** which empty into the cloaca. Eggs are released from the ovary into the coelom, carried in coelomic fluid to the ostia, and then down the oviducts by ciliary action to the outside. At **amplexus** (the courtship embrace) a male clasps a female and fertilizes the eggs externally as they are laid in the water.

During breeding season, the thumbs of the male frogs of some species enlarge, presumably to assist in clasping a female during amplexus. Why would a male need to clasp a female so firmly? _____ What might be trying to displace the male? _____

_____

Recently, research has found that a top-selling weed killer (atrazine) in the United States dramatically affects the sexual development of frogs in both the laboratory and the field. Male frogs exposed to the herbicide show indications of being hermaphrodites, with the development of both testes and ovaries. Does your frog show any of these signs? _____

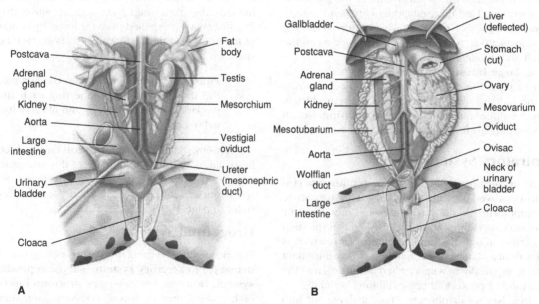

Figure 19-8
Urogenital system of a frog, ventral views. **A,** Male. **B,** Female.

Oral Report

Be able to demonstrate your dissection and give the functions of the structures you have studied.

Trace the route of food through the digestive tract and tell what happens to it at each stage.

Trace the route of eggs and spermatozoa and be able to explain the anatomy and physiology of excretion and reproduction.

Understand the mechanics and physiology of respiration and tell how the mechanics of respiration in frogs differ from those in humans.

EXERCISE 19E
Circulatory System

The shift from gill to lung breathing during the evolution of amphibians required important changes in circulation. Two new problems arose. The first was to provide a blood circuit to the lungs. This was accomplished by converting the last pair of aortic arches (which in fishes carried blood through the last gill arch) into **pulmonary arteries** to serve the lungs. New **pulmonary veins** then developed to return oxygenated blood to the heart. The second problem was to separate this new **pulmonary circuit** from the rest of the body's circulation such that oxygenated blood from the lungs would be selectively sent to the body and deoxygenated blood from the body would be sent to the lungs. This was achieved by partitioning the heart into a double pump, with each side serving each circuit. In this way, a **double circulation** comprising separate **pulmonary** and **systemic** circuits was formed. As you will see in your dissection of a frog, amphibians approached this modification only partway: the atrium, which was single in fish, is completely divided into two atria, but the ventricle remains undivided. Complete separation is seen in birds and mammals, which have completely divided hearts of two atria and two ventricles.

To assist your study of circulation, you will dissect a frog that has had the arterial system injected with red or yellow latex and the venous system with blue latex. If only the arteries are injected, the veins may be filled with dark, clotted blood.

Dissect carefully and do not cut or injure the blood vessels. With a probe, you may loosen the connective tissue that holds them in place. Cut away a midsection of the pectoral girdle and pin back the arms, so that the heart is fully exposed. Carefully remove the **pericardium,** the sac that contains the heart.

Identify the thick-walled, conical **ventricle** (Figures 19-9 and 19-10); the thin-walled **left and right atria;** the

conus arteriosus, arising from the ventricle and dividing to form the **truncus arteriosus** on each side; and, on the dorsal side of the heart, the thin-walled **sinus venosus,** formed by convergence of three large veins—two **precaval veins** and one **postcaval vein.***

Venous System

The **precava (anterior vena cava)** (Figure 19-10) is formed by the union of (1) the **external jugular** from the tongue and floor of the mouth; (2) the **innominate** (L. *in,* not, + *nomen,* named), made up from the **subscapular vein** from the shoulder and the **internal jugular** (L. *jugulum,* collarbone) from the brain; and (3) the **subclavian** (L. *sub,* under, + *clavus,* key, below the clavicle), which receives blood from the arm and dorsal body wall.

The **postcava (posterior vena cava)** extends from the sinus venosus through the liver to the region between the kidneys. It receives **hepatic veins** from the liver, **renal veins** from each kidney, and **ovarian** or **spermatic veins** from the gonads.

Pulmonary veins transport blood from the lungs to the left atrium. How does oxygen content of the blood in these veins differ from that in any other vein? _____

Portal Systems

Ordinarily veins carry blood directly from a capillary bed to the heart. This plan is interrupted in amphibians by capillary beds in two portal systems—the hepatic portal and renal portal systems.

Hepatic Portal System. In the hepatic portal system, blood is carried to capillaries of the liver by two veins: (1) the **ventral abdominal vein** in the ventral body wall collects from the pelvic veins, which are branches of the femoral veins; it empties into the liver; and (2) the **hepatic portal vein** receives the splenic, pancreatic, intestinal, and gastric veins. From the capillary bed in the liver, the blood is picked up by **hepatic veins** and is carried to the postcava and then the sinus venosus. The hepatic portal system, present in all vertebrates, is of great importance because it delivers nutrients absorbed from the gut directly to the liver. This guarantees that the liver will have first opportunity to store and process food materials before they are released into general circulation. In this way, blood leaving the liver remains relatively uniform, regardless of digestive activities underway.

**"Caval" derives from the Latin *cavus,* meaning hollow, and refers to the sinus venosus into which both the precaval veins (also called the anterior vena cava) and postcaval vein (= posterior vena cava) drain. The caval veins of tetrapod vertebrates replace the cardinal veins of fishes (see pp. 288–289).

Renal Portal System. Amphibians also inherited a *renal* portal system from their fish ancestors. Most of the blood returning from the hindlegs is interrupted in its journey toward the heart to be diverted into a network of capillaries in the kidneys. The **renal portal vein,** found along the margin of each kidney, is formed by union of the **sciatic** and **femoral veins** (see Figure 19-9). Then, from the kidney, blood is collected by the **renal veins** and carried to the **postcava.** All vertebrates except mammals have a renal portal system. You will see, then, that both hepatic and renal portal systems fit the definition of a portal system as one that begins and ends in capillaries.

Arterial System

The **carotid, pulmocutaneous,** and **systemic arches** (known collectively as the **aortic arches**) arise from the **truncus arteriosus** (Figure 19-10).

Carotid Arch

The **common carotid artery** divides into the (1) **internal carotid** to the roof of the mouth, eye, brain, and spinal cord and (2) **external carotid (lingual)** to the floor of the mouth, tongue, and thyroid gland (see Figure 19-9).

Pulmocutaneous Arch

The third arch divides into a short **pulmonary artery** to the lungs and a longer **cutaneous artery** to the skin. Unlike the carotid and systemic arches, which carry oxygenated blood to the body, the pulmocutaneous arch carries *deoxygenated* blood to the lungs and skin, where the blood can be oxygenated.

Systemic Arch

Each systemic arch (one from each side) passes along the side of the esophagus to join middorsally to form the **dorsal aorta** (see Figure 19-9). Each gives off several arteries before joining, among these the **subclavian artery** to the shoulder.

Find the **dorsal aorta** by lifting the kidneys to see it. The dorsal aorta supplies all the body posterior of the head except lungs and skin. Major branches of the dorsal aorta are

1. **Celiacomesenteric artery,** which in turn gives rise to **celiac** (Gr. *koilia,* belly) **artery** to the stomach, pancreas, and liver, as well as **anterior mesenteric artery** to the spleen and intestines

2. Six pairs of **urogenital arteries** to the kidneys, fat bodies, and gonads

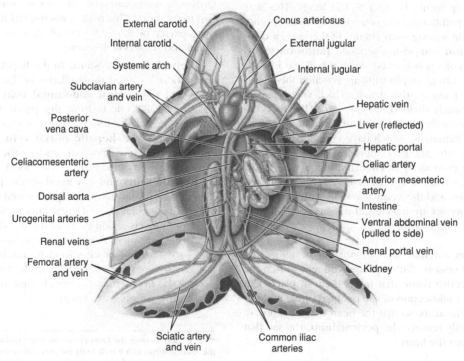

Figure 19-9
Circulatory system of a frog. Arterial, red; venous, blue.

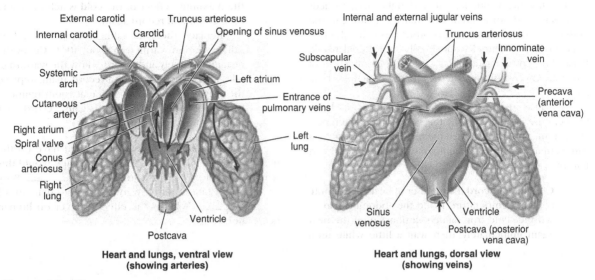

Figure 19-10
Structure of a frog heart. **Left,** Ventral view of frontal section. **Right,** Dorsal view. What structure collects deoxygenated blood returning to the heart and is formed by the convergence of three large veins? _____ What structure may help prevent mixing of oxygenated and deoxygenated blood as it leaves the heart (use your textbook to help you if necessary)? What artery carries deoxygenated blood to the skin, where the blood can be oxygenated? _____

3. **Lumbar arteries** (not shown in Figure 19-9) to the muscles of the back

4. **Common iliac** (L. *ilia,* flanks) **arteries,** formed by the division of the dorsal aorta; each iliac gives off a **femoral artery** to the thigh, as well as branches to the urinary bladder, abdominal wall, and rectum; the iliac then continues into the hindleg as the **sciatic artery**

Heart

 Make a frontal section of the heart (Figure 19-10), dividing it into dorsal and ventral valves.

Find the opening from the sinus venosus into the **right atrium** and the opening from the pulmonary veins into the **left atrium.** Why is the ventricle more muscular than the atria? _____
_____

The **conus arteriosus,** which receives blood from the **ventricle,** divides to form a left and right truncus arteriosus. Valves to prevent backflow of blood guard entrances to the atria and conus.

Even though an amphibian heart is three-chambered, with two atria and one undivided ventricle, there is nevertheless an effective separation of oxygenated and deoxygenated blood in the heart. Oxygenated blood from the lungs is sent preferentially to the body, whereas deoxygenated blood from the body is directed toward the pul-

mocutaneous arch. This partitioning is aided by a spiral fold inside the conus arteriosus and by pressure changes within the heart with each heart contraction. Technically the frog heart can be thought of as having five chambers, since both the sinus venosus and the conus arteriosus are contractile and assist in pumping blood.

Written Report

 Fill in the report on blood circulation on pp. 315–316.

Oral Report

 Demonstrate your dissection of the circulatory system to your instructor and be able to explain orally any phase of its anatomy or functions. Be able to trace the flow of blood into the heart from body tissues, through the pulmonary circuit, and back to the body tissues.

Observing the Heartbeat

 Open a pithed frog as you did the preserved frog, but avoid cutting the abdominal vein. Cut carefully through the pectoral girdle, keeping the scissors well up to avoid injuring the heart. Pin back the forelimbs and keep the heart well moistened with frog Ringers solution.

Identify the ventricle, left and right atria, truncus arteriosus, and aortic arches. Watch the heartbeat and note the series of alternating contractions—first the two atria, then the ventricle, and finally the arterial trunk. Raise the ventricle carefully to view the contraction of the sinus venosus immediately before contraction of the atria.

A frog is an **ectothermic** animal; that is, its body temperature is influenced by the environmental temperature, rather than by internal means (endothermic). You can examine the effect of temperature changes on heart rate by a simple experiment.

 Count and record the number of beats per minute at room temperature. Flood the abdominal cavity with ice-cold frog saline solution. Count the beat again immediately; then wait a little while until the maximum effect of the cold is achieved, and then count and record again.

Replace the cold saline solution with frog saline solution warmed to about 40° C. Count the beat immediately and record. Allow the warmth to take effect; then count and record again. Replace the warmed saline with saline at room temperature and count the heart rate again. Record your results on pp. 315–316.

What effect does temperature change have on the heart rate? _____ What advantage would this reaction to cold have for a frog? _____ Why should the solution not be warmed to more than 40° C? _____ What is the effect of fever on human heart rate? _____

Frog Circulation

Name _____

Date _____

Section _____

LAB REPORT

1. Trace the shortest route a corpuscle could take on each of the following trips, underscoring each place where it would go through a **capillary bed.**

   a. Ventricle to lung and return _____

   _____

   _____

   b. Ventricle to brain and return _____

   _____

   _____

   _____

   c. Systemic arch to intestine to right arm _____

   _____

   _____

   _____

   d. Hindleg to left atrium by way of renal portal _____

   _____

   _____

   _____

2. What are the chief gains and losses that take place in the blood in the following organs?

   a. Lung _____

   _____

   b. Kidney _____

   _____

   c. Intestinal wall _____

   _____

d. Liver _____

_____

_____

e. Muscles _____

_____

_____

3. Describe the shortest route from the **left atrium** to an **arm** and back to the **left atrium.**

_____

_____

_____

_____

_____

_____

4. Effect of temperature on heart rate

Rate of contraction

at room temperature   _____   /min (first count)

of cooled heart   _____   /min (first count)

of cooled heart   _____   /min (later count)

of warmed heart   _____   /min (first count)

of warmed heart   _____   /min (later count)

at room temperature   _____   /min (later count)

EXERCISE 19F

Nervous System

The nervous and endocrine systems are the coordinating systems of the body, integrating activities of the various organ systems.

The nervous system is composed of (1) the **central (cerebrospinal)** nervous system, consisting of the brain and spinal cord, which are housed in the skull and spinal column and are concerned with integrative activity, and (2) the **peripheral** nervous system, made up of the paired cranial and spinal nerves and the **autonomic** nervous system. These make up a system for the conduction of sensory and motor information throughout the body. The autonomic system consists of a pair of autonomic nerve cords together with their ganglia and nerve fibers, which innervate the viscera.

Brain and Spinal Cord

 Place the frog *dorsal surface up*. Remove the skin from the head and back. Cut through the skull just back of the nares. Beginning here, use the tip of a scalpel or forceps to chip away small pieces from the top of the cranium, being careful not to injure the delicate tissue beneath. Expose the entire brain from the olfactory nerves to the vertebral column. Now, beginning with the first vertebra, snip through each side of each vertebra between the neural spine and the articular processes (see Figure 19-2A) and remove the dorsal piece to expose the spinal cord. Continue until the whole cord is exposed (Figure 19-11).

The central system is enclosed in two membranes called the **meninges.** The tough **dura mater** usually clings to the cranial wall and neural canal; the thinner **pia mater** adheres to the brain and cord.

 Remove the dura mater from the brain and cord and identify the following parts.

Dorsal View of the Brain and Spinal Cord

1. The **forebrain** consists of cerebral hemispheres and diencephalon (Figure 19-12). The **cerebral hemispheres** constrict anteriorly to form **olfactory lobes,** from which the **olfactory nerves** (cranial nerves **1**) extend to the nares. The **diencephalon** is a depressed region behind the cerebrum. In the center of the diencephalon is a small stalk that was attached to the **parietal complex;** this structure, which lies just beneath the roof of the skull, is usually torn off when the cranium is removed. The parietal complex consists of an **epiphysis,** or **pineal gland,** that produces the hormone melatonin, and the **parietal organ,** which is a rudimentary third eye. The optic nerves **(2)** arise on the ventral side of the diencephalon.

2. The **midbrain** bears on the dorsal side two prominent **optic lobes.** Cranial nerves **3** and **4** arise in the midbrain.

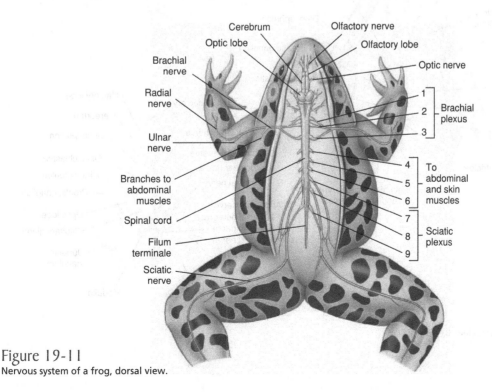

Figure 19-11
Nervous system of a frog, dorsal view.

3. The **hindbrain** consists of the **cerebellum** and **medulla.** The last six cranial nerves arise from the medulla.

4. The **spinal cord** is a continuation of the medulla and ends in the urostyle.

Ventral View of the Brain and Spinal Cord

 With the brain under water, cut the olfactory nerves and carefully lift the anterior end of the brain, gently working it loose. Continue loosening and lifting to remove the brain and spinal cord in one piece; then place them in a dish of water.

On the ventral side (Figure 19-12B), locate the **optic chiasma,** where the **optic nerves** meet and cross. Posterior to the optic chiasma is a slight extension of the diencephalon, to which is attached posteriorly the **hypophysis,** or **anterior lobe** of the pituitary gland. This is sometimes broken off in dissection, remaining in the floor to the cranium. There are 10 pairs of cranial nerves.

Consult your textbook for the functions of the various parts of the brain.

Spinal Nerves

 Lift the tip of the urostyle and cut around it carefully, preventing injury to the spinal nerves below. Continue your dissection, removing bone and muscle above the spinal nerves until they are completely exposed.

The 10 pairs of spinal nerves (see Figure 19-11) emerge through small openings between the vertebrae and appear as white threads in the dorsal body wall. The first three nerves on each side form a **brachial plexus** (a network of nerves that interchange fibers) to the arm, neck, and shoulder. The next three are in the body wall. The seventh to tenth (the tenth is a very small nerve) form the **sciatic plexus** to the leg.

The sciatic plexus on each side gives off to the hindleg a **femoral nerve** and a large **sciatic nerve,** the largest nerve in the body.

Oral Report

Be prepared to demonstrate from your dissection all the component parts of a frog's nervous system so far studied. From your textbook, find out their various functions.

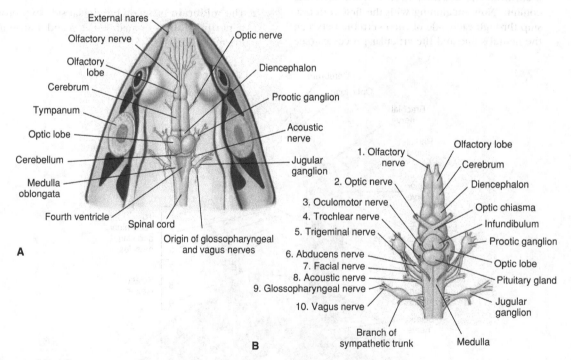

Figure 19-12
Brain of a frog. **A,** Dorsal view. **B,** Ventral view.

EXERCISE 20

The Nonavian Reptiles

EXERCISE 20

Painted Turtle

EXERCISE 20
Painted Turtle

Amphibians and nonavian reptiles are similar in that both are ectothermic tetrapods. However, they differ in several important characteristics. One of the most important ways they differ is that nonavian reptiles have an amniotic egg, an egg that allows reproduction and development outside of water. Nonavian reptiles also have a tough, protective skin; better-developed lungs; a more efficient circulatory system; and a more complex nervous system.

Modern nonavian reptiles—lizards, snakes, crocodilians, turtles—belong to the **diapsid** lineage, a group characterized by having a skull with two pairs of windowlike openings in the cheek (temporal) region. This is a derived condition that lightened the skull, furnished edges for jaw muscle attachment, and provided space that allowed jaw muscles to bulge when the jaw was closed. Interestingly, turtles lack these openings and are often considered to be living representatives of an early **anapsid** (no opening) group. Research published in the last 15 years using morphological and genetic evidence suggests that the skull openings were lost in early turtle evolution and that the current condition evolved secondarily from ancestors having temporal openings.

Turtles have changed little over the past 200 million years, and, although they are highly specialized and much modified from the earliest known amniote fossils, they reveal several features that distinguish the reptilian lineages. A turtle's shell, the anatomical feature that makes it instantly recognizable, is undoubtedly one secret of their success, providing protection to an otherwise ungainly animal.

Painted Turtle

Phylum Chordata
    Subphylum Vertebrata
        Class Reptilia
            Order Testudines (Chelonia)
                Genus *Chrysemys*
                    Species *Chrysemys picta*

Where Found

Painted turtles, *Chrysemys picta*, are familiar aquatic turtles of ponds, marshes, lake edges, and slow streams. They are widely distributed in the central and northern United States, as far south as Georgia and Louisiana and north along the southern edge of the Canadian provinces. Painted turtles feed on aquatic vegetation, crayfish, snails, and insects.

External Structure

 If living turtles are available, study locomotion and external features for adaptations that distinguish this group.

The anatomical form of a turtle is unusually broad and flattened, compared with that of other reptiles, with limbs extending laterally from the sides and bent downward at elbow and knee. As a result, a turtle's gait is slow and seemingly awkward, although not as inefficient as it might appear—it has, after all, served this successful group for some 200 million years, whereas numerous more agile reptiles have disappeared. The protective shell of a turtle, its exoskeleton, includes the dorsal **carapace** (Sp. *carapacho,* shell) and the ventral **plastron** (Fr., breastplate). Some turtles have hinged plastrons and can close their plastrons tightly. Other species rely more on their snapping jaws for defense and have greatly reduced plastrons. The bones of the carapace are covered with horny **scutes** (homologous to the epidermal scales of other reptiles). Although a turtle's shell is confining, it is not the explanation for the awkward gait, since a sprawling posture with the body dragging on the ground was characteristic of early land dwellers in general. The subsequent evolution of the shell, however, did prevent any further refinement in locomotion.

The head is stoutly protected with bone. A peculiarity of turtles is their lack of teeth. Instead, the edges of the jaws are formed into sharp ridges covered with strong, horny beaks. Locate the **external nares** (nostrils). Note that they are set close together at the tip of the snout, enabling the turtle to breathe while remaining almost completely submerged. The eyes are well developed. (Turtles, like lizards, have an abundance of cones in the retina, providing them a colorful view of the world.) The eyes are provided with upper and lower eyelids and an additional eyelid at the anterior corners, the transparent **nictitating** (L. *nictare,* to wink) **membrane,** which can be pulled across the eye to moisten and cleanse the cornea.

As in most turtles, the neck is long and flexible and folds dorsoventrally to allow retraction of the head within the protective confines of the shell. In a different suborder of turtles, distributed in the Southern Hemisphere, the neck folds sideways when the head is retracted.

Skeleton

 Examine a mounted skeleton of a painted turtle. Handle with care and use a probe or dissecting needle, not a pencil, in pointing.

Examine carapace and plastron of the shell (Figure 20-1). The plastron, normally united to the carapace by bony bridges, will have been removed in the mounted skeleton. Note that bones of the carapace are covered by horny scutes that do not coincide in number or position with the underlying bone. There are five central scutes of epidermal origin on the outside, but on the inside there are eight central bony plates (of dermal origin) fused to the thoracic vertebrae. Notice the growth lines in the scutes, formed as new keratin is laid down at the edges of the expanding scutes. These cannot be used to determine a turtle's age because new growth is influenced by many environmental factors.

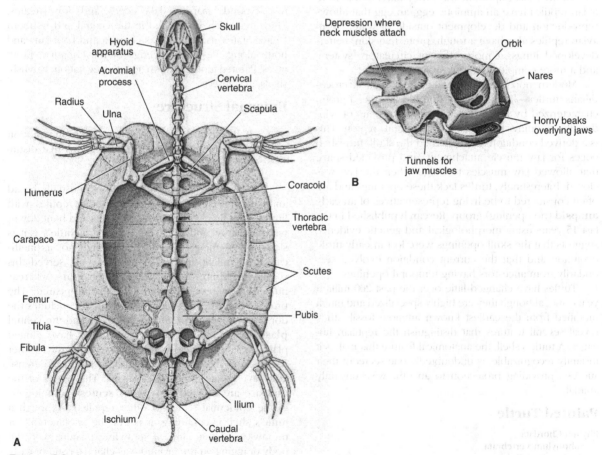

Figure 20-1

Skeleton of a painted turtle. **A,** Ventral view of entire skeleton. **B,** Lateral view of skull.

As in other vertebrates, the **endoskeleton** comprises two divisions, an **axial skeleton** consisting of skull, vertebrae, and ribs, and an **appendicular skeleton** consisting of the pectoral and pelvic girdles and limb bones.

A turtle skull is completely roofed over with the braincase (Figure 20-1B). Locate openings for the eyes, nostrils, and ears. Note wide excavations at the rear where the skull has been scalloped out to receive the neck muscles. There are also tunnels on each side at the rear of the upper jaw that provide space for powerful jaw muscles. These excavations for muscles in the anapsid skull of turtles are not true skull openings ("fenestrations") of the kind found in the diapsid skull of other reptiles. Beneath the lower jaw is the **hyoid** (Gr. *hyoeides,* Y-shaped) **apparatus,** a complex of bones, mostly fused, that support the tongue (Figure 20-1A). The hyoid apparatus is derived from remnants of gill arches of fish ancestors.

The vertebral column consists of 8 **cervical vertebrae** that form the bony support of a turtle's flexible neck; 10 **thoracic vertebrae** fused to the carapace; 2 **sacral vertebrae** with expanded ends fused to the pelvic girdle (frogs and other amphibians never have more than 1 sacral vertebra); and 25 to 30 **caudal vertebrae.** Note the strong articulating processes (called zygopophyses) of the elongate cervical vertebrae. The articulations are arranged to allow a turtle to withdraw its neck into an S-shaped bend. The thoracic (trunk) vertebrae have elongate centra, and each gives rise to a rib on each side. Note that the central 8 pairs of ribs extend laterally from the vertebrae like flying buttresses to fuse with, and lend strength to, the shell.

Turtles have stout pectoral and pelvic girdles to support the limbs and bear the animal's weight. Both girdles are much modified, compared with those of other reptiles. The pectoral girdle lacks a sternum (because the plastron serves a sternum's function), and the strutlike bones of the pectoral girdle form an odd tripartite scaffold between the carapace and plastron. An elongate **scapula** meets and articulates with the carapace dorsally. Fused to the scapula is the **acromial** (Gr. *akros,* summit, + *omos,* shoulder) **process** projecting anteriorly and at right angles to the scapula. Also lying at right angles to the two scapulas are the paddlelike **coracoid** (Gr. *korax,* crow, + *eidos,* form) **processes,** which are joined by cartilage at their medial margins. The pelvic girdle consists of the **ilia** (sing. **ilium**) attached to the ribs of two sacral vertebrae and, on either side, a broad **ischium** and **pubis.** The limbs of a turtle are stout but otherwise typical of reptiles and contain the same elements found in other vertebrate tetrapod pentadactyl limbs.

Internal Structure

Internal structure will be studied with preserved turtles.

Oral Cavity and Pharynx

 To open the mouth, first trim away some of the neck skin if necessary to expose the entire head. Cut through the temporal muscle on either side of the jaw; then force a strong knife blade between the jaws. Force the jaws apart enough to allow cutting the angle of the jaws with heavy scissors or bone shears.

Open the mouth widely. The oral (buccal) cavity (Figure 20-2), the space enclosed by the jaws, leads into the **pharynx,** a cavity extending from the posterior border of the tongue to the esophagus. Note the horny beaks covering the toothless jaws and the triangular **tongue** that is firmly attached throughout its length. The **glottis** is a narrow, slitlike opening posterior to the tongue that leads into the larynx. The external nares lead through the nasal passages to the **internal nares,** which open on the roof of the mouth. There is no secondary palate in turtles, but the roof of the mouth is vaulted and bears a pair of **palatal folds** that help direct the air toward the glottis. (The secondary palate, present in crocodilians and mammals, is a bony plate that completely separates respiratory and food passages, thus providing a channel for free passage of air from nose

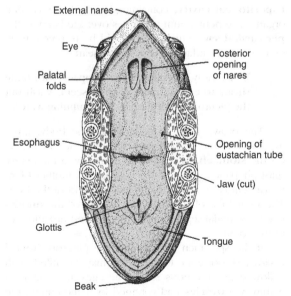

Figure 20-2
Oral cavity and pharynx of a painted turtle.

to pharynx; the secondary palate allows an animal to manipulate food in its mouth while breathing through its nose.) Locate the **eustachian (auditory) tubes** in the roof of the pharynx; these lead to the middle ear cavity on each side of the head. At the posterior margin of the pharynx is the **esophagus.**

Digestive System

 If not already done, cut through the bridges uniting the carapace and plastron with a bone saw or hacksaw. Strong bone shears are usually required to break through the anterior and posterior margins of these bony bridges to complete the separation. Remove the plastron by slicing carefully through adhering tissue and muscle, holding the scalpel *close* to the under surface of the plastron.

With the plastron removed, you will see much of the viscera covered by several muscles of the pectoral and pelvic girdles, with their origins on the plastron.

 Peel back and cut off the large, fan-shaped pectoralis major muscle near its insertion on the humerus. Cut through and remove the coracoid bone of the pectoral girdle and its muscles on both sides to expose the anterior viscera. Trim away the superficial muscles of the pelvic girdle.

The entire coelom is enclosed by a thin, tough, transparent membrane, the **parietal peritoneum.** Carefully trim away this membrane to reveal the **pleuroperitoneal cavity,** containing most of the visceral organs. The peritoneum continues over the heart as the **pericardial sac,** which also should be trimmed away on the ventral surface to expose the heart.

 Break away the sides of the carapace with bone shears to expose more of the viscera. Wash out the pleuroperitoneal cavity with running water.

The brown **liver** extends across the body, passing dorsal to the heart (Figure 20-3). The left lobe covers the **stomach,** to which it is bound by a mesentery (gastrohepatic ligament). Use a probe or another blunt instrument carefully to free the stomach from the liver. The right lobe of the liver covers part of the **duodenum** (the initial segment of the small intestine) and part of the colon.

If the specimen is a female, the pleuroperitoneal cavity just posterior to the liver may be filled with yellow eggs of various sizes. The eggs are contained within two **ovaries** and confined by a mesentery, the **mesovarium.**

Look beneath (dorsal to) the heart to find a tough membrane, the **transverse septum,** separating the pericardial cavity from the rest of the pleuroperitoneal cavity.

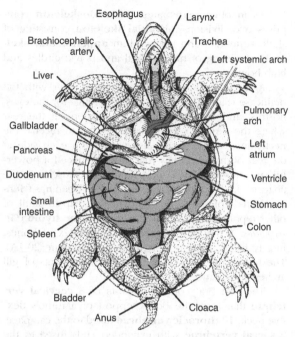

Figure 20-3

Internal anatomy of a painted turtle. In desert species, the bladder can be large and used as a water reservoir. Notice how tightly the organs sit in the body cavity. Why might turtles have physiological adaptations for dealing with extended periods of breath-holding? (Hint: how is the physiology impacted when its legs and head are withdrawn into the shell?) _____

Now identify the components of the digestive system (Figure 20-3). Push the left lobe of the liver to the right and trace the ventral surface of the stomach forward to the **esophagus.** Following the gut posteriorly, find the duodenum; the **pancreas,** a slender, pale gland lying along the anterior border of the duodenum; and the **gallbladder,** a dark green sac embedded in the dorsal side of the right liver lobe. It may be necessary to break away the posterior margin of the right liver to expose the gallbladder. The gallbladder stores and concentrates bile from the liver; the green color is contributed by a variety of pigments present in the bile. The duodenum gives rise to the **small intestine** proper, which coils several times before emptying into the **colon** (large intestine). The colon terminates at the **cloaca,** which also receives ducts from the ovaries (oviduct) and kidneys (ureter, or metanephric duct).

Respiratory System

 With bone shears, cut through the acromial processes on both sides of the thoracic region and trim away the tissue in the neck region. Make a light midventral incision in the neck and retract tissue to expose the trachea.

Follow the **trachea** anteriorly, carefully scraping away muscle and connective tissue from the trachea and hyoid bone, beneath which the trachea disappears. Cut through the two horns of the hyoid bone on both sides, lateral to the trachea, and carefully free the hyoid from underlying trachea and larynx (Figure 20-3).

The glottis, seen earlier, opens into the **larynx,** an enlarged vestibule that leads into the trachea. Note the complex of cartilages and associated muscles (the latter partly removed with the hyoid bone) that open and close the glottis. In many animals, the larynx contains vocal cords, but most turtles are voiceless, able to do little more than make a hissing sound by rapidly expelling air from their lungs. If turtles cannot vocalize, how might they communicate with each other? _____

_____

Follow the trachea posteriorly, where, with the esophagus, it drops middorsally between large blood vessels emerging from the heart. At this point the trachea divides into two **bronchi** (sing. **bronchus**). Trace the left bronchus to the lung. Reflect the left lobe of the liver and stomach to the right and cut through the peritoneum to expose the **left lung.** The left bronchus will be seen lying between the left pulmonary artery and vein.

Slice open the lung with a lateral incision. The lung is basically saclike, although modestly subdivided into **alveolar pockets,** giving the inner wall a honeycomb appearance. The lung is mostly confined to a separate pleural cavity by an extension of the transverse septum, the **pleuropericardial membrane.** In mammals these membranes become incorporated into the muscular diaphragm. But turtles have no diaphragm and must use other muscles to expand and compress the lungs. The volume of the body cavity is relatively fixed by the shell. What would happen to the internal volume if the turtle extended its head and legs? _____

_____

Would air go into the lungs or be pushed out? _____

_____

Circulatory System

We will confine our study of the circulatory system to the heart and major vessels entering and leaving the heart (Figure 20-3).

As noted earlier, the heart lies within a pericardial sac. Lift the ventricle to see the **sinus venosus,** which receives blood from the major **systemic veins,** the precaval and postcaval veins. Deoxygenated blood from the body drains from the sinus venosus into the **right atrium,** which empties into the right side of the ventricle. Oxygenated blood from the lungs enters the left atrium via **pulmonary veins** and is pumped from the left atrium into the left side of the heart.

The turtle ventricle is only partly divided by a septum (complete in crocodilians), but very little admixture of oxygenated and deoxygenated blood occurs. From the ventricle, three large arterial trunks extend forward; these represent the subdivision of the conus arteriosus of fishes and amphibians.

1. The trunk farthest to the turtle's left is the **pulmonary arch,** which divides immediately into right and left pulmonary arteries. The pulmonary arch takes deoxygenated blood from the right ventricular chamber and distributes it to the lungs.

2. The middle trunk is the **left systemic arch (left aorta),** which gives off branches to the stomach, pancreas, liver, and duodenum. It receives oxygenated blood from the left side of the ventricle.

3. The third trunk is the **right systemic arch (right aorta).** It is concealed from view by the **brachiocephalic** (Gr. *brachion,* arm, + *kephale,* head) **(innominate) artery,** a large branch that the right systemic arch gives off immediately after leaving the heart. The right systemic arch also receives oxygenated blood from the left ventricular chamber. Small **coronary arteries** spring from the base of the brachiocephalic and branch over the heart. The brachiocephalic divides at once into four arteries: **right** and **left subclavian arteries,** which supply the neck region, pectoral girdle, shoulder muscles, and forelimbs; and **right** and **left carotid arteries,** which supply the head.

Although you will not trace the arteries farther, the left and right systemic arteries unite posteriorly in a V shape to form the **dorsal aorta.** This vessel continues posteriorly in the median dorsal line, giving off branches that supply most of the visceral organs and all of the muscles of the trunk and hindlimbs.

NOTES

The Birds
Class Reptilia
Subclass Aves

EXERCISE 21
Pigeon

EXERCISE 21
Pigeon
Pigeon (rock dove)

Birds, described by English zoologist Thomas Huxley as "glorified reptiles," do indeed bear the stamp of their reptilian heritage in many subtle ways. But birds have become so highly specialized into flying machines with all the constraints that design for flight requires that the truth of Huxley's comment is not instantly evident to one gazing casually at a bird.

The demands of flight, far more than anything else, have shaped the form and function of birds—and have disguised their reptilian past. Virtually every adaptation found in flying birds focuses on two features: more power and less weight. This will be the central theme of this exercise.

Pigeon (Rock Dove)

Phylum Chordata
    Subphylum Vertebrata
        Class Reptilia
            Subclass Aves
                Order Columbiformes
                    Family Columbidae
                        Genus *Columba*
                          Species *Columba livia,* rock dove

Where Found

The common pigeon (rock dove), so familiar to city dwellers, is of Old World origin but has been introduced throughout the world. It is not migratory, yet it has excellent navigational proficiency; it is the homing pigeon used in carrying messages in wars from the time of Caesar's conquest of Gaul through World War II. It is one of the swiftest birds in flight. Many domesticated varieties have been developed over centuries of breeding; Charles Darwin was a pigeon fancier. The "city pigeon" is highly variable in coloration.

Feathers

 Examine a flight (contour) feather.

Identify the central **shaft** (also called the **rachis** [Gr. *rhachis,* spine]), which is a continuation of the **quill** that is thrust into the feather follicle of a living bird. The shaft bears numerous **barbs,** which spread laterally to form the feather's expansive webbed surface, the **vane.**

Flex the feather in your hands, noting its resilience and toughness, despite its remarkable light weight. If you run your fingers down the vane toward the quill, you will separate some of the barbs that are normally linked together by tiny **barbules.** Note that considerable force is needed to separate the barbs. Because detachment happens in the course of a bird's daily activities, it spends time each day preening: zipping the barbs back together by drawing the feather through its bill. You can do the same with your fingers. Why would preening be so important for a bird? _____

 Examine a prepared slide of a contour feather, using a dissecting microscope or low power of a compound microscope.

The microscope reveals barbules that extend out at roughly 45° angles in both directions from each barb and are equipped with numerous tiny hooks. Note how adjacent rows of barbules overlap and fit into each other. The hooks of barbules on one barb become fixed to the grooves in barbules on the neighboring barb.

There are several types of feathers that may have been placed on display. The **contour feathers** that you have just examined give the bird its outward form; contour feathers used in flight are called **flight feathers. Down feathers** are soft tufts, lacking hooks, that are found on young birds or beneath the contour feathers of adult birds. Down feathers have excellent insulative value and function mainly to conserve heat. **Filoplume feathers** are hairlike feathers thought to play a sensory role. These feathers, consisting of a weak shaft with a tuft of short barbs at the tip, are the "hairs" visible on plucked fowl.

Skeleton

 Study the mounted pigeon skeleton and unmounted bird bones on display.

A pigeon skeleton (Figure 21-1), like that of other birds, is a marvel of lightness combined with strength. It is even lighter than it looks because many of the limb and girdle bones are hollow. If a long bone, such as the humerus, has been broken or cut open for examination, note its tubular form and the internal struts that have developed where stresses must be borne. Many of the bird's bones are "pneumatized": that is, they are penetrated by extensions of the air sac system and thus contain buoyant warm air rather than bone marrow, which is typical of mammalian bones. (Some bird bones do contain marrow, but much of a bird's red and white blood cell production occurs in the spleen and liver.)

A striking feature of a bird skeleton is its rigidity. Of the axial skeleton, only the neck remains flexible. The remaining vertebrae are fused together with the pelvic girdle to form a stiff, boxlike framework to support the legs and provide rigidity for flight. The double-headed **ribs,** too, are mostly fused with the **thoracic vertebrae** and with the **sternum.** Unlike in mammals, nearly all of which have 7 cervical vertebrae, the number of **cervical vertebrae** in birds varies from 8 to 24, depending on the species (long-necked birds have the most). Note the complex articulations of the cervical vertebrae of this most flexible part of the pigeon's body. How many cervical vertebrae has the pigeon? _____

_____

The last rib-bearing thoracic vertebra is fused with five **lumbar,** two **sacral,** and five **caudal** vertebrae to form a thin, platelike structure, the **synsacrum.** The **ilium** of the pelvic girdle is also fused with the

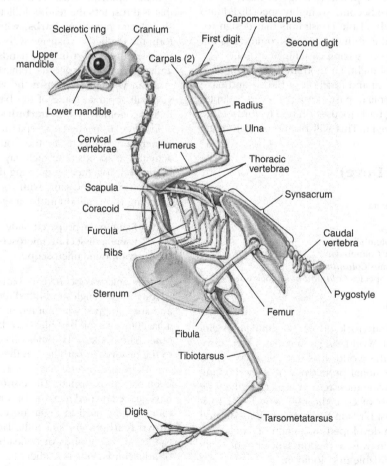

Figure 21-1

Skeleton of a pigeon. Why is the keel of the sternum so large? _____ What bone is formed by the fusion of 13 vertebrae? _____ What bone is sometimes called the "wishbone"? _____ How would you describe the fibula of the bird, as compared with other vertebrates (about the same, reduced, enlarged)? _____

synsacrum. This very light but stout arrangement provides further rigidity to the body frame. Finally note the short, bony tail, consisting of five free **caudal vertebrae** that carry four caudal vertebrae fused into a **pygostyle,** which supports the tail feathers.

A pigeon skull is composed of individual bones that are completely united in adults to form a single thin-walled, lightweight structure. Birds are descended from archosaurian reptiles, which belong to the diapsid lineage of amniotes; this lineage is characterized by skulls having two openings, or fenestra, in the temporal region. Birds are so highly specialized, however, that it is difficult to see any trace of diapsid origin in their skulls. A large, bulging **cranium** encloses the brain, which is much larger, relative to body size, than the brain of a turtle; the complex coordinating problems of bird flight require far more central nervous coordination than does the plodding locomotion of a turtle. A pigeon's large eyes are housed in sockets and encircled in front by a protective ring of shinglelike, bony plates, the **sclerotic ring.** The **beak** consists of a **lower mandible** hinged to the skull in a way that provides wide-gaping action. The **upper mandible** (also called the maxilla) is fused to the skull in pigeons, but some birds (parrots, for example) have kinetic skulls with movable bony elements that allow the upper mandible to tilt upward when the bird opens its mouth.

We will turn our attention now to the appendicular skeleton. Examine the pectoral girdle. It is a tripod of paired bones, the **scapula, coracoid,** and **furcula** ("wishbone"). The scapula is a thin, bladelike bone tied to the ribs by ligaments. The stout coracoid bone unites the scapula and **sternum.** Describe the sternum. _____ Why is it so large? _____ Both muscles that depress the wing (pectoralis) and those that raise the wing (supracoracoideus) are attached to the sternum. Where scapula and coracoid unite, there is a hollow depression, into which the ball of the chief bone of the wing, the **humerus,** fits. The supracoracoideus is attached by a tendon to the upper side of the humerus so that it pulls from below by an ingenious "rope-and-pulley" kind of arrangement (Figure 21-2). In this way, muscle weight is kept below the center of gravity, providing greater flight stability.

The pelvic girdle, as we have seen, is a fused structure that is almost paper thin but is strengthened by bony ridges that can be seen by looking at the underside of the girdle. The **femur** (thighbone) is directed forward and is virtually buried in the flesh of a living bird. The **tibiotarsus** is the main bone of the shank ("drumstick"); the **fibula** is reduced to a thin splint. The ankle is greatly modified. Some of the proximal pebble-like tarsal bones of the tetrapod limb are united with the tibia to form the tibiotarsus, and the distal tarsal bones are fused with the metatarsals to form a single elongate **tarsometatarsus.** A pigeon, like most other

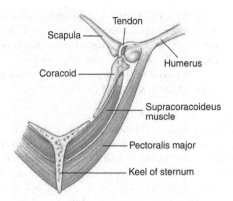

Figure 21-2
The major flight muscles of a bird are arranged to keep the center of gravity low in the body. Both the supracoracoideus and the pectoralis are anchored on the sternum keel. Contraction of the pectoralis muscle pulls the wing downward. As the pectoralis relaxes, the supracoracoideus muscle contracts and, acting as a pulley system, pulls the wing upward.

birds, has four digits, three directed forward and the fourth directed backward.

The bones of the forelimbs are highly modified for flight. Note how the wing folds into a compact Z shape when the bird is at rest. Identify the **humerus** and locate the expanded dorsal surface for the attachment of the pectoral muscles. The **radius** and **ulna** are longer than the humerus, and the ulna, the larger of the two, carries the secondary flight feathers. Most modified are the wrist and digits, which carry the primary flight feathers. Identify the two **carpals** (wrist bones) and two elongate **carpometacarpals** (palm bones), so-called because they are formed by the fusion of three carpal and three metacarpal bones. There are only three **digits** (fingers). The first digit, the **alula,** or "thumb," carries quill-like feathers. The second finger is by far the largest; this, together with the palm bones, carries primary flight feathers. The third digit, like the first, is reduced to a small bone (not shown in Figure 21-1) that carries a single, outermost flight feather.

Internal Structure and Function of the Digestive System

We will limit our study of a pigeon's internal anatomy to the digestive system, which is readily accessible by dissection. Begin by removing the skin and feathers from the ventral side of a pigeon.

 With a scalpel, make a midventral incision from the upper neck to the cloaca. Using the blunt end of the scalpel, separate the skin and feathers from the underlying musculature of the neck, breast, and abdomen. Be careful in the neck region not to damage the crop, which lies just beneath the skin at the base of the neck. Cut away the loosened skin from the breast musculature down to the wing insertion and from the abdomen. It is not necessary to remove the skin and feathers from the head, back, wings, legs, and tail.

To examine the oral cavity, cut through the angle of the jaws with heavy scissors.

The muscular **tongue,** used for manipulating food, is narrow and sharply pointed in front (Figure 21-3). The tongue of most birds, pigeons included, is poorly supplied with taste buds, but all birds can probably taste food to some extent. Seed eaters especially use vision and touch rather than taste as the principal means of evaluating their food; the inside of the mouth is liberally supplied with touch endings.

On the roof of the mouth, find the **palatine folds** (Figure 21-3). These are fleshy folds that extend from the lateral borders of the upper jaw to the midline. Probe between the midline slit of the palatine folds to expose a dorsal passage through which air passes from the nostrils to the glottis. The **pharynx** is the common chamber of the mouth and nasal cavity, beginning at the caudal end of the palatine folds. The **glottis,** the opening to the **larynx,** is a slitlike opening on a raised area just posterior to the tongue.

Find the opening to the **esophagus,** which extends from the pharynx to the stomach. In seed-eating birds, such as pigeons, the esophagus swells into a storage chamber, the **crop,** located at the base of the neck (Figure 21-4).

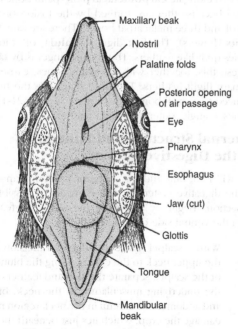

Figure 21-3
Oral cavity of a pigeon.

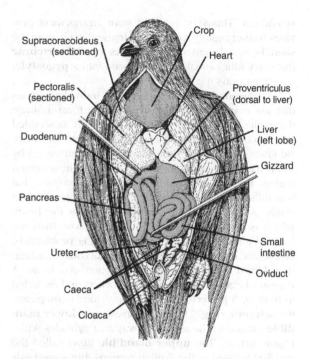

Figure 21-4
Internal anatomy of a pigeon.

 Locate the bilobed crop just anterior to the keel of the sternum and make a midventral incision with a scalpel to expose the interior.

An expansible crop allows seed eaters to swallow food quickly and store it for a period while seeds are softened with mucus before entering the stomach. In pigeons the crop not only stores food but also secretes a mixture of desquamated cells and fluid, called "pigeon milk," which the parents regurgitate to feed their young.

To expose more of the digestive system, the sternum must be removed.

 Pass a sharp scalpel down both sides of the breastbone keel to cut free the breast musculature.

The large breast muscles are the **pectoralis** and the **supracoracoideus,** the strong flight muscles mentioned earlier in your study of the skeleton. Use your fingers to force these muscles away from the keel. Note the silvery fascia that separates these two muscles.

 Continue to dissect away the breast muscles from the keel, base of the sternum, and coracoid. With heavy scissors, and using care to prevent damaging underlying organs, cut through the ribs, anterior end of the sternum, and coracoid on both sides and remove to expose the viscera. Remove any remaining skin from the ventral side of the abdomen as far posteriorly as the cloaca.

From Figure 21-4, identify the exposed visceral organs: heart, liver (two lobes), gizzard, and intestine. Note that the body organs are rather firmly supported by mesenteries. The body wall is lined with **parietal peritoneum,** and the visceral organs (except the kidneys) are covered with **visceral peritoneum.**

 Remove the heart after severing the pulmonary and aortic arches and the sinus venosus.

All birds have two stomachs: an anterior glandular stomach, the **proventriculus,** and a posterior muscular stomach, the **gizzard** (Figure 21-4). Pass a probe through the opening in the crop and into the spindle-shaped proventriculus. The proventriculus produces an acid-rich secretion containing a peptide enzyme that attacks protein foods. The muscular stomach, or gizzard, is especially thick in seed eaters, such as pigeons, and lined with a horny, keratinous material that serves as grinding plates for mechanically reducing food. Seed and grain eaters also swallow grit (rough granules of sand or stone). Why would birds intentionally swallow grit? _____

A bird's intestine is the principal organ of digestion. Its length and dimensions differ with the bird's diet: long, coiled, and relatively thick-walled in seed eaters but shorter and thinner-walled in meat- and fruit-eating birds. Find the origin of the looped **duodenum,** the initial segment of the small intestine, where it emerges from the gizzard beside the junction of the proventriculus with the gizzard. The **pancreas** lies in a ligament that connects the halves of the duodenal loop. Trace the small intestine to the straight large intestine. Locate a pair of bud-like **caeca** at the junction of small and large intestines. These small sacs are of uncertain function in pigeons, but, in some birds (grouse, for example), they are much longer and appear to function in the absorption of water and amino acids.

The large intestine empties into the **cloaca,** which also receives the ureters and genital ducts.

The bilobed **liver,** noted earlier, is as large as or larger than the liver of mammals of equal size. Its function in birds is similar to its function in mammals: it is the central organ of metabolic regulation, which monitors and adjusts the circulating levels of metabolites. The liver also has numerous other functions, including the synthesis of bile, storage of glycogen, inactivation of toxins, synthesis of plasma proteins, removal of damaged blood cells, and storage of iron- and fat-soluble vitamins.

Although the respiratory system will not be explored in this exercise, the **lungs** can be seen flattened against the body wall by retracting the digestive organs to one side. Although the lungs are the center of the breathing system, birds have a complex system of air sacs (usually collapsed and difficult to locate in a preserved pigeon), which serve as reservoirs for fresh air. These are interconnected in such a way that perhaps 75% of inspired air bypasses the lungs and flows directly into air sacs. On expiration some of this fully oxygenated air is shunted through the lung, while used air passes directly out. As a consequence of this remarkable system, the lungs receive fresh air during both inspiration and expiration. Birds are negative pressure breathers like mammals, but unlike mammals they lack a muscular diaphragm. Air is pulled in (inspiration) by thoracic and abdominal muscles that expand the thoracic cavity. During expiration abdominal muscles contract to push air out of the air sacs.

Oral Report

 Familiarize yourself with a pigeon skeleton and digestive system. Be prepared to name the major elements of the skeleton and explain how a pigeon skeleton is adapted for the demands of flight. Be prepared to trace the route of food through the digestive system and explain its fate en route. How is a pigeon's digestive system adapted for a herbivorous diet?

NOTES

EXERCISE 22

The Mammals
Fetal Pig

Fetal Pig

Class Mammalia
  Subclass Theria
    Infraclass Eutheria
      Order Artiodactyla
        Genus *Sus*
          Species *Sus domesticus*

Mammalia are those animals whose young are nourished by milk from the breasts of the mother. Mammals have a muscular diaphragm, a structure found in no other class, and a four-chambered heart. Most are covered with hair. Their nervous system is especially well developed. Their eggs develop in a uterus, with placental attachment for nourishment (except the monotremes, which lay eggs, and the marsupials, in which the placental attachment is only weakly and briefly developed).

Order Artiodactyla includes the even-toed, hoofed mammals, such as deer, sheep, cattle, and camels. These usually have two toes, but some, such as hippopotamuses and pigs, have four toes.

Fetal pigs are an especially desirable laboratory example of a mammal. They are easy to obtain, relatively inexpensive, and easily stored in individual plastic bags. Fetal pigs are obtained from the uteri of sows slaughtered for market. Because they are unborn, their bones are still largely cartilaginous, which makes the specimens pliable and easy to handle. They have an umbilical cord, by which they were attached to the placenta in the uterus.

The embryo depends on maternal blood to bring it nutrients and oxygen and to carry off the waste products of metabolism because its own organs cannot serve these functions until birth. This exchange of materials between fetal blood and maternal blood takes place within the placenta of the mother's uterus. The difference between fetus and adult is largely physiological, but there are also a few morphological differences, especially in the circulatory system, which you will observe in your specimen.

The period of gestation in a pig is 16 to 17 weeks, as compared with 20 days in a rat, 8 weeks in a cat, 9 months in a human being, 11 months in a horse, and 22 months in an elephant. Pig litters average 7 to 12 but may have as many as 18 piglets. The pigs are about

---

EXERCISE 22A

Skeleton
Axial skeleton
Appendicular skeleton

EXERCISE 22B

Muscular System
Organization of skeletal muscles
Muscles of the forequarter
Muscles of the hindquarter

EXERCISE 22C

Digestive System
Head and throat
Abdominal cavity
Thoracic cavity and neck region
Digestive tract

EXERCISE 22D

Urogenital System
Urinary system

EXERCISE 22E

Circulatory System
Heart

EXERCISE 22F

Nervous System
Spinal nerves
Autonomic nervous system
Brain

EXERCISE 22G

Respiratory System
Demonstration

---

30 cm long at birth and weigh from 1 to 1.5 kg (about 2 to 3 pounds). The age of a fetus may be estimated from the length of its body:

At 3 weeks, the fetus is about 1.3 cm long.
At 7 weeks, the fetus is about 3.8 cm long.
At 14 weeks, the fetus is about 23 cm long.
At full term, the fetus is about 30 cm long.

External Structure

 Before proceeding with the regular exercises, look at the external structure of a pig.

On the head, locate the **mouth,** with fleshy lips, and **nostrils** at the tip of the snout. The snout has a tough rim for rooting and bears **vibrissae,** stiff sensory hairs (whiskers). Each eye has two lids and a small membrane in the medial corner, which represents the nictitating membrane. Fleshy pinnae, or ear flaps, contain the external auditory opening.

On the trunk, locate the **thorax,** supported by ribs, sternum, and shoulder girdle with forelimbs attached; **abdomen,** supported by a vertebral column and muscular walls; **sacral region,** comprising the pelvic girdle with hindlimbs attached; **umbilical cord;** five to eight pairs of **mammae,** or nipples, on the abdomen; and **anus** at the base of the tail.

What is the **sex** of your specimen? _____ In males the **urogenital opening** is just posterior to the umbilical cord; **scrotal sacs** form two swellings at the posterior end of the body (the **penis** can sometimes be felt under the skin as a long, thin cord passing from the urogenital opening back between the hindlegs). In females the urogenital opening is just ventral to the anus and has a fleshy tubercle projecting from it.

Examine the cut end of the umbilical cord. Note the ends of four tubes in the cord. These represent an umbilical vein, two umbilical arteries, and an allantoic duct, all of which during fetal life are concerned with transporting food, oxygen, and waste products to or from the placenta of the mother's uterus.

Notice that the entire body of a fetal pig is covered with a thin cuticle called the **periderm.**

EXERCISE 22A
Skeleton

The skeleton of an adult pig, although different in size and proportion from skeletons of other mammals, such as dogs, cats, and humans, is, nonetheless, quite similar. Bones are homologous, and the origins and insertions of muscles as described for one can usually be traced on the others.

Because of its immature condition, the skeleton of a fetal pig is unsuitable for classroom study. However, if you are planning to dissect the muscles of a fetal pig, it is essential to be familiar with the bones. Skeletons of a cat or dog can be used quite satisfactorily for this purpose. Figures 22-1 and 22-2, showing a cat skeleton, will help you in your identification.

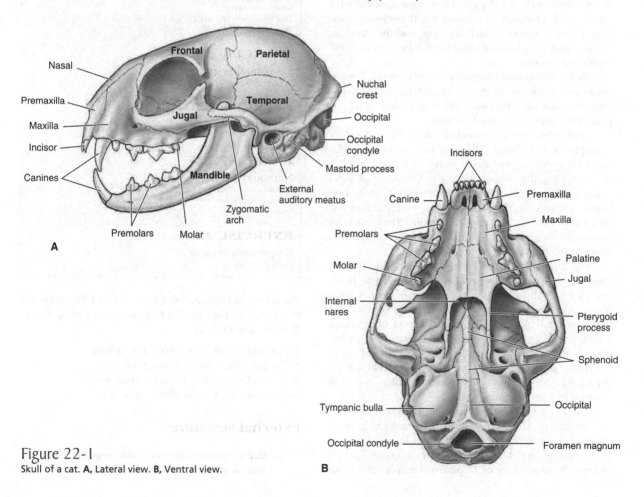

Figure 22-1
Skull of a cat. **A,** Lateral view. **B,** Ventral view.

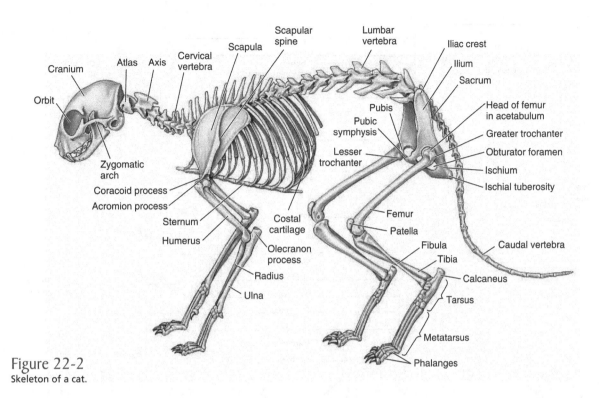

Figure 22-2
Skeleton of a cat.

⭐ As you study the mounted skeleton of a dog or cat, compare the parts with those of the fetal pig skeleton (Figure 22-3). Then try to locate these parts and visualize their relationships within the flesh of a preserved pig. As you do, notice the similarities with a human skeleton (Figure 22-4).

As in a frog, a pig skeleton consists of an **axial skeleton** (skull, vertebral column, ribs, and sternum) and an **appendicular skeleton** (pectoral and pelvic girdles and their appendages).

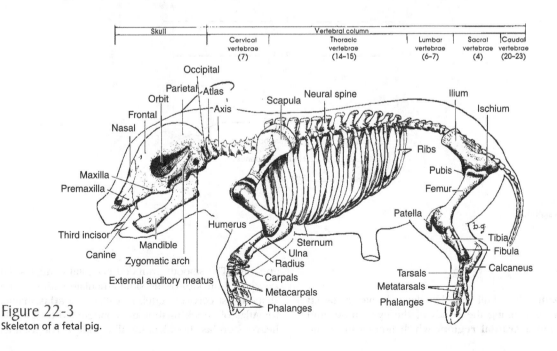

Figure 22-3
Skeleton of a fetal pig.

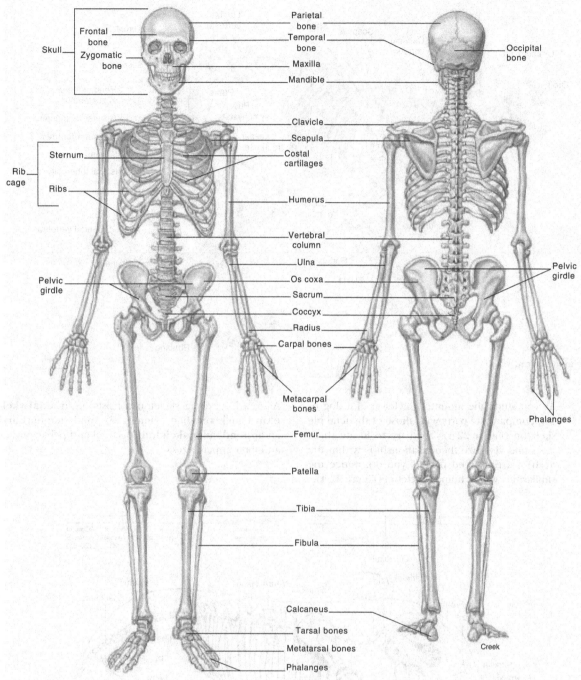

Figure 22-4
Human skeleton.

Axial Skeleton

Skull. The skull can be divided into a **facial region,** containing the bones of the eyes, nose, and jaws, and a **cranial region,** which houses the brain and ears. The smooth, rounded occipital condyles (Gr. *kondylos,* knuckle) of the skull articulate with the ring-shaped first cervical vertebra (called the **atlas,** named for Atlas of Greek mythology, condemned to hold the heavens on his shoulders for all eternity). The foramen magnum ("great opening") is the opening at the posterior end of the braincase for the emergence of the spinal cord. Many important bones of the skull can be identified with the help of Figure 22-1.

Vertebral Column. Note the five types of vertebrae—**cervical,** in the neck; **thoracic,** bearing the ribs; **lumbar,** without ribs but with large transverse processes; **sacral,** fused together to form a point of attachment for the pelvic girdle; and **caudal,** the tail vertebrae. In humans three to five vestigial caudal vertebrae are fused to form the coccyx of the tail bone. All vertebrae are built on the same general plan, with recognizable individual differences (see Figures 19-2, 22-2, and 22-3).

Ribs. Observe the structure of a rib and its articulation with a vertebra. Each rib articulates with both the body of the vertebra and a transverse process. The **shaft** of the rib ends in a **costal** (L. *costa*, rib) **cartilage,** which attaches to the sternum or to another costal cartilage and so indirectly to the sternum. A cat has 1 pair of free, or floating, ribs. A pig has 14 or 15 pairs of ribs, of which 7 pairs attach directly to the sternum and 7 or 8 attach indirectly. How many does a human have? _____

Sternum. The sternum is composed of a number of ossified segments, the first of which is called the **manubrium,** and the last of which is called the **xiphisternum.** Those in between are collectively called the **body** of the sternum.

Appendicular Skeleton

Pectoral Girdle and Its Appendages. The pectoral girdle comprises a pair of triangular **scapulae,** each with a lateral **spine** and a **glenoid fossa** at the ventral point for attachment with the head of the humerus. The **forelimb** (see Figures 22-2 to 22-4) includes (1) the **humerus;** (2) two forearm bones—a shorter, more medial **radius** and a longer, more lateral **ulna,** with an **olecranon** (ol-ek're-non) **process** at the proximal, or elbow, end; (3) the **carpus,** consisting of two rows of small bones; (4) the **metacarpals** (five in a cat and human and four in a pig); and (5) the **digits,** or toes, made up of **phalanges.**

Pelvic Girdle and Its Appendages. The pelvic girdle in adult mammals consists of a pair of **innominate** (L., without name) **bones,** each formed by the fusion of the **ilium** (L., flank), **ischium** (Gr. *ischion,* hip), and **pubis** (L., mature). A lateral cavity, the **acetabulum** (L., vinegar cup), accepts the head of the femur. The pubic bones and the ischial bones of opposite sides unite at **symphyses,** and the ilia articulate with the sacrum, so that the innominates and the sacrum together form a complete ring, or **pelvic canal.** Each pelvic appendage includes (1) the **femur,** or thigh bone; (2) the larger **tibia** and more slender fibula of the shank;

(3) the ankle, or **tarsus,** comprising seven bones, and fibular tarsal (**calcaneus;** cal-ka'nee-us; L. *calx,* heel), forming the projecting heel bone; (4) the **metatarsals** (five in a cat, of which the first is very small, and four in a pig); and (5) the **digits,** or toes (four in both a cat and a pig), composed of **phalanges.**

Structure of a Long Bone

Longitudinal and transverse sections through a long bone (Figure 22-5) illustrate a shell of **compact bone,** within which is a type of **spongy bone (cancellous bone),** the spaces of which are filled with **marrow.** The **shaft** (also called the **diaphysis;** di-af'uh-sis; Gr. *dia,* through, + *phyein,* to grow) is usually hollowed to form a **marrow cavity.** In a young mammal, there is only red marrow, a blood-forming substance, but this is gradually replaced in adults with yellow marrow, which is much like adipose tissue. The extremities (**epiphyses;** ee-pif'uh-sees; Gr. *epi,* upon, + *phyein,* to grow) of the bone usually bear a layer of **articular cartilage.** The rest of the bone is covered with a membrane, the **periosteum** (pear-ee-os'te-um; Gr. *peri,* around, + *ostrakon,* shell). Arteries, veins, nerves, and lymphatics pass through the compact bone to supply the marrow and cells responsible for bone formation and maintenance.

Growth of a Bone

The primitive skeleton of an embryo consists of cartilage and fibrous tissue, in which bones develop by a process of ossification (p. 54). Bones that develop in fibrous tissue—namely, some bones of the cranium and face—are called membranous bones. Most bones of the body develop from cartilage and are designated as endochondral ("within cartilage") bones.

In a typical long bone, there are usually three primary centers of ossification—one for the diaphysis, or shaft, and one for each epiphysis, or extremity (Figure 22-5). As long as this cartilage persists and grows, new bone may form, and the length may increase.

Articulations

An articulation, or joint, is the union of two or more bones or cartilages by another tissue, usually fibrous tissue, cartilage, or a combination of the two.

Three types of joints are recognized—synarthrosis, diarthrosis, and amphiarthrosis.

Synarthrosis. A synarthrosis (sin-ar-thro'sis; Gr. *syn,* with, + *orthron,* joint) is an immovable joint. Interlocking margins of the bones are united by fibrous tissue. Example: sutures of the skull.

Diarthrosis. A diarthrosis (Gr. *dis,* twice, + *arthron,* joint) is a movable joint. Ends of articulating

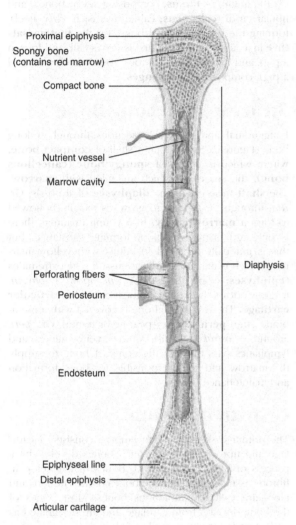

Proximal epiphysis

Spongy bone
(contains red marrow)

Compact bone

Nutrient vessel

Marrow cavity

Diaphysis

Perforating fibers

Periosteum

Endosteum

Epiphyseal line

Distal epiphysis

Articular cartilage

Figure 22-5
Diagram of longitudinal section of a long bone.

bones are covered with cartilage and enclosed in a joint capsule of fibrous tissue. The capsule contains a joint cavity lined with a vascular synovial membrane that secretes a lubricating fluid. Examples: most of the joints—knee, elbow, and others.

Amphiarthrosis. An amphiarthrosis (am-fee-ar-thro'sis; Gr. *amphi*, both, + *arthron*, joint) is a slightly movable joint. The bones are joined by a flattened disc of fibrocartilage. The bones of the joint are bound together by ligaments. These are tough bands or sheets composed mostly of white, fibrous tissue and are pliable but not elastic (except for the nuchal ligament at the back of the neck). Examples: pubic symphysis and joints between the vertebrae.

EXERCISE 22B
Muscular System

Because the muscles of a fetal pig are softer and the separations of the muscles less evident than in a lean cat or frog, a pig has been less used for muscle dissection in beginning classes. However, if full-term pigs (30 cm or more in length) are used, and careful attention is given to the dissection, even beginning students can demonstrate a great many of the muscles, along with their origins and insertions. Uninjected pigs are quite satisfactory for this work; in fact, in some ways they are easier to work with than injected pigs.

A human being has approximately 700 identified and named skeletal muscles. A pig probably has fewer (because it lacks our five-fingered manual dexterity) but still possesses hundreds of muscles. Only about 40 of the largest and most conspicuous will be studied. Even so, many introductory courses lack sufficient laboratory time in which to dissect these 40, so your instructor may be selective, or some of the dissection may be done on an extra-credit basis.

Organization of Skeletal Muscles

Skeletal muscle is under voluntary control; that is, it is innervated by motor fibers. Skeletal muscle can contract effectively to about 30% of its resting length. However, the force that a muscle develops is not the same throughout its shortening length. If a muscle is stretched out fully, little force can be developed. Similarly, when a muscle is fully contracted, its force again diminishes. You know from your own experience that it is difficult to lift a heavy object with your forearm fully extended but that it becomes easier as your arm approaches a 90° angle. But, when the muscle is maximally shortened, the force you can exert again declines.

Skeletal Muscle Is Organized into Functional Bundles. Muscle fibers are bound together by a fibrous connective tissue called **fascia** (fa'shē-uh; pl. **fasciae,** fa'shē-ē; L., bundle) into bundles called **fasciculi** (fa-sick'yu-li; L. *fasciculus,* small bundle). Fasciculi are in turn organized in various ways into an entire muscle. The most common type of muscle is a **parallel muscle,** in which the fasciculi are arranged side by side parallel to the long axis of the muscle. Other muscles are arranged in sheets with broad attachments; still others are arranged in a circle, such as those that form sphincters around orifices.

How Muscles Are Connected. Skeletal muscles are connected to cartilage, bone, ligaments, and skin either directly by their investing fascia or indirectly by means of tendons or aponeuroses, never by actual muscle fibers themselves. If the muscle fibers come very close to the bone, we say the muscle has a "fleshy attachment." A **tendon** is a narrow band of tough, fibrous connective tissue, and an **aponeurosis** (Gr. *apo,* from, + *neuron,* sinew) is a broad, thin sheet of tough connective tissue that connects the muscle to its place of attachment.

Origin, Insertion, and Action. A muscle begins at its **origin,** which in general is the stationary end. It ends at its **insertion,** which is the end that moves. The movement produced by a muscle is its **action.** For example, the biceps brachii of a human arm originates on the scapula and inserts on the radius of the forearm. Its action is to flex the forearm. Sometimes these rules for origin and insertion do not easily apply. If, for example, a muscle extends between a broad aponeurosis and a narrow tendon, the aponeurosis is considered the origin and the tendon the insertion. Some muscles have several tendons at one end and only one at the other end; in this case, the muscle has multiple origins but only one insertion. Multiple origins in such instances are called **heads.** Even these rules do not apply to every muscle, and in the end it is better to know what a muscle does (its action) than to try to know every origin and insertion.

Naming Actions. Anatomists have long used descriptive terms for dynamic motion; such terms prevent having to use complicated notations such as "bends the foreleg toward the body" or "raises the arm toward the shoulder." **Flexion** (flek'shun) moves a distal part of a limb toward the next proximal part—for example, bending the fingers or the elbow. "Flexion" also refers to the bending of the head or trunk toward the ventral surface. **Extension** is the opposite movement; it *increases* the angle between articulating elements. Straightening the arm or the fingers is an extension movement. Muscles causing these movements are called **flexors** and **extensors.**

Adduction (L. *ad,* to, + *ducere,* to lead) refers to a movement of the distal end of a bone—for example, the humerus or femur—that brings it closer to the ventral median line of the body. In **abduction** (L. *ab,* from) such a bone is moved farther away from the ventral median line, as in raising the arm out to one side. Muscles that cause these movements are **adductors** and **abductors,** respectively. (It will be helpful if you can remember the meanings of the prefixes *ad* [meaning *to*] and *ab* [meaning *from*]).

Protractors in a tetrapod (an animal with four legs) may be defined as muscles that move the distal ends of bones—for example, the femur or humerus—forward longitudinally; **retractors** move them backward. A **depressor** may cause a part, such as the mandible or an eyelid, to be lowered; a **levator** raises such a part. **Rotation** is the turning of a part: for example, the rotation of the radius on the ulna or the first vertebra (atlas) on the second (axis). Several other muscle action terms are used by human anatomists (for example, "inversion,"

"eversion," "pronation," and "supination"), but learning the actions defined in this section will suffice for our study of a fetal pig.

Naming Muscles. The names of muscles are descriptive and may be derived from one or more of the following: (1) **position** (the brachialis is an arm muscle, the pectoralis is a chest muscle, and the cutaneous lies just under the skin); (2) **action** (adductor longus, depressor rostri); (3) **shape** (deltoid); (4) **direction** (transversus abdominus); (5) **number of divisions** (the biceps is two-headed, the digastric is two-bellied); and (6) **attachments** (the sternomastoid is attached to the sternum and to the mastoid process of the skull). Many names combine two or more of these descriptive elements (the extensor carpi obliquus is an extensor; it is attached to the carpus, which it extends; and its fibers run in an oblique direction).

Dissection of Fetal Pig Muscles

Before beginning a dissection of the muscles, be sure you are familiar with the external structure of the animal, as given in the introduction to this chapter (p. 331).

It is absolutely essential to study bones and muscles together as functional units. The shape, attachments, and actions of the muscles have meaning only in connection with the bones that they cover, hold in place, and move. Refer often to the skeleton as you dissect the muscles. Feel for and identify the bones underlying the muscles you are dissecting.

If your pig has been injected, there will be an incision in the neck through which one of the jugular veins was injected. *Use the side opposite this incision for the dissection of lateral muscles.* In the neck region, as you dissect the musculature, refer also to the section on the salivary glands (p. 344) and identify the glands and blood vessels mentioned there.

 The animal first must be skinned. Make a longitudinal middorsal incision through the skin from head to tail (making sure the cut is through the skin only). Make a midventral incision from chin to groin and circular incisions through the skin around the neck, chest, and groin. Then, starting with a corner of skin in the dorsal neck region, lift the skin with forceps and use a probe or the *blunt edge* of a scalpel to push back the muscle underneath. Continue removing pieces of skin until you have uncovered the entire body and legs (unless the instructor asks you to do only one side or only the forequarter).

The outer layer of muscle is a thin, superficial layer of **cutaneous muscle,** many fibers of which are attached directly to the skin. *Try not to remove this muscle layer with the skin.*

After the pig is skinned, there is usually a great deal of fat and connective tissue still covering the muscles.

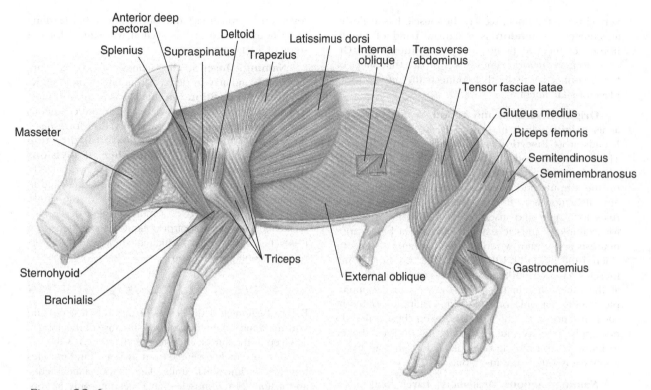

Figure 22-6

Superficial muscles of a fetal pig, lateral view. What muscle is most responsible for chewing? _____ Clench your teeth and feel your own muscle that closes your jaw. What muscle elevates the shoulder? _____ What anterior superficial thigh muscle flexes the hip joint and extends the knee? _____

Much of this can be removed by gentle rubbing with a paper towel or by careful scraping with a scalpel.

Identify the outer layer of cutaneous muscle. In the neck and face region, this cutaneous layer is called the **platysma** (pla-tiz′ma; Gr., flat piece); in the trunk region, it is called the **cutaneous maximus.** These muscles are used in twitching the skin to shake off insects, dirt, or other irritants. This thin layer of muscle is *not shown in the illustrations*. After identifying this layer, *remove it carefully* to identify the superficial muscles underneath. Remember that these muscles are very thin; remove them carefully so as not to destroy the other muscles you are to identify.

 To locate the borders of muscles, scrape off the overlying connective tissue and fascia and look for the direction of the muscle fibers. A muscle edge may be seen where there is a change in direction of fibers. Try to slip the flat handle of the scalpel between the layers of muscle at this point. *Do not cut the muscles or tear them with a dissecting needle.* Try to loosen each muscle and find out where it is attached but *do not cut a muscle unless instructed to do so.* When you are told to cut a muscle to locate deeper muscles, cut through the belly of the muscle but leave the ends attached for identification.

Figure 22-6 shows the more superficial muscles after removal of the cutaneous and platysma layer.

If, after skinning the animal, you find the muscles are still too soft to separate, exposure to air will help to harden them in a few hours. Dipping the pig in preservative or sponging a little preservative over its surface and keeping it overnight in a plastic bag should make it easier to handle.

The following muscles are grouped loosely into two groups—muscles of the forequarter and muscles of the hindquarter. The first group contain some of the muscles of the face and neck as well as those of the shoulder, chest, and forelimb. The second group includes muscles of the back, abdomen, and hindlimb. This is not an exhaustive list, but it includes the chief superficial muscles and many of the muscles of the second layer.

Muscles of the Forequarter

Muscles of the Face, Neck, Chest, and Shoulder (Table 22.1)

Beginning with the throat muscles, locate the most ventral pair, the **sternohyoids,** marking the ventral midline of the neck and covering the larynx (Figure 22-7). These muscles retract and depress the hyoid and the base of the tongue, as in swallowing. Immediately internal to

TABLE 22.1

Muscles of the Forequarter

Muscle	Origin	Insertion	Action
Muscles of the Face, Neck, Chest, and Shoulder			
Sternohyoid	Anterior end of sternum	Hyoid bone	Retracts and depresses hyoid and base of tongue, as in swallowing
Sternothyroid	Sternum	Larynx	Retracts larynx
Digastric	By tendon from mastoid process of skull	Medial surface of mandible	Depresses mandible
Mylohyoid	Medial surface of mandibles	Hyoid bone	Raises floor of mouth and hyoid bone
Masseter	Zygomatic arch	Lateral surface of mandible	Elevates jaw and closes mouth
Sternocephalic	Anterior end of sternum	Mastoid process of skull	Turns head; two muscles together depress head
Brachiocephalic	Two origins: nuchal crest and mastoid process of skull	Proximal end of humerus and fascia of shoulder	Singly, inclines head; when head is fixed, draws limb forward; together extend head
Superficial pectoral	Sternum	By a broad aponeurosis on medial surface of humerus	Adducts humerus
Posterior deep pectoral	Posterior half of sternum and cartilages of fourth to ninth ribs	Proximal end of humerus	Retracts and adducts forelimb
Anterior deep pectoral	Anterior part of sternum	Scapular fascia and aponeurosis that covers dorsal end of supraspinatus	Adducts and retracts limb
Trapezius	Nuchal crest of skull and neural spines of first 10 thoracic vertebrae	Spine of scapula	Elevates shoulder
Latissimus dorsi	Some of the thoracic and lumbar vertebrae and four ribs preceding last rib	Medial surface of humerus	Draws humerus upward and backward and flexes shoulder
Deltoid	Scapular aponeurosis	By an aponeurosis on proximal end of humerus	Flexes shoulder and abducts arm
Rhomboideus	Second cervical to ninth or tenth thoracic vertebrae	Medial surface of dorsal border of scapula	Draws scapula mediodorsally or rotates it
Rhomboideus capitis	Occipital bone	Dorsal border of scapula	Draws scapula forward and rotates shoulder
Splenius	First four or five thoracic neural spines	Occipital and temporal bones and first few cervical vertebrae	Singly, inclines head and neck to one side; together, elevate head and neck
Ventral serratus	Cervical part on transverse processes of last four or five cervical vertebrae; thoracic part on lateral surfaces of last eight or nine ribs	Medial surface of scapula	Singly, cervical part draws shoulder forward and thoracic part backward; together, shift weight to limb of contracting side; both sides together form elastic support that suspends trunk between scapulas; raise thorax
Supraspinatus	Anterior and dorsal portion of scapula and scapular spine	Proximal end of humerus	Extends humerus
Infraspinatus	Lateral surface and spine of scapula	Lateral surface of proximal end of humerus	Abducts and rotates forelimb

TABLE 22.1
Muscles of the Forequarter—cont'd

Muscle	Origin	Insertion	Action
Muscles of the Foreleg			
Triceps brachii	Long head: posterior border of scapula	All three heads insert on medial and lateral surfaces of olecranon process of ulna	Extend forearm
	Lateral head: lateral side of proximal end of humerus		
	Medial head: medial surface of proximal end of humerus, covering insertion of teres major		
Brachialis	Proximal third of humerus, ventral to lateral head of triceps	Medial surface of distal end of radius and ulna	Flexes elbow
Biceps brachii	Ventral surface of scapula near glenoid fossa	Proximal ends of radius and ulna	Flexes elbow

the sternohyoid on each side is the long **sternothyroid,** which retracts the larynx. Note that each has a lateral and a medial branch; separate these muscles to locate the small, dark, compact **thyroid gland** lying on the ventral side of the trachea.

The **digastric** muscle is the major depressor of the mandible—that is, it opens the jaw. It originates by a strong tendon from the base of the skull. Stretching ventrally between the mandibles as a thin transverse sheet is the **mylohyoid;** it compresses the floor of the mouth and assists in swallowing. The large muscle of the cheek is the **masseter.** This muscle and another (the temporal, not shown in Figure 22-8) are the major muscles that elevate the jaw and close the mouth.

Locate the **sternocephalic,** a flat muscle band that passes diagonally across the throat posterior to the submaxillary gland and beneath the parotid gland; it turns the head. When both sternocephalics contract together, the head is depressed. Posterior to the sternocephalic is the **brachiocephalic,** a large, band-shaped muscle that originates on the skull and inserts on the shoulder. This muscle raises the head, or, if the head is fixed in position by other muscles, it draws the forelimb forward. It originates on two different processes (nuchal crest and mastoid process) of the skull.

Examine the muscles that position the shoulder girdle and move the forelimb (Figure 22-7). The **superficial pectoral** (equivalent to the pectoralis major of humans) adducts the humerus. The **posterior deep pectoral** and **anterior deep pectoral** both retract and adduct the forelimb. The most superficial muscle of the back (after removal of the cutaneous maximus) is the thin and triangular **trapezius** (Figure 22-8). This muscle elevates the shoulder and moves the scapula.

The **latissimus dorsi** (see Figure 22-6) is a large, broad muscle that fans out across the back; it flexes the shoulder and is a major retractor of the humerus.

Now carefully cut through the trapezius at its insertion on the spine of the scapula and separate it from the underlying muscles. A triangular muscle just beneath the trapezius is the **rhomboideus.** Anterior to this is the straplike **rhomboideus capitis.** Both of these muscles act upon the scapula to rotate it or draw it forward or dorsally. Beneath the rhomboideus capitis, locate the triangular **splenius,** which helps elevate and turn the head.

Cut the latissimus dorsi at its origin along the spine and remove most of the muscle, leaving only a centimeter or two at its insertion on the humerus. Locate the **ventral serratus** (Figure 22-8), an extensive, fan-shaped chest muscle that originates on the cervical vertebrae and several ribs and inserts on the scapula beneath the insertion of the rhomboideus muscles. It shifts the scapula forward and backward and serves as a muscular support to sling the weight of the trunk.

Arising near the insertion of the trapezius on the scapula is the **deltoid.** It inserts on the humerus and protracts (moves forward) the upper foreleg. Carefully trim away the deltoid muscle at both origin and insertion. Beneath it lies the **infraspinatus,** which abducts and rotates the forelimb. Anterior to this is the **supraspinatus,** a fleshy muscle on the anterior surface of the scapula; it extends the humerus.

Muscles of the Foreleg

The largest muscle is the **triceps brachii,** an extensor of the forearm (Figures 22-7 and 22-8). It arises from three heads: a triangular-shaped, long head at the posterior border of the scapula; a lateral head from the

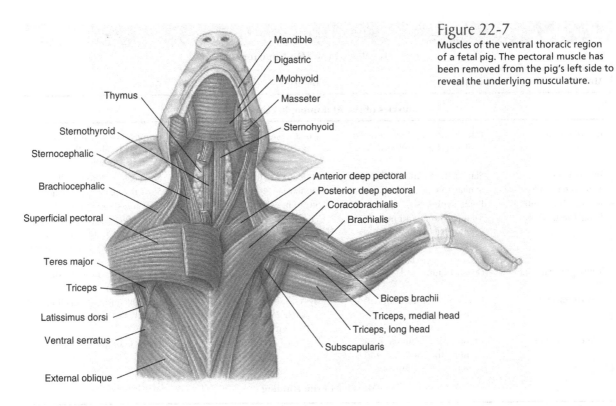

Figure 22-7
Muscles of the ventral thoracic region of a fetal pig. The pectoral muscle has been removed from the pig's left side to reveal the underlying musculature.

Mandible
Digastric
Mylohyoid
Masseter
Sternohyoid
Thymus
Sternothyroid
Sternocephalic
Brachiocephalic
Superficial pectoral
Anterior deep pectoral
Posterior deep pectoral
Coracobrachialis
Brachialis
Teres major
Triceps
Latissimus dorsi
Ventral serratus
Biceps brachii
Triceps, medial head
Triceps, long head
Subscapularis
External oblique

Figure 22-8
Muscles of the neck and shoulder of a fetal pig, lateral view. The trapezius muscle has been removed to reveal underlying musculature.

Trapezius (cut and removed)
Ventral serratus
Rhomboideus
Longissimus dorsi
Splenius
Spine of scapula
Infraspinatus
Masseter
Supraspinatus
Thymus
Larynx
Ventral serratus
Sternohyoid
Sternocephalic
External oblique
Brachiocephalic
Anterior deep pectoral
Brachialis
Triceps, long head
Triceps, lateral head

lateral surface of the humerus; and a medial head from the medial surface of the humerus. Two smaller muscles lying on the anterior and ventral surfaces of the humerus are the **brachialis** and **biceps brachii;** both act upon the elbow to flex the forearm.

Muscles of the Hindquarter

Muscles of the Abdomen, Back, and Hip (Table 22.2)
Three thin sheets of muscle lie in the lateral abdominal wall. Most superficial is the **external oblique,** lying immediately beneath the cutaneous (see Figure 22-6). Beneath this is the **internal oblique;** this is revealed by cutting a window high up on the external oblique. Then, by separating fibers of the internal oblique, you will see the **transverse abdominal,** the deepest layer and thinnest of the three muscles (and most difficult to see). All three muscles insert on the **linea alba,** a tendinous band that extends from the pubis to the sternum (Figure 22-9). Together, these muscles support the abdominal wall and compress the viscera during

TABLE 22.2
Muscles of the Hindquarter

Muscle	Origin	Insertion	Action
Muscles of the Abdomen, Back, and Hip			
External oblique	Lateral surface of last 9 or 10 ribs and lumbodorsal fascia	Linea alba, ilium, and femoral fascia	Compress abdomen, arch back; singly, it flexes trunk laterally
Internal oblique	Similar to external oblique	Similar to external oblique	Similar to external oblique
Transverse abdominal	Similar to external oblique	Similar to external oblique	Similar to external oblique
Rectus abdominus	Pubic symphysis	Sternum	Constricts abdomen
Longissimus dorsi	Sacrum, ilium, and neural processes of lumbar and thoracic vertebrae	Transverse processes of most vertebrae and lateral surfaces of ribs except the first	Singly, flexes spine laterally; together, extend back and neck; rib attachments may aid in expiration
Tensor fasciae latae	Crest of ilium	Fascia over knee, patella, and crest of tibia	Flexes hip joint and extends knee joint
Biceps femoris	Lateral part of ischium and sacrum	By a wide aponeurosis to patella and fascia of thigh and leg	Abducts and extends limb; may also flex knee joint
Gluteus medius	Fascia of longissimus dorsi, ilium, and sacroiliac and sacrosciatic ligaments	Proximal end of femur	Abducts thigh
Muscles of the Hindleg			
Quadriceps femoris, a large muscle group consisting of			
1. Rectus femoris	Ilium	Patella and its ligament	Extends shank
2. Vastus lateralis	Proximal end of femur	Patella and its ligament	Extends shank
3. Vastus medialis	Proximal end of femur	Patella and its ligament	Extends shank
4. Vastus intermedialis	Proximal end of femur	Patella and its ligament	Extends shank
Gracilis	Pubic symphysis and ventral surface of pubis	Patellar ligament and proximal end of tibia	Adducts hindlimb
Sartorius	Iliac fascia and tendon of psoas minor (external iliac vessels lie between two heads)	Patellar ligament and proximal end of tibia	Adducts hindlimb and flexes hip joint
Semimembranosus	Ischium	Distal end of femur and proximal end of tibia, both on medial side	Extends hip joint and adducts hindlimb
Semitendinosus	First and second caudal vertebrae and ischium	Proximal end of tibia and calcaneus	Extends hip and tarsal joint and flexes knee joint
Adductor	Ventral surface of pubis and ischium and tendon of origin of gracilis	Proximal end of femur	Adducts hindlimb and extends and rotates femur inward
Pectineus	Anterior border of pubis	Medial side of shaft of femur	Adducts hindlimb and flexes hip
Iliacus	Ventral surface of ilium and wing of sacrum	Proximal end of femur together with psoas major	Flexes hip and rotates thigh outward
Psoas major	Ventral sides of transverse processes of lumbar vertebrae and last two ribs	With iliacus on proximal end of femur	Flexes hip and rotates thigh outward

expiration and defecation. Beneath the external oblique and extending between the pelvic girdle and ribs on each side of the midventral line is a longitudinal band of muscle, the **rectus abdominus** (Figure 22-9). It also supports and constricts the abdomen.

Dorsal and lateral to the vertebral column, locate the **longissimus dorsi,** a very long muscle extending from the sacrum to the neck (see Figure 22-8). Acting together these muscles extend the back and neck; acting singly each flexes the spine laterally.

The most anterior superficial thigh muscle is the **tensor fasciae latae** (see Figures 22-6 and 22-10); it flexes the hip joint and extends the knee joint. Posteriorly the most superficial thigh muscle is the **biceps femoris** (see Figures 22-6 and 22-10). Its action is complex, acting across both the hip and knee joints to retract the thigh and flex the shank. Between the tensor fasciae latae and biceps femoris, and partially covered by them, is the **gluteus medius** (see Figures 22-6 and 22-10). It abducts the thigh.

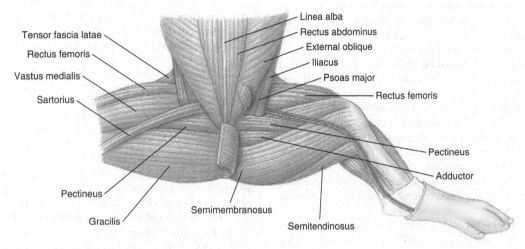

Tensor fascia latae
Rectus femoris
Vastus medialis
Sartorius
Pectineus
Gracilis
Semimembranosus
Semitendinosus
Linea alba
Rectus abdominus
External oblique
Iliacus
Psoas major
Rectus femoris
Pectineus
Adductor

Figure 22-9
Muscles of the hindlimb of a fetal pig, ventral view. The gracilis and sartorius have been cut and removed from the pig's left leg.

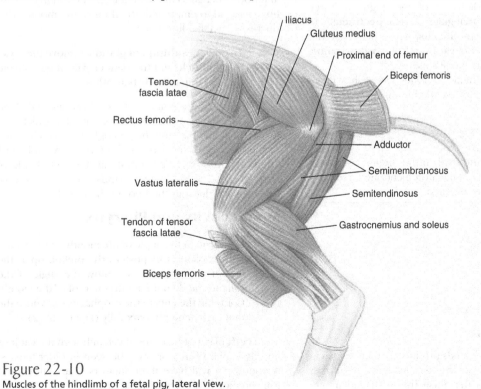

Iliacus
Gluteus medius
Proximal end of femur
Biceps femoris
Tensor fascia latae
Rectus femoris
Adductor
Semimembranosus
Semitendinosus
Vastus lateralis
Gastrocnemius and soleus
Tendon of tensor fascia latae
Biceps femoris

Figure 22-10
Muscles of the hindlimb of a fetal pig, lateral view.

Muscles of the Hindleg

The **quadriceps femoris** is a large muscle group covering the anterior and lateral sides of the femur that comprises four muscles: **rectus femoris,** a thick muscle on the anterior side of the femur; **vastus lateralis** (Figure 22-10), lateral to the rectus femoris and partly covering it; **vastus medialis** (Figure 22-9), on the medial surface of the rectus femoris; and **vastus intermedialis,** a deep muscle lying beneath the rectus femoris. All four of these muscles converge on the patella (knee-cap) and then continue as the patellar ligament to insert on the tibia. These are extensors of the shank.

The posteromedial half of the thigh is covered with a thin, wide muscle, the **gracilis** (Figure 22-9). It adducts the thigh and flexes the shank. Just anterior to the gracilis is the **sartorius,** a thin band of muscle that covers the femoral blood vessels; it is delicate and easily destroyed if not identified. Cut through the gracilis and sartorius to reveal the large **semimembranosus** muscle in the medial portion of the thigh (Figure 22-9). It extends the hip joint and adducts the hindlimb. Just posterior to the semimembranosus is the thick, band-shaped **semitendinosus;** it acts mainly to extend the hip. The semimembranosus and semitendinosus, together with the biceps femoris, are the hamstring muscles of humans.

The **adductor,** lying anterior to the semimembranosus and covered by the gracilis, is a triangular-shaped muscle that, as its name suggests, adducts the femur—that is, draws it toward the midline.

Also on the medial side of the thigh are three smaller muscles: the triangular-shaped **pectineus,** an adductor of the thigh; the **iliacus,** which flexes the hip and rotates the thigh outward; and the **psoas major,** which acts the same as the iliacus.

Some of the shank muscles are shown in Figure 22-10 but are not described in this exercise.

Identification

Be able to identify and explain the origin, insertion, and action of as many of the aforementioned muscles as your instructor has assigned.

EXERCISE 22C
Digestive System

Head and Throat

Salivary Glands

Three pairs of salivary glands produce a continual background level of fluid secretions containing lysozymes and immunoglobulins that flush the teeth and mouth

cavity and help keep bacterial growth under control. Much larger quantities of saliva are produced during meals. These secretions contain lubricating glycoproteins called **mucins** and a large amount of **salivary amylase** (α-amylase), which begins the breakdown of complex carbohydrates, such as starch.

 On the right side of the face, neck, and chin, carefully remove the skin if you have not already done so. A muscle layer will tend to adhere, but push this layer back into place gently so as not to destroy the glands beneath. Now carefully remove the thin muscles back of the angle of the jaw and beneath the ear to uncover the **parotid gland.** Do not destroy any large blood vessels.

The triangular parotid (pa-rot′id; Gr. *para,* beside, + *ous,* ear) gland is broad, thin, and rather diffused, extending from almost the midline of the throat to the base of the ear (Figure 22-11). Do not confuse the salivary glands, which are choppy and lobed in appearance, with the lymph nodes, which are more smooth and shiny. The **parotid duct** comes from the deep surface of the gland and follows the ventral border of the masseter (cheek) muscle along the external maxillary vein to the corner of the mouth (Figure 22-11).

The **submaxillary (= mandibular) gland** lies under the parotid gland and just posterior to the angle of the jaw. It is darker, compact, and oval. Its duct comes from the anterior surface of the gland and passes anteriorly, medial to the mandible, and through the sublingual gland to empty into the floor of the mouth. This duct is very difficult to trace.

 To find the **sublingual glands,** remove the mylohyoid muscle and the slender pair of geniohyoid muscles immediately beneath it.

On each side, a whitish, elongated sublingual gland is located between the diagastric muscle, which lies inside the mandible, and the genioglossus, which is one of the muscles of the base of the tongue. A sublingual artery and vein will be seen along the ventral side of each gland. The sublingual glands empty by way of several short ducts to the floor of the mouth.

Mouth Cavity and Pharynx

 Cut through the angle of the mouth on both sides with scissors. Cut posteriorly, pulling open the mouth as you proceed. Follow the angle of the tongue and do not cut into the roof of the mouth. Continue the cuts to the esophagus to expose the oral cavity and pharynx fully (Figure 22-12).

Teeth may not be erupted yet, although the canines and third pair of incisors may be seen in older fetuses. A young pig will have three incisors, one canine, and four premolars on each side of each jaw.

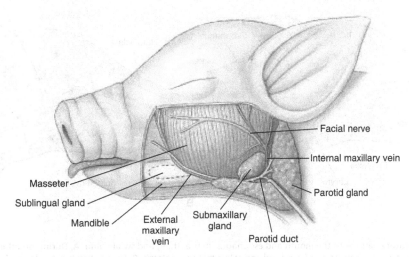

Figure 22-11
Dissection of the head and neck of a fetal pig to show some superficial veins, nerves, and salivary glands.

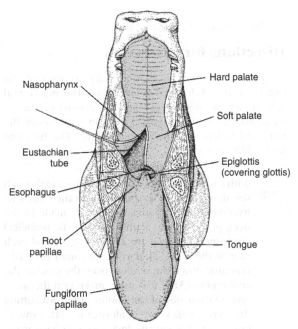

Figure 22-12
Oral cavity of a fetal pig.

 Remove the flesh along the right jaws and carefully cut away enough of the jawbone to expose buds of the embryonic teeth.

The third incisors and canines are first to erupt; second incisors are last.

The mouth cavity is roofed by a narrow, bony **hard palate,** sheathed ventrally with mucous membranes ridged into transverse folds. Extending posteriorly from the hard palate is the **soft palate,** composed of thick

membrane. The hard and soft palates of mammals completely separate the oral cavity from the air passages above, an innovation that allows a mammal to chew a mouthful of food at leisure while breathing freely through its nose. Only crocodilians among other vertebrates have a hard palate; a soft palate is unique to mammals.

Open the mouth wide, drawing down the tongue, to locate, at the posterior end of the soft palate, the opening into the **nasopharynx** (fair'inks; Gr. *pharyngx,* gullet), the space above the soft palate. It connects with the nasal passages from the nostrils.

 To expose the nasopharynx, make a midline incision of the soft palate. Locate the small openings on each side of the roof of the nasopharynx.

From these openings, the **eustachian tubes** (named after B. Eustachio, an Italian physician) lead to the middle ear.

Posterior to the nasopharynx is the **laryngeal pharynx,** which connects the oral cavity with the **esophagus.** Both nasal and laryngeal pharynx are derived from the pharynx of ancestral chordates, which evolved as a filter-feeding apparatus. Pharyngeal (gill) pouches develop in this region in all vertebrate embryos. In fishes these pouches break through to develop into gill chambers, but in tetrapods they become transformed into other structures: middle ear cavity and glandular tissue (thyroid, parathyroid, and thymus).

The **larynx** lies in the floor of the laryngeal pharynx. Locate the flaplike **epiglottis,** which folds up over the **glottis** (open end of the larynx) to close it when food is being swallowed. Note that, in the mouth, air passages are *dorsal* to the food passage. In the throat, however, air is carried through the larynx and trachea, which are *ventral* to the food passage (esophagus).

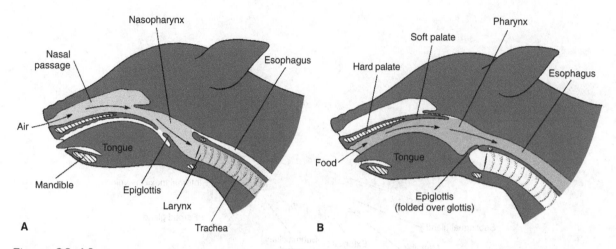

A

B

Figure 22-13

Relationship of respiratory passage to the mouth and esophagus, in breathing and swallowing. **A,** During breathing, the glottis is open to receive air from nostrils and is protected from food and saliva by the epiglottis. **B,** For swallowing, the larynx is pushed anteriorly, causing the epiglottis to fold over the glottis, thus closing air passage to the lungs. Feel your Adam's apple (larynx) as it moves up when you swallow.

These passageways cross in the pharyngeal cavity (Figure 22-13). When the animal is respiring, the epiglottis fits up against the opening into the nasopharynx, allowing air into the larynx but preventing the entrance of saliva or food from the mouth. During swallowing the larynx is pushed forward, causing the epiglottis to fold over the glottis, thus opening the food passage while closing off the air passage.

 Continue your dissection of the neck region by making a midventral incision down the neck.

After parting the skin and clearing away some tissue around the larynx, you will expose the **thymus,** a large, soft, irregular mass of glandular tissue lying lateral to the sternohyoid muscles (Figure 22-14). It is an extensive gland in the fetus and young animal but after puberty it decreases in size, although continuing to function throughout life. The thymus extends caudally under the sternum, with its posterior portion overlying the heart. The thymus is part of the body's lymphoid system and is filled with lymphocytes of all sizes and is especially rich in T cells, which are important in immunological responses.

As tissue is cleared from the larynx, find the **trachea** (windpipe) extending caudally from it. The trachea is stiffened by a series of C-shaped cartilage rings, which are incomplete dorsally where the trachea lies against the esophagus.

Tracing the trachea posteriorly, you will see the **thyroid gland,** a small, dark red, oval gland lying on the trachea beneath the sternothyroid muscles (Figure 22-14). The thyroid is an endocrine gland that produces thyroxin and triiodothyronine, two hormones that promote growth and development and regulate the metabolic rate.

Abdominal Cavity

Directions for Dissection

To proceed further, it is necessary to expose the organs of the abdominal cavity. Place the pig ventral side up in the dissecting pan. Tie a cord or rubber band around one forelimb, loop the cord under the pan, and fasten it to the other forelimb. Do the same to the hindlegs.

 With a scalpel, make a midventral incision through the skin and muscles, but not into the body cavity, continuing the incision already made in the neck posteriorly to within 1 cm of the umbilical cord (incision 1, Figure 22-15). Cut around each side of the cord (2). If your specimen is female, continue down the midline from the cord to the anal region (3). If it is male, make two incisions, one on each side of the midline, to avoid cutting the penis, which lies underneath (3a). Now, in either sex, deepen the incisions you have made in the abdominal region through the muscle layer to reach the body cavity, taking care not to injure the underlying organs. With scissors, make two lateral cuts on each side, one just anterior to the hindlegs (4) and the other posterior to the ribs (5), and turn back the flaps of the body wall (6). Flush out the abdominal cavity with running water.

All visceral organs are invested in mesentery and held in place with connective tissue. Loosen this tissue carefully to separate organs, tubes, and vessels,

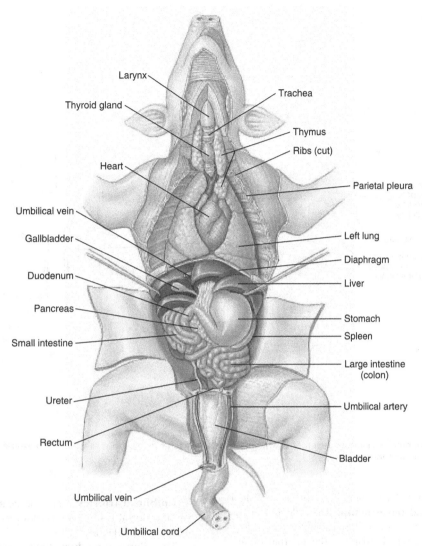

Figure 22-14

Internal anatomy of a fetal pig, ventral view. The first part of the small intestine (just past the stomach) is called the _____.
The liver has how many lobes? _____ What long, reddish organ both serves as an important lymph organ and has important immunological function? _____

being careful not to cut or tear them. _Do not remove any organs unless you are specifically directed to do so._ Be careful in all your preliminary dissection not to destroy blood vessels or nerves, to keep them intact for later dissection of the circulatory and nervous systems.

It is important to remember that instructions referring to the "right side" refer to the animal's right side, which will be on your left as the animal lies ventral side up in the dissection pan.

Notice that the umbilical cord is attached anteriorly by a tube, the **umbilical vein.**

 Tie a string around the umbilical vein in two places and sever the vein between the two strings.

The strings will identify this vein later. Lay the umbilical cord between the hindlegs and identify the following parts.

The **body wall** consists of several layers: (1) tough external **skin,** (2) two layers of **oblique muscle** and an inner layer of **transverse muscle** (try to separate the layers and determine the direction of the fibers), and (3) an inner lining of thin, transparent **peritoneum.**

The **diaphragm** is a muscular, dome-shaped partition separating the peritoneal cavity (abdominal cavity) from the thoracic cavity, which together constitute the coelom. _Do not remove the diaphragm._

The peritoneum is the smooth, shiny membrane that lines the abdominal cavity and supports and covers

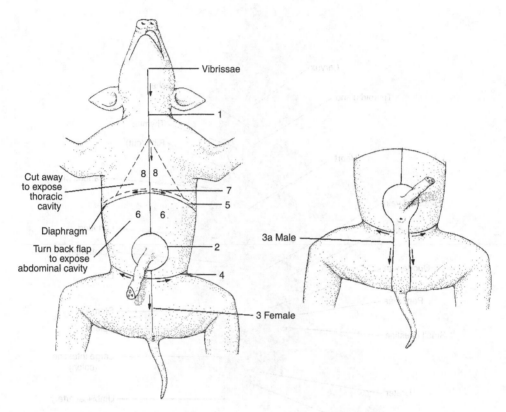

Figure 22-15

Cutting diagram. The numbers indicate the order in which each incision is to be made. Incisions 1 through 6 expose the abdominal cavity; 7 and 8 expose the thoracic cavity.

the organs within it. That which lines the body walls is called the **parietal peritoneum.** It is reflected off the dorsal region of the body wall in a double layer to form the **mesenteries,** which suspend the internal organs, and then continues around the organs as a cover, where it is called the **visceral peritoneum.**

The **liver** is a large, reddish gland with four main lobes lying just posterior to the diaphragm. The greenish, saclike **gallbladder** may be seen under one of the central lobes (Figure 22-14).

The **stomach** is nearly covered by the left lobe of the liver. The **small intestine** is loosely coiled and held by mesenteries. Note the blood vessels in the mesentery that supports the digestive tract. The **large intestine** is compactly coiled on the left side posterior to the stomach.

The **spleen** is a long, reddish organ attached by a mesentery to the greater curvature of the stomach. The spleen contains one of the largest concentrations of lymphatic tissue in the body. It phagocytizes spent blood components and salvages the iron from hemoglobin for reuse. It is also immunologically important in initiating immune responses by B cells and T cells.

Umbilical arteries are two large arteries extending from the dorsal wall of the coelom to and through the umbilical cord (Figure 22-14).

The **allantoic bladder,** the fetal urinary bladder, is a large sac lying between the umbilical arteries. It connects with the allantoic duct in the umbilical cord.

Kidneys are two large, bean-shaped organs attached to the dorsal wall dorsal to the intestines. They are *outside* the peritoneal cavity in the **cisterna magna** and are separated from the other abdominal organs by the peritoneum.

Thoracic Cavity and Neck Region

 With scissors, begin just anterior to the diaphragm and cut along the midventral line through the sternum to a point midway between the forelegs. Keep the lower blade of the scissors up to prevent injuring the heart underneath. Now make a lateral cut on each side just anterior to the diaphragm (see incision 7, Figure 22-15).

This exposes the thoracic cavity but leaves the diaphragm in place.

The **mediastinal septum,** which separates the right and left lung cavities, is a thin, transparent tissue attached to the sternal region of the thoracic wall (Figure 22-16).

 Separate the mediastinal septum carefully from the body wall. Now lift up one side of the thoracic wall and look for the small **internal thoracic artery** and **vein** (also called sternal or mammary) embedded in the musculature of the body wall. Carefully separate these vessels on each side and lay them down over the heart and lungs for future use. Now you may cut away some of the ventral thoracic wall (see incision 8, Figure 22-15) to allow a better view of the thoracic cavity containing the left and right **lungs** and the **heart.**

Pleura (Gr., side) is the name given to the peritoneum that lines each half of the thoracic cavity and covers the lungs (Figure 22-16). The peritoneum lining the thoracic cavity is the **parietal** (L. *paries,* wall) **pleura;** the part applied to the lungs is the **visceral** (L., bowels) **pleura.** The small space between is the **pleural cavity,** in which lubricating **pleural fluid** prevents friction. The portions of the parietal pleurae on the medial side next to the heart are called the **mediastinal pleurae.** The **mediastinum** is the region between the mediastinal pleurae. It contains the pericardium and heart and roots of the big arteries and veins, as well as the trachea, the esophagus, part of the thymus, and other parts.

The double-walled **pericardium** enclosing the heart is made up of an outer **parietal pericardium** and a **visceral pericardium** applied to the heart with pericardial fluid in the space between.

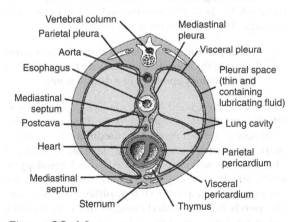

Figure 22-16
Diagrammatic transverse section through the thorax in the region of the ventricles to show the relations of the pleural and pericardial membranes, mediastinum, and lung cavities.

Digestive Tract

The digestive system consists of the alimentary canal, extending from mouth to anus, and glands such as salivary glands, liver, and pancreas, that assist in its function of converting food into a form that can be assimilated for growth and energy requirements. You have already studied the anterior portions of the alimentary canal: mouth cavity and salivary glands. We will now consider the digestive tract proper, beginning with the esophagus.

The **esophagus** is a soft, muscular tube that leads from the pharynx to the stomach. Locate it in the neck region posterior to the larynx, where it is attached to the dorsal side of the trachea by connective tissue. Find the esophagus in the thoracic cavity posterior to the lungs; in the abdominal cavity, find where it emerges through the diaphragm at the cardiac end of the stomach. The muscles at the anterior end of the tube are striated (voluntary), gradually changing to smooth muscle. How does this affect swallowing? _____

The **stomach** (see Figure 22-14) is a large, muscular organ that breaks up food and thoroughly mixes it with gastric juice. Identify its **cardiac end** near the heart, its **pyloric end** that joins the duodenum, its **greater curvature** where the spleen is attached, and its **lesser curvature.** The **fundus** (L., bottom) is the anterior blind pouch. The contents of the fetal digestive tract, made green by pigments in the bile salts, are called **meconium** and contain epithelium sloughed from the mucosa lining, sebaceous secretions, and amniotic fluid swallowed by the fetus. Open the stomach longitudinally, rinse out, and find (1) the **rugae,** or folds, in its walls; (2) the opening from the esophagus; and (3) the **pyloric** (Gr. *pylōros,* gatekeeper) **valve,** which regulates the passage of food into the duodenum.

The **small intestine** includes the **duodenum** (doo-uh-de'num or doo-od'in-um; L., "twelve-each," referring to its length in humans, which equals about 12 finger-widths), or first portion, which lies next to the pancreas and receives the common bile duct and pancreatic duct, and the **jejunum** and **ileum,** indistinguishable in the fetal pig, which make up the remainder of the small intestine.

 Remove a piece of the intestine, open it, and examine it *under water* with a hand lens or dissecting microscope. Observe the minute, fingerlike **villi** (sing. **villus;** L., shaggy hair), which greatly increase the absorptive surface of the intestine.

Most digestion and absorption take place in the small intestine.

The **large intestine** includes a long, tightly coiled **colon** and a straight, posterior **rectum,** which extends through the pelvic girdle to an **anus.** Its primary function is absorption of water and minerals from the liquified chyme that enters it.

Find the **cecum,** a blind pouch of the colon at its junction with the ileum. In humans and anthropoid apes, the cecum has a narrow diverticulum (a tube, blind at distal end) called the **vermiform** (L., worm-shaped) **appendix.** Open the cecum (on its convex side opposite the ileum) and note how the entrance of the ileum forms a ring-shaped **ileocecal valve.** The posterior end of the rectum will be exposed in a later dissection.

Digestive Glands. The **liver,** a large, brownish gland posterior to the diaphragm, has four main lobes: left and right lateral lobes and left and right central lobes. One of the many important functions of the liver is the production of **bile,** a fluid containing bile salts, which are steroid derivatives responsible for the emulsification of fats. Bile is stored and concentrated in the **gallbladder,** a small, greenish, oval sac embedded in the dorsal surface of the right central lobe of the liver. The liver is connected to the upper border of the stomach by a tough, transparent membrane, the **gastrohepatic ligament,** in which are embedded blood vessels (in the left side) and ducts (in the right side). Carefully loosen the gallbladder and note its tiny **cystic duct.** This unites with **hepatic ducts** from the liver to form the **common bile duct,** which carries bile to the duodenum. Probe the gastrohepatic ligament and adjoining liver tissue carefully to find these ducts. Do not injure the blood vessels lying beside them.

The **pancreas** is a mass of soft glandular tissue in the mesentery between the duodenum and the end of the stomach. Push the small intestine, except the duodenum, to the left to explore the gland. Its pancreatic juice is carried by a **pancreatic duct** to the pyloric end of the duodenum. The pancreas is a double gland having both endocrine and exocrine portions. Its endocrine portion produces two hormones, insulin and glucagon, which are of great importance in carbohydrate and fat metabolism. The exocrine portion secretes pancreatic juice—a mixture of water, electrolytes, and enzymes. The enzymes include carbohydrases, which digest sugars and starches; lipases, which split lipids; and proteases, which break down proteins. The pancreas is the only source of lipases in the digestive system.

Other digestive juices are secreted by the **mucosa lining** of the stomach and of the small intestine.

Histological Study of the Intestine. Examine a cross section of human or other mammalian small intestine and compare it with the histological structure of amphibian intestine. Examine mammalian liver and pancreas slides.

Identification

Be able to locate and give the functions of the parts of the digestive system.

EXERCISE 22D
Urogenital System

Urinary System

 Read the directions carefully and dissect cautiously. Do not tear or remove any organs, blood vessels, or ducts. Instead, separate them carefully from the surrounding tissues. You will dissect the urogenital system of only one sex, then exchange your dissected specimen with another student who has dissected the opposite sex. Therefore, prepare your specimen with the care you would give to a demonstration dissection.

The urinary system consists of a pair of kidneys, pair of ureters, urinary bladder, and urethra (shared with the reproductive system in males).

The fetal **urinary bladder** is the **allantoic** (Gr. *allas,* sausage) **bladder,** a long sac located between the umbilical arteries (Figure 22-17). It narrows ventrally to form the **allantoic duct,** which continues through the umbilical cord and is the fetal excretory canal. The bladder narrows dorsally to empty into the **urethra,** the adult excretory canal. The urethra will be dissected later. After birth the allantoic end of the bladder closes to form the urinary bladder.

Kidneys are dark and bean-shaped. They lie *outside* the peritoneum on the lumbar region of the dorsal body wall. Uncover the right kidney carefully. The depression on the median side of each kidney is called the **hilus.** Through it pass the renal blood vessels and the **ureter,** or excretory duct. Follow the left ureter posteriorly to its entrance into the bladder. Be careful of small ducts and vessels that cross the ureter. (Note the small **adrenal gland,** an endocrine gland lying close to the medial side of the anterior end of the kidney and embedded in fat and peritoneum.)

 Slit open the right kidney longitudinally, cutting in from the outer border. Remove the ventral half of the kidney and lay it in a dish of water.

Study with a hand lens or dissecting scope. Identify the **cortex** (L., bark), or outer layer, containing microscopic renal corpuscles; **medulla** (L., marrow, pith), or deeper layer, containing the radially arranged blood vessels and collecting tubules; and **renal pyramids,** which contain groups of collecting tubules coming together to empty through **papillae** into the pelvis. The **pelvis** is a thin-walled chamber that connects with the ureter. Divisions of the pelvis into which the papillae empty are referred to as **calyces** (ka′luh-sez; sing. **calyx**) (Figure 22-17).

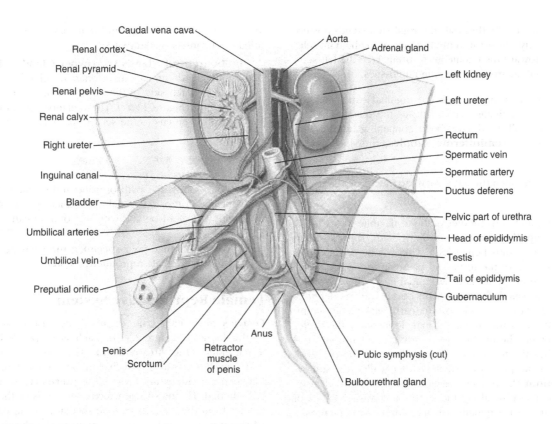

Figure 22-17
Male urogenital system of a fetal pig. The right kidney has been longitudinally sectioned to show internal structure.

 For a description of the anatomy and physiology of excretion, read your textbook. Examine the demonstration specimens of sheep kidneys on display. You will be expected to understand the structure and functioning of the kidney and its functional unit, the nephron.

Male Reproductive System

The location of the testes in the fetus depends on the stage of development of the fetus. Each testis originates in the abdominal cavity near the kidney. During the development of the fetus, a prolongation of the peritoneum, the **processus vaginalis,** grows down into each half of an external pouch, the scrotum. Later the testis "descends" into the **scrotum** through the **inguinal canal,** where it lies within the sac, or sheath, formed by the processus vaginalis. The inguinal canal is the tubular passage connecting the abdominal cavity with the scrotal sac (Figure 22-17). The descent of both testes into the scrotum is usually completed shortly before birth. Part of the cutaneous scrotum can be seen ventral to the anus.

Lay the umbilical cord and allantoic bladder between the legs and locate the **urethra** (Gr. *ouron,* urine) at the dorsal end of the bladder. The urethra bends dorsally and posteriorly to disappear into the pelvic region. Find the sperm ducts (pl. **vasa deferentia;** sing. **vas deferens**), two white tubes that emerge from the openings of the **inguinal** (L., groin) canals, cross over the umbilical arteries and ureters, and come together medially to enter the urethra. Also emerging from each inguinal ring are the spermatic artery, vein, and nerve. Together with the vas deferens, these make up the **spermatic cord,** which leads to the testis.

Now lay the bladder up over the abdominal cavity and locate the thin, hard, cordlike **penis** under the strip of skin left posterior to the urogenital opening. The penis lies in a sheath in the ventral abdominal wall, ending at the **urogenital opening.**

 Carefully separate the penis from surrounding tissue; then cut away the skin and muscle that covered and surrounded it. Complete the removal of any skin remaining on the inside of the thigh and rump and carefully separate away the underlying fascia. The thin-walled scrotal sac extends posteriorly across the ventral surface of the high muscles toward the cutaneous scrotum. Free the left scrotal sac from the surrounding tissues.

Pass a probe through the inguinal canal into the processus vaginalis, which houses the **testis.** The testis is a small, hard, oval body containing hundreds of microscopic **seminiferous tubules,** in which sperm develop.

 Cut open the left scrotal sac to expose the testis.

The seminiferous tubules of the testis unite into a much coiled **epididymus** (Gr. *epi,* upon, + *didymos,* testicle). The epididymus begins as a whitish lobe on the anterior surface of the testis and passes posteriorly around one side of the testis to its caudal end, where it unites with the **vas deferens** (sperm duct). The vas deferens (L. *vas,* vessel, + *deferre,* to carry off) passes cranially through the inguinal canal, loops over the ureter and enters the urethra, as already seen. A fibrous cord attaches the testis and the epididymis to the posterior end of the processus vaginalis. It is called the **gubernaculum** (L., rudder). A narrow band of muscle (the cremaster) runs along the lateral and posterior part of the processus vaginalis parallel with the vas deferens.

 Separate tissues on each side of the penis in the pelvic region; then, being careful not to injure the penis or cut too deeply, use a scalpel to cut through the cartilage of the pelvic girdle.
  Spread the legs apart to expose the **urethra** and its connection with the penis.

The urethral canal extends throughout the length of the penis and serves as a common duct for both sperm and urine.

 Now, beginning at its juncture with the bladder, follow the urethra posteriorly and locate the following **male glands.**

Seminal Vesicles. Seminal vesicles are a pair of small glands on the dorsal side of the urethra. These glands contribute a secretion to the semen that is rich in fructose, a six-carbon sugar that stimulates previously inactive but mature spermatozoa to become highly motile. In humans secretion of the seminal vesicles makes up more than 60% of the volume of the semen.

Prostate Gland. The prostate gland is poorly developed in the fetus; it lies between and often partly covered by the seminal vesicles but may be difficult to find. Alkaline secretions of the prostate assist in neutralizing acids normally present in the urethra, as well as in the vagina of females. In humans, prostate secretion is

known to contain a compound that may help prevent urinary tract infections in males.

Bulbourethral Glands (=Cowper Glands). Bulbourethral glands are a pair of narrow glands about 1 cm long on each side of the urethra near its junction with the penis (Figure 22-17). These glands add a thick, sticky alkaline mucus to the semen that has lubricating properties.

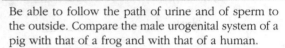

Identification

Be able to follow the path of urine and of sperm to the outside. Compare the male urogenital system of a pig with that of a frog and with that of a human.

 Now exchange your specimen for a female and study the female reproductive system.

Female Reproductive System

Ovaries are small, pale organs lying just posterior to the kidneys (Figure 22-18). Each is suspended by a mesentery, the **mesovarium** (Gr. *mesos,* middle, + L. *ovarium,* ovary), which can be seen extending between the kidney and ovary. The **uterus** (L., womb) is Y-shaped. **Horns of the uterus** (the arms of the Y) extend from the ovaries to unite medially at the **body of the uterus,** which leads to a **vagina** (L., sheath). It is in the horns of the uterus, not the body of the uterus, that fetal pigs develop. (Most mammals have a similar Y-shaped uterus, called **bicornuate** ["double-horned"], but in higher primates, including humans, the two uterine horns are completely fused, a condition called **simplex.**) Each uterine horn is suspended by a mesentery, the **broad ligament.** Follow the uterine horn anterior to the ovary, where it gives rise to a highly convoluted **oviduct** (also called **fallopian tube,** after G. Fallopio, Italian anatomist). The oviduct coils around the ovary and terminates at a wide, ciliated funnel, the **infundibulum** (L., funnel). In adult pigs, eggs released from the ovary at ovulation are swept into the opening **(ostium)** of the infundibulum by ciliary currents.

To expose the rest of the reproductive system, the pelvis must be cut open.

 Lay the allantoic bladder anteriorly over the abdominal viscera. Cut through the muscle medially between the legs and through the pelvic girdle. Be careful not to cut through the urethra or vagina. Spread the legs apart and separate the urethra from the surrounding tissue. (Note where the ureters join the dorsal end of the bladder.)

Lay the bladder and urethra to one side. Follow the body of the uterus posteriorly to a slight constriction called the **cervix.** From here the tube widens and is

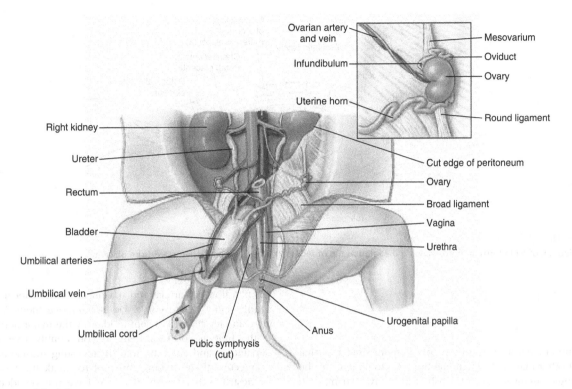

Figure 22-18

Female urogenital system of a fetal pig. What structures serve as excretory ducts for the kidneys? _____ What structure drains the bladder? _____ Embryonic pigs develop in what paired structures? _____

called the **vagina.** The vagina and urethra soon join to form a **urogenital sinus,** which is a short common passageway for the two systems.

The **vulva** is the external opening of the urogenital sinus, ventral to the anus. The ventral side of the vulva extends out to form a pointed **genital papilla.** A small, rounded **clitoris** may be seen extending from the ventral floor of the urogenital sinus. This is not always evident.

In adults, at copulation, the male penis places the spermatozoa, contained in a seminal fluid, into the vagina. The sperm must pass through the uterus to the oviduct to fertilize the egg. After fertilization the zygote passes down to the horn of the uterus to develop. Note how the horns are adapted for carrying a litter. How does this compare with the human uterus? _____ How is the developing fetus nourished? _____ How are waste products from the fetus disposed of? _____

The placenta of a pig is known as a **chorioallantoic,** or **diffuse, placenta** (Figure 22-19). In the uterus of a dog and some other carnivores, the placenta is called a zonary placenta because the chorionic villi are located in a girdlelike zone, or band, around the middle of each pup rather than over the whole

surface of the chorion, as in the pig. A human placenta is disc-shaped.

If you have not studied the male system, trade your specimen for a male and make a thorough study of the male system.

Identification

Be able to trace the path of an unfertilized egg from the ovary to the uterus. Compare with a frog.

Be able to trace the path of urine in females. Are any parts shared by both urinary and reproductive systems? _____

Oral Report

Be able to identify and give the functions of the reproductive organs of both male and female pigs.

Written Report

On separate paper, compare the mammalian and amphibian reproductive systems as illustrated by your study of a pig and frog. How is each adapted to its own type of reproduction?

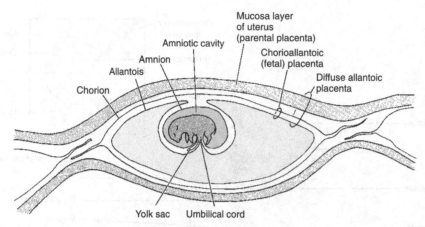

Figure 22-19

Diagram of a pig fetus in utero, showing the relationship of fetal and parental membranes in a diffuse placenta.

EXERCISE 22E

Circulatory System

The circulatory system of a pig is quite similar to that of other mammals, including humans. In contrast to the single-circuit system of a fish, with its two-chambered heart, and the incomplete double circuit of a three-chambered amphibian heart, a mammal has an effective four-chambered heart, which allows the blood two complete circuits: a **systemic** circuit through the body, followed by a **pulmonary** circuit to the lungs for oxygenation. The right side of the heart receives oxygen-poor blood returning from the body tissues and pumps it to the lungs; the left side receives oxygen-rich blood returning from the lungs and pumps it to the body tissues.

The study of fetal pig circulation has the added advantage of illustrating not only typical mammalian circulation but also typical **fetal circulation.** The changes in circulation necessary for the transition from a non-breathing, noneating fetus to an independent individual with a fully independent circulation are both crucially important and elegantly simple.

Uninjected vessels will contain only dried blood (or they may be empty) and therefore will be fragile, flattened, and either brown or colorless. If injected, the arteries will have been filled with latex or a starchy injection mass through one of the arteries in the cut umbilical cord and will be firm and pink or yellow. The veins will have been injected through an external jugular vein in the neck and will be blue. Sometimes, however, the injection medium does not fully penetrate the vasculature. The lymphatic system will not be studied.

Uncover and separate the vessels with a blunt probe and trace them as far into the body as possible, but be careful not to break or remove them. Nerves often follow an artery and a vein and will appear as tough, shiny, white cords. Do not remove them. You may, in fact, find it efficient to identify the major nerves at this time as you find them. As you identify a vessel, separate it and carefully remove investing muscle and connective tissue, taking care not to break the vessel or destroy other vessels that you have not yet identified. Do not remove any body organs unless specifically directed to do so.

As it is often difficult to trace the arterial system without damaging the venous system, which lies above it, you will study the veins first. However, because corresponding arteries and veins usually lie side by side, it is often convenient to study both systems at the same time.

Keep in mind that there is considerable variation among individual pigs in the points of vessel bifurcation, especially in the venous system of the neck and shoulder region. *The venous arrangement in your pig almost certainly will not look exactly like the manual illustrations.* Make notes or sketches of any variations that you find in your specimen. With careful dissection, both veins and arteries can be left intact.

Heart

 Note carefully the shape and slope of the diaphragm and how it forms the posterior boundary of the thoracic cavity. Then cut the diaphragm away from the body wall to make entrance into the thoracic cavity more convenient.

Open the pericardial sac and examine the heart. It has two small, thin-walled atria and two larger, muscular-walled ventricles.

Right Atrium (Anterior and Ventral). Lift the heart (Figure 22-20) and see the precaval and postcaval veins that empty into the right atrium. The **postcava**

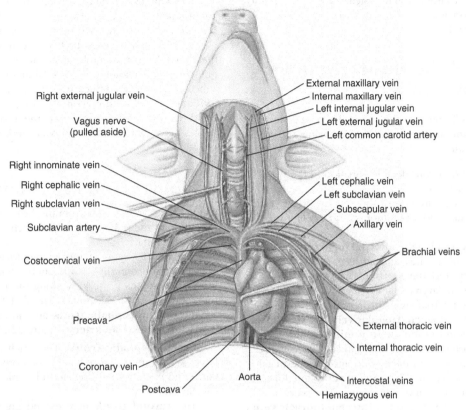

Figure 22-20
Veins of head, shoulders, and forelimbs of a fetal pig. The internal thoracic veins, shown laterally on the opened thoracic cavity, actually lie ventral to the heart.

from the abdominal region emerges through the diaphragm; the **precava** comes through the space between the first ribs (Figure 22-20).

Left Atrium (Anterior and Dorsal). The left atrium receives the **pulmonary veins** on the dorsal side. Note the conspicuous, earlike right and left auricles (L. *auricula,* ear) lying on each side of the heart. The term "auricle" is often incorrectly used as a synonym for "atrium"; however, the term should be reserved for the earlike flap that protrudes from each atrium.

Right Ventricle. The right ventricle is large and thick-walled. The **pulmonary artery** leaves the right ventricle and passes over the anterior end of the heart to the left, where it divides back of the heart to go to the lungs.

Left Ventricle. The left ventricle is larger and covers the apex of the heart (posterior). It gives off the large **aorta,** which rises anteriorly just behind (dorsal to) the pulmonary artery. The **coronary sulcus** is the groove on the surface of the heart between the right and left ventricles. It contains the **coronary artery** and **vein,** which supply the tissues of the heart itself.

General Plan of Circulation

In mammalian circulation (after birth), the systemic and pulmonary systems of circulation are separate. Blood from all parts of the body except the lungs returns by way of the large **precava** (anterior vena cava) and **postcava** (posterior vena cava) to the **right atrium.** From there it goes to the **right ventricle** to be pumped out through the **pulmonary arteries** to the lungs to be oxygenated. The blood returns through the **pulmonary veins** to the **left atrium** and then to the **left ventricle,** which sends it through the **aorta** to branches that carry blood finally to capillaries of all parts of the body. The venous system returns it again to the right side of the heart to begin another circuit. Mammals have a **hepatic portal system** but no renal portal system, as in amphibians.

Before birth, when the lungs are not yet functioning, a fetus depends on the placenta for nutrients and oxygen, which are brought to it through the **umbilical vein.** Therefore, the general plan of circulation is modified in a fetus, so that most of the pulmonary circulation is short-circuited directly into the systemic bloodstream to be carried to the placenta instead of the lungs. Only enough blood goes to the lungs to nourish the lung tissue until birth.

Veins of the Head, Shoulders, and Forelimbs

 Carefully remove the remainder of the sternum and the first rib without damaging the veins beneath.

You will find considerable variation in the veins of individual specimens.

The precaval division of the venous circuit carries blood from the head, neck, thorax, and forelimbs to the heart.

Begin by locating the **internal jugular vein,** found lying along the trachea and adjacent to the common carotid artery and the vagus nerve (Figure 22-20). It drains the brain, larynx, and thyroid.

Trace the internal jugular vein posteriorly to its confluence with the **external jugular vein** and **subclavian vein;** these join to form the **innominate vein.** Follow the two innominate veins (right and left) through the opening at the level of the first rib into the chest cavity. Here they join to form the **precaval vein** (anterior vena cava), which enters the right atrium. The precava also receives, at this level, a pair of **internal thoracic veins** lying on each side of the sternum. This is the vein that, along with the accompanying artery, you detached from the ventral muscle wall of the chest cavity (Exercise 22C). You will also find its continuation in the abdominal muscle wall.

Another vessel entering the precava dorsolaterally close to the heart is the **costocervical trunk.** It receives several veins from the neck and dorsal thorax.

Lift the heart and left lung and push them to the right. The unpaired **hemiazygous (= azygous) vein** lies in the chest cavity along the left side of the aorta and receives from the left and right intercostal veins. Follow the hemiazygous anteriorly to the point at which it crosses the aorta and goes under the heart. Lift up the heart to see the vein cross the pulmonary veins and enter the right atrium along with the postcava.

Return now to the neck region and locate the **external jugular vein.** This vein was probably used to inject the venous system and will be tied and severed on one side of the neck. The external jugular is formed by the union of the **internal maxillary** (dorsal) and the **external maxillary** (ventral) near the angle of the jaw. These vessels drain superficial parts of the head.

Joining the base of the external jugular (or sometimes the subclavian) is the **cephalic vein,** a large, superficial vein from the arm and shoulder. It lies just beneath the skin.

The **subclavian vein** extends from the shoulder and forelimb. It is a deeper vein, which follows the subclavian artery. (There may be from one to three subclavian or brachial veins. If there are more than one, there may be considerable anastomosing [networklike branching and rejoining of vessels] among them.) The subclavian, as it continues into the arm, is called the **axillary** (L. *axilla,* armpit) in the armpit and the **brachial** (Gr. *brachion,* upper arm) in the upper arm. Large nerves of the brachial nerve plexus overlie these veins.

Arteries of the Head, Shoulders, and Forelimbs

Arteries carry blood away from the heart, and, with the exception of the pulmonaries, all branch from the main artery, the aorta.

The **aorta** begins at the left ventricle (ascending aorta), curves dorsally (aortic arch) behind the left lung, and extends posteriorly along the middorsal line (descending, or dorsal, aorta). The first two branches are the **brachiocephalic trunk** and, just to the left of it, the **left subclavian artery** (Figure 22-21).

Brachiocephalic Trunk. The brachiocephalic is a large, single artery that extends anteriorly a short distance and branches into the carotid trunk and the right subclavian artery.

The **carotid trunk** may extend anteriorly for as much as a centimeter, or it may divide at once into the **left** and **right common carotid** arteries, which form a Y over the trachea and extend up each side of it. Each common carotid artery follows an internal jugular vein and the vagus nerve toward the head, giving off branches to the esophagus, thyroid, and larynx. Near the head, each common carotid gives off an **internal carotid,** a deep artery passing dorsally to the skull and brain and an **external carotid,** which is a continuation of the common carotid that supplies the tongue and face.

The **right subclavian artery** arises from the brachiocephalic and continues into the right arm as the **axillary** in the armpit, **brachial** in the upper arm, and **radial** and **ulnar** in the lower arm. The **subscapular** extends to the deep muscles of the shoulder and branches off the axillary part of the artery.

Left Subclavian Artery. The left subclavian arises directly from the aorta. Otherwise, it is similar to the right subclavian artery.

Each of the subclavian arteries gives off several branches, which include the **internal thoracic artery** and **thyrocervical artery.** The internal thoracic artery (also called the mammary or sternal artery and, in humans, an artery used in coronary bypass operations) is the artery you detached earlier. It supplies the ventral muscular wall of the thorax and abdomen.

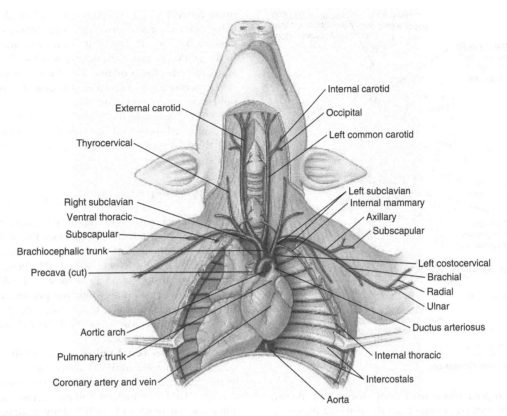

Figure 22-21

Arteries of head, shoulders, and forelimbs of a fetal pig. The internal thoracic arteries, shown laterally, actually lie ventral to the heart. What pair of arteries supplies blood to the tongue and face? _____ What artery supplies blood to the thyroid and parotid glands? _____ Near the head, the common carotid artery splits into what two arteries? _____

The thyrocervical (=internal cervical) artery arises from the subclavian at the same level as the internal thoracic. It supplies the thyroid and parotid glands and some of the pectoral muscles.

Pulmonary Circulation

Pulmonary Trunk. The pulmonary trunk arises from the right ventricle, ventral to the aorta. Follow it as it branches into **right** and **left pulmonary arteries,** which carry oxygen-poor blood to the lungs. Scrape away some lung tissue to find branches of these vessels.

Pulmonary Veins. Pulmonary veins empty oxygen-rich blood into the left atrium.

 Probe gently under the left atrium to expose the veins.

You should be able to find the large trunk entering the heart just under the hemiazygous vein and a pair of vessels servicing each lobe of the lungs.

Fetal Shortcuts

Foramen Ovale. This is a fetal opening in the wall between the right and left atria. Part of the blood from the right atrium can pass through the foramen ovale directly to the left atrium, where it can go to the left ventricle, to the aorta, and back into the systemic circulation without going to the lungs at all (Figure 22-22). The remainder of the blood enters the pulmonary trunk.

Ductus Arteriosus. This is the short connection between the pulmonary trunk and the aorta. Trace this connection, which begins where the smaller pulmonary arteries branch off toward the lungs. Part of the blood from the right ventricle goes to the lungs, and part is shunted through the ductus arteriosus to the aorta (Figure 22-22).

Ductus Venosus. This is a third fetal shortcut that connects the umbilical vein with the postcava, passing through a channel in the liver tissue. During fetal life, the anterior part of the postcaval vein carries a mixture

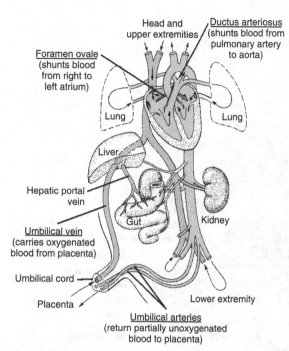

Figure 22-22
Scheme of fetal circulation.

of oxygen-poor blood from body tissues and oxygen-rich blood (and nutrients) from the placenta by way of the umbilical vein (the vein tied and cut earlier). After birth both the umbilical vein and the ductus venosus degenerate.

 You will be able to see the arrangement of the vessels in the liver tissue by using a probe to scrape or "comb out" the liver tissue to separate it from the vessels. Wash out the loose tissue.

Some of the vessels you see will probably be hepatic ducts.

Changes in Circulation at Birth

Two crucial events happen at the moment of birth: (1) the placental bloodstream upon which the fetus has depended is abruptly cut off, and (2) pulmonary circulation immediately assumes the task of oxygenating the blood. One of the most extraordinary aspects of mammalian development is the perfect preparedness of the circulatory architecture for this event.

When a newborn piglet (or human) takes its first breath, vascular resistance through the lungs is suddenly lowered as the lungs expand. The ductus arteriosus functionally constricts almost immediately, and the lungs receive full blood circulation. Blood then returns from the pulmonary veins to the left atrium, raising

pressure in this chamber enough to close the flaplike valve over the foramen ovale. With blood no longer passing between the right and left atria, the foramen ovale gradually grows permanently closed, leaving a scar called the **fossa ovalis.** The ductus arteriosus also closes permanently, becoming a ligament between the pulmonary artery and aortic arch.

With severing of the umbilical cord, flow through the umbilical vein and arteries ceases immediately, and these vessels are eventually reduced to fibrous cords.

Postcaval Venous Circulation

The **postcava** carries blood to the heart from the hindlimbs and trunk. Follow it from the right atrium through the intermediate lobe of the lung and through the diaphragm to the liver (Figure 22-23). Push the intestines to the left side, clean away most of the dorsal portion of the liver, and note where the **postcava** emerges and continues posteriorly. Clean away the peritoneum that covers the postcava, and find the following veins that enter it on each side.

One or two **renal veins** extend from each kidney. Do both right and left veins enter at the same level? _____The narrow, band-shaped adrenal gland (=suprarenal gland) lying against the anteromedial border of each kidney is drained by a small **adrenal vein** that may enter the renal vein or may empty directly into the postcava. It is accompanied by the adrenal artery. Just posterior to the adrenal vein and at about the same level as the renal veins, find the **parietal vein** extending to the body wall, accompanied by the parietal artery. The **genital vein** and **artery** serve the testes and ovaries. In males the vein is called the **spermatic vein** and is incorporated together with the spermatic artery into the spermatic cord to the testis. In females it is called the **ovarian vein;** it lies suspended in the mesovarium along with the ovarian artery.

Follow the postcava posteriorly to its bifurcation into the **common iliac veins.** These in turn divide into **internal** and **external iliac veins.** The internal iliac vein (hypogastric) is the medial branch extending dorsally and posteriorly into the deep tissue and draining blood from the rectum, bladder, and gluteal muscles. The external iliac vein is the lateral branch and the largest vein entering the common iliac. It drains the foot and leg and is formed by the union of the large **femoral vein,** which extends ventrally toward the knee, and **deep femoral vein,** which extends dorsally and posteriorly into the deep muscles of the thigh. It also receives a lateral branch, the **circumflex iliac vein,** which drains the muscles of the abdomen and upper thigh.

Hepatic Portal System

The hepatic portal system is a series of veins that drain the digestive system and spleen. Blood is collected in the **hepatic portal vein,** which carries it to liver capillaries. As blood laden with nutrients from the intestine passes through the liver, the liver may store excess sugars in the form of glycogen, or it may give up sugar to the blood if sugar is needed. Some of the amino acids formed by protein digestion may also be modified here. Blood from the liver capillaries is collected by **hepatic veins,** short veins that empty into the postcava.

The hepatic portal system in your specimen may not be injected. Unless these vessels are injected or are filled with dry blood, they may be difficult to locate. Try to examine an injected specimen.

Lift up the liver, stomach, and duodenum and draw the intestine posteriorly to expose the pancreas. Loosen the pancreatic tissue from the hepatic portal vein that runs through it. Now lay the duodenum over to your right and see how the vein enters the lobes of the liver near the common bile duct (in the gastrohepatic ligament). Lay the small intestine over to your left and fan out the mesenteries of the small intestine to see how the veins from the intestines are collected into the **anterior**

mesenteric vein (Figure 22-23). This joins with the small **posterior mesenteric vein** from the large intestine and with veins from the stomach and spleen to form the **hepatic portal vein.**

Arteries of the Trunk and Hindlegs

Descending Aorta. The descending aorta follows the vertebral column posteriorly, first lying dorsal and then ventral to the postcava (Figure 22-23). After passing through the diaphragm, the aorta gives rise to a single large artery, the **celiac artery.** To find it, clip away the diaphragm and remove the tissue around the aorta at the anterior end of the abdominal cavity. Be very careful not to destroy the celiac ganglion and sympathetic nerves (described in Exercise 22F). The celiac artery divides almost immediately into arteries serving the stomach, spleen, pancreas, liver, and duodenum.

Just posterior to the celiac, find another unpaired artery, the **anterior mesenteric artery.** This vessel must be dissected from the surrounding tissue. It sends branches to the pancreas, small intestine, and large intestine.

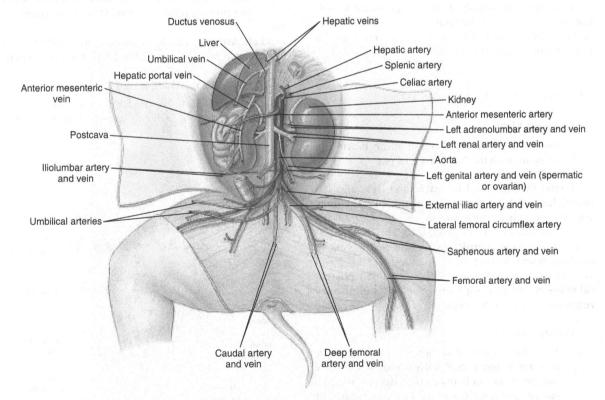

Figure 22-23
Circulation of trunk and hindlegs of a fetal pig.

Locate next the paired **parietal arteries, renal arteries,** and **spermatic** or **ovarian arteries.** Posterior to these is the single **posterior mesenteric artery,** which divides and sends branches to the colon and rectum. It will probably have been broken off during earlier dissection of the abdominal cavity.

At its posterior end, the aorta now divides into two large lateral **external iliac arteries** to the legs, two medial **internal iliac arteries** to the sacral region, and a small continuation of the aorta into the tail, the **caudal artery.** Trace one of the external iliac arteries. It first gives off a lateral **circumflex artery** that supplies some of the pelvic muscles, then penetrates the peritoneal body wall to enter the leg as the **femoral artery.** Note that nearly all of the caudal arterial circulation is accompanied by corresponding venous circulation, already described. Follow the femoral artery to the point where, on its median side, it gives off a **deep femoral artery.** This artery serves the deep muscles of the thigh.

Locate the origin of the **internal iliac arteries.** Each internal iliac gives off at once a large **umbilical artery** and then, as a smaller vessel, continues dorsally and posteriorly into the sacral region beside the internal iliac vein, giving off branches to the bladder, rectum, and gluteal muscles.

In a fetus, the umbilical arteries are major vessels that return blood from the fetus to the placenta by way of the umbilical cord. After birth they become smaller and serve the urinary bladder.

Structure of the Heart

External View.

Use fresh or preserved pig or sheep hearts and compare with the heart of a fetal pig.

Locate the right and left **atria** and right and left **ventricles.** Find the **coronary sulcus** and **coronary artery** and **vein,** which supply the muscles of the heart. Now identify on the ventral side the large, thick-walled **pulmonary trunk,** leaving the right ventricle, and large **aorta,** leaving the left ventricle. On the dorsal side, find the large, thin-walled **precaval** and **postcaval veins** entering the right atrium and the **pulmonary veins** entering the left atrium.

Frontal Section.

Now make a frontal section, dividing the heart into dorsal and ventral halves. Start at the apex and direct the cut between the origins of the pulmonary and aortic trunks. Leave the two halves of the heart attached at the top. Wash out the heart cavities (or, if injected, carefully pull out the latex filling).

The cavities of the heart are lined with a shiny membrane, the **endocardium.** Identify the chambers and valves at the entrance to each chamber that prevent a backflow of blood.

Right Atrium. The right atrium is thin-walled, with openings from the precava, postcava, and hemiazygous veins. Find the entrance of these veins. Now, in the dorsal half of a fetal pig heart, probe for an opening between the two atria. This is the **foramen ovale,** one of the fetal shortcuts.

Right Ventricle. The right ventricle is thick-walled. The tricuspid valve (also called the right atrio-ventricular valve) prevents backflow of blood to the atrium (Figure 22-24). The valve is composed of three **cusps,** or flaps of tissue, that extend from the floor of the atrium and are connected by fibrous cords, the **chordae tendineae** (ten-din′ee-ee), to **papillary muscles** projecting from the walls of the ventricle.

In the ventral half of the heart, the opening into the pulmonary artery is guarded by **semilunar valves.**

Cut the pulmonary artery close to the heart and remove the latex. Slit the vessel for a short distance into the ventricle and look into it to see the three cusps, or pockets of tissue. Determine how they would work to allow passage into the vessel but prevent return of blood into the ventricle.

Left Atrium. The left atrium is thin-walled. Find the entrance of the pulmonary veins that return oxygen-rich blood to the heart.

Left Ventricle. The left ventricle is the most muscular chamber of the heart, for it must send freshly oxygenated blood at high pressure to all tissues of the

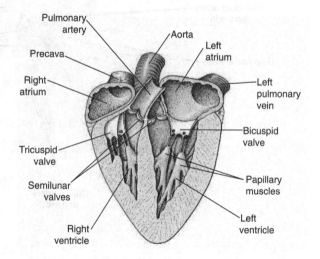

Figure 22-24
Frontal section of a sheep heart.

body. The bicuspid valve (also called the left atrioventricular valve) guards the entrance from the left atrium. Find the cusps of this valve. Push the valve open and closed to see how it works.

Find the three-cusped **semilunar valve,** which prevents backflow from the aorta (Figure 22-24).

Notice the difference in the thickness of the walls of arteries and veins. Of what are these walls composed? _____Would you find the same kind of muscle in the heart as in the vessels? _____ What is the pacemaker of the heart? _____ Consult your text.

Identification

Be familiar with direction of blood flow throughout the body. Be able to describe how fetal circulation differs from postnatal circulation. Be able to trace blood from any part of the heart to any part of the body and back to the heart.

Written Report

On separate paper, list the two chief differences between mammalian and amphibian circulatory systems, as illustrated by your study of a pig and frog. How are these differences adaptive to an all-terrestrial or half-aquatic life?

EXERCISE 22F
Nervous System

The nervous system can be divided into the **central nervous system (CNS),** containing the spinal cord and brain, and **peripheral nervous system (PNS),** containing all the neural tissue outside the central nervous system. The PNS is the link between an animal's environment and its CNS, and it contains both **sensory** components that bring sensory information to the CNS and **motor** components that carry neural commands from the CNS to peripheral effectors (usually muscles). Such neural information, in the form of nerve impulses, is conducted over axons that are bundled together into **peripheral nerves** (also called nerve trunks). Peripheral nerves comprise both **spinal nerves** that communicate with the spinal cord and **cranial nerves** that are connected to the brain.

The **autonomic nervous system** is a subdivision of the PNS that provides automatic control over visceral activities, such as coordination of the cardiovascular, respiratory, digestive, and reproductive functions.

Consult your textbook for additional information on the nervous system and be able to relate this material to your dissection. In your dissection of the nervous system of a fetal pig, you will first look for the spinal nerves and plexuses and then look for the sympathetic

nerve trunks and some of their ganglia. These you will find in the neck region and body cavities. Then you will study a preserved mammalian brain.

Spinal Nerves

Each spinal nerve arises from the spinal cord as two roots: a **dorsal root** containing the axons of sensory nerves and a **ventral root** containing motor neurons that control peripheral effectors (Figure 22-25). Each dorsal root bears a prominent **ganglion** that contains the cell bodies of the sensory neurons. The ventral roots bear no ganglia because the cell bodies of the motor neurons are contained within the spinal cord. Spinal nerves emerge from the vertebral column through openings between the individual vertebrae called **intervertebral foramina** (sing. **foramen**). After exiting through a foramen, each spinal nerve divides into three branches: a small **dorsal branch** that supplies the muscles and skin of the dorsal part of the body, a large **ventral branch** that supplies the skin and muscles of the ventral and lateral part of the body and limbs, and a small **communicating branch** that joins ganglia of the autonomic nervous system. The major named spinal nerves to be studied in this exercise are all ventral branches.

There are 33 pairs of spinal nerves in a fetal pig (31 pairs in humans) and each is identified by its association with the vertebra through which it exits: 8 cervical, 14 thoracic, 7 lumbar, and 4 sacral (Figure 22-26).

Brachial Plexus

In your search for arteries and veins in the foreleg, you saw a group of tough, white nerves extending into the arm. These are the sixth, seventh, and eighth cervical and first thoracic nerves, which, with their interconnecting branches, form the brachial plexus (a plexus is a network of nerves produced by the convergence of fibers in complex ways; the term literally means interwoven).

Clear away connective tissue and sever blood vessels if necessary to uncover as many of these nerves as possible and trace them back to their emergence from the vertebrae, being careful not to destroy any of the branches. Each nerve sends branches to join neighboring nerves.

Starting at the level of the first rib and moving anteriorly are three nerves into the foreleg that come from the seventh and eighth cervical and the first thoracic nerves—the ulnar, median, and radial nerves. The subscapular and suprascapular nerves come from the fifth, sixth, and seventh cervical nerves and are also part of the brachial plexus.

Ulnar. The ulnar is the most posterior of the brachial nerves. It follows the bend of the elbow to the underside of the foreleg and foot.

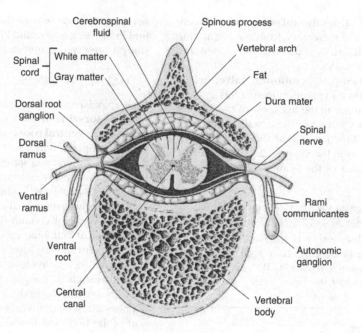

Figure 22-25
Section of spinal column of a mammal, showing spinal roots and branches of spinal nerve.

Median. The median nerve follows the brachial artery and vein along the inside of the foreleg.

Radial. The radial is the larger nerve. It lies underneath the median and passes into the deep muscles of the foreleg. By skinning the lateral side of the arm and shoulder and dissecting under the muscles (triceps), you may find the radial nerve where it crosses over to the lateral side of the foreleg and passes down the dorsal (radial) side of the foreleg and foot.

Subscapular Nerve. The subscapular nerve is from parts of the sixth and seventh cervical nerves. It branches into the muscles under the scapula.

Suprascapular Nerve. This large nerve is from the fifth and sixth cervical nerves to the muscles above the scapula.

You can probably also locate the fourth, third, and second cervical nerves, but the first is difficult to find.

Thoracic and Lumbar Nerves

Thoracic nerves lie in the intercostal spaces, running parallel with the intercostal arteries and veins. Trace one or two back to the vertebral column.

Posterior to the ribs in the dorsal body wall, the first four lumbar nerves lie just under the peritoneum. They angle out posterolaterally from the vertebral column. Trace some of these.

Lumbosacral Plexus

The lumbosacral plexus is formed by the ventral branches of the fifth, sixth, and seventh lumbar and first sacral nerves; it sends large nerves into the hindlegs.

To identify the nerves making up the plexus, you may have to clip the iliac artery and vein from the postcava and remove some of the muscle along the backbone. The **femoral nerve** and **saphenous nerve** (which branches from the femoral) follow arteries of the same names. The large **sciatic nerve** follows the internal iliac artery and vein into the deep sacral region. The nerve emerges with the vessels close to the backbone and travels around the end of the ischium to follow the femur (Figure 22-26).

 If you wish to trace the sciatic into the leg, skin the dorsal side of the pelvis and thigh and lay aside the layer of muscle along the backbone for 3 to 4 cm above the tail.

Autonomic Nervous System

The autonomic nervous system (ANS) is concerned with involuntary body functions that are not controlled by the cerebrum and do not ordinarily affect consciousness. It governs (1) heart muscle; (2) smooth involuntary muscle, such as that of the digestive tract, and blood vessels; and (3) secretions of various glands. The ANS is composed of two divisions, **sympathetic** and **parasympathetic,** and each of these divisions has a characteristic anatomical and functional organization. One important characteristic of *both* divisions is that there is always a synapse imposed between the CNS where the autonomic fibers originate and the peripheral effectors where they end. The first neuron with its body in the spinal cord is called a **preganglionic neuron.** Its

PERIPHERAL NERVOUS SYSTEM   AUTONOMIC NERVOUS SYSTEM

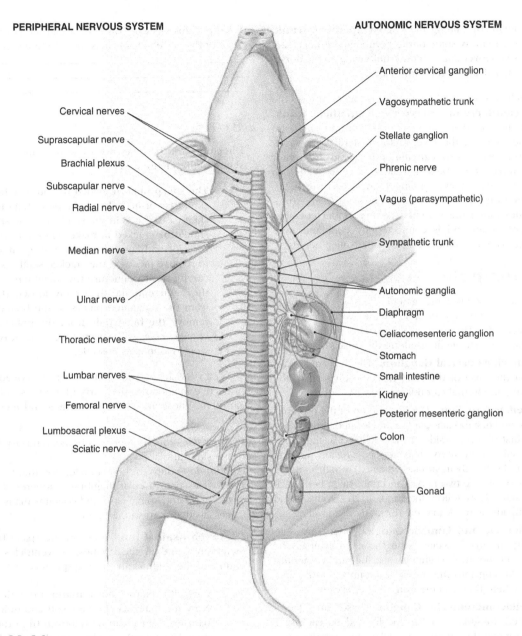

Cervical nerves

Suprascapular nerve

Brachial plexus

Subscapular nerve

Radial nerve

Median nerve

Ulnar nerve

Thoracic nerves

Lumbar nerves

Femoral nerve

Lumbosacral plexus

Sciatic nerve

Anterior cervical ganglion

Vagosympathetic trunk

Stellate ganglion

Phrenic nerve

Vagus (parasympathetic)

Sympathetic trunk

Autonomic ganglia

Diaphragm

Celiacomesenteric ganglion

Stomach

Small intestine

Kidney

Posterior mesenteric ganglion

Colon

Gonad

Figure 22-26

Peripheral nervous system and sympathetic division of the autonomic nervous system of a fetal pig. **Left (pig's right)**, peripheral nervous system. **Right (pig's left)**, sympathetic trunk and major ganglia.

axon extends out some distance from the spinal cord to a ganglion, where it synapses with the second neuron in the series, the **postganglionic neuron.** This neuron extends the remaining distance to the effector organ, a muscle or gland.

In the sympathetic division of the ANS, preganglionic fibers all emerge from the thoracic and lumbar segments of the spinal cord and pass to **sympathetic ganglia** located close to the spinal cord. Many of these ganglia are interconnected into an elongate **sympathetic trunk** (Figure 22-26).

In the parasympathetic division of the ANS, preganglionic fibers emerge from the cranial (brain stem) and sacral segments of the spinal cord. Preganglionic fibers are quite long, extending all the way from the CNS to the peripheral effector organ. Here they synapse with short postganglionic fibers. Although the parasympathetic outflow travels over several different cranial and sacral nerves, nearly 75% of its outflow is carried by a single nerve, the **vagus nerve** (tenth cranial nerve).

Begin by finding the **vagosympathetic trunk.** Clean away some of the peritoneum if necessary to uncover one of these trunks lying on the dorso-medial side of the carotid artery.

Each vagosympathetic trunk is made up of the **vagus (tenth cranial) nerve** and **sympathetic trunk,** which are united in a common sheath and enter the thoracic cavity at the level of the first rib. The vagus nerve is a mixed nerve carrying both sensory and motor (parasympathetic) fibers. It follows the esophagus to the abdominal cavity, sending branches to the heart, bronchi, stomach, and intestines. The sympathetic trunk continues along the vertebral column under cover of the peritoneum and is connected by communicating branches (rami communicantes) to the spinal nerves.

Sympathetic Ganglia

There are several large ganglia in the sympathetic system that you may be able to find with some care (Figure 22-26). These are usually paired and appear as irregular, whitish swellings along the trunks.

Anterior Cervical Ganglion. This is a small ganglion at the base of the skull near the division of the external and internal carotids.

Stellate Ganglion. This is made up of the posterior cervical and first thoracic ganglia and located under cover of the first rib on the side of the trachea near the origin of the subclavian artery. It is at this ganglion that the vagus and sympathetic trunks separate. From this region, try to separate the two nerves and trace them both back to the skull. Now follow the vagus to the stomach and the sympathetic trunk into the dorsal thoracic wall.

Thoracic and Lumbar Ganglia. These are segmentally arranged swellings on the main sympathetic trunks. Lift the trunk slightly to see the rami communicantes dipping into the muscle to connect with spinal nerves where they emerge from the vertebrae.

Celiacomesenteric Ganglia. These are large, elongated, irregular ganglia, one located on each side of the aorta at the origin of the celiac and anterior mesenteric arteries. They send branches to the stomach, intestine, kidney, and genital organs.

Posterior Mesenteric Ganglion (Unpaired). This is a small ganglion on the posterior mesenteric artery. It sends branches to the intestine and to the ovaries or testes.

Do you see any pattern of similarity between the nervous systems of a pig and frog? _____ By observing charts or diagrams, compare the nervous system of a pig with that of a human being. What conclusions can you draw about the nervous system of vertebrates in general? _____

_____

_____

What conclusions can you draw about the nervous systems of the vertebrates versus that of the invertebrates?

_____

_____

_____

Brain

Directions will be given for dissection and study of a sheep brain (Figure 22-27).

 The sheep brain provided to you may be in the skull case or may already be dissected out of the skull case. If it is in the skull case, the skull case should be cracked to make removal of the brain easier. Gently use forceps or the tip of a scalpel to remove pieces of the cracked skull case, being careful not to puncture the membrane covering the brain underneath. Gently loosen the brain from the remaining pieces of the braincase. To remove the brain fully from the braincase, the cranial nerves will have to be cut, but leave nerve stumps as long as possible.

Both the brain and spinal cord are covered with protective membranes that carry blood vessels to nourish them. These are called **meninges** and include the following:

Dura mater—tough outer membrane; tends to cling to the skull in places

Arachnoid—clings to the pia mater; too thin to identify

Pia mater—fine vascular membrane; adheres closely to the brain and spinal cord and contains many blood vessels that nourish the brain

Cerebrospinal fluid flows in the space between membranes and in the cavities, or ventricles, of the brain and the central canal of the spinal cord.

 Carefully remove **dura mater** from the brain. Now the brain will be very soft and quite easily damaged, but it can be removed from the braincase. Lift it gently and look for the cranial nerves on the ventral side where they pass into the floor of the braincase. Clip the nerves, leaving the stubs on the brain cut as long as possible. Cut the spinal cord 2.5 to 5 cm below the brain, leaving one or two stubs of spinal nerves in place.

Dorsal Surface of the Brain

Cerebrum (Cerebral Hemispheres). The cerebrum is divided into left and right oval lobes separated by the **longitudinal fissure.** The cortex (outer layer) is made up of raised convolutions called **gyri** (jī'rē), separated by fissures called **sulci** (sul'kē). The cortex contains most of the gray matter of the brain. A groove,

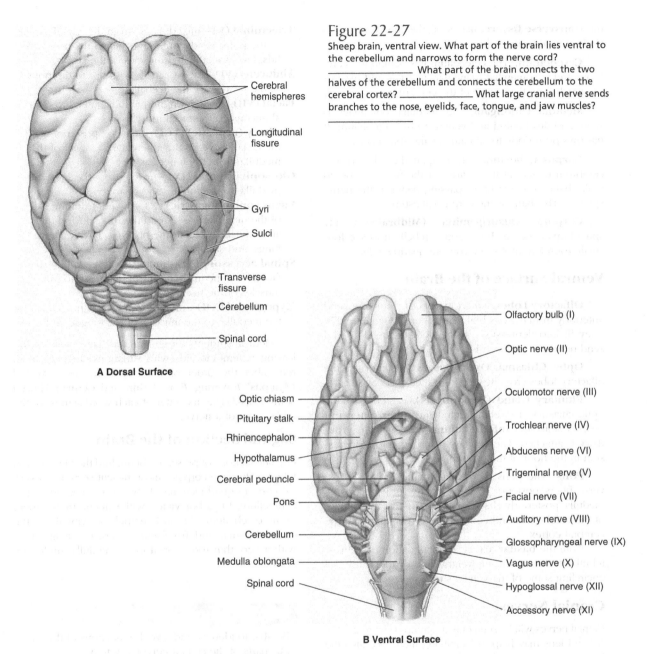

Cerebral
hemispheres

Longitudinal
fissure

Gyri

Sulci

Transverse
fissure

Cerebellum

Spinal cord

A Dorsal Surface

Figure 22-27

Sheep brain, ventral view. What part of the brain lies ventral to
the cerebellum and narrows to form the nerve cord?
_____ What part of the brain connects the two
halves of the cerebellum and connects the cerebellum to the
cerebral cortex? _____ What large cranial nerve sends
branches to the nose, eyelids, face, tongue, and jaw muscles?
_____

Olfactory bulb (I)

Optic nerve (II)

Oculomotor nerve (III)

Trochlear nerve (IV)

Abducens nerve (VI)

Trigeminal nerve (V)

Facial nerve (VII)

Auditory nerve (VIII)

Glossopharyngeal nerve (IX)

Vagus nerve (X)

Hypoglossal nerve (XII)

Accessory nerve (XI)

Optic chiasm

Pituitary stalk

Rhinencephalon

Hypothalamus

Cerebral peduncle

Pons

Cerebellum

Medulla oblongata

Spinal cord

B Ventral Surface

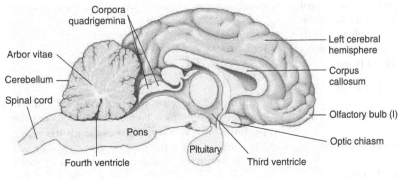

Corpora
quadrigemina

Arbor vitae

Cerebellum

Spinal cord

Left cerebral
hemisphere

Corpus
callosum

Olfactory bulb (I)

Optic chiasm

Pons

Pituitary

Fourth ventricle

Third ventricle

C Midsaggital Section

the **transverse fissure,** marks off the cerebrum posteriorly from the cerebellum.

Cerebellum. The cerebellum lies behind the cerebrum and is somewhat triangular. Its folds and fissures are much finer than those of the cerebrum.

Medulla Oblongata. The medulla oblongata is small and lies behind and ventral to the cerebellum. It narrows posteriorly to continue as the spinal cord.

Corpus Callosum. Spread apart the lobes of the cerebrum to see, at the bottom of the fissure, a broad white band of nerve fibers passing between the hemispheres. This band is the corpus callosum.

Corpora Quadrigemina (Midbrain). Gently spread apart the cerebrum and cerebellum to see four small, rounded knobs, the corpora quadrigemina.

Ventral Surface of the Brain

Olfactory Lobes. Olfactory lobes (=bulbs) extend anteriorly from the cerebral hemispheres (Figure 22-27). They fit into depressions in the floor of the skull and send nerves to the nostrils.

Optic Chiasma. Optic nerves posterior to the olfactory lobes cross here to form the optic chiasma.

Pituitary Gland (Hypophysis). Posterior to the optic chiasma, a swelling called the **tuber cinereum** bears a stalk, the **infundibulum,** on which the **pituitary** is attached. The pituitary gland fits into a depression in the floor of the cranium.

Pons. The pons is a broad, raised area of transverse fibers posterior to the pituitary and joining the medulla posteriorly. Its fibers connect the two halves of the cerebellum and connect the cerebellum with the cerebral cortex.

Note the **basilar artery,** a continuation of the vertebral arteries, in the midventral line of the brain and encircling some of the ventral structures.

Cranial Nerves

Cranial nerves will be seen only as stumps (Figure 22-27). A hand lens may help in identifying them. See also the human brains on display in the laboratory. Some cranial nerves carry only sensory fibers to the brain from the eyes, nose, or ears. Some carry only motor fibers, which innervate the muscles or glands of certain areas; others carry both sensory and motor fibers. All are paired.

Olfactory (I)—sensory; from the nose to the olfactory lobes

Optic (II)—sensory; from the eyes to the optic chiasma

Oculomotor (III)—motor; small; anterior to the pons; to the muscles of the eyeball

Trochlear (IV)—motor; smallest; lateral to the oculomotor; to the muscles of the eyeball

Trigeminal (V)—mixed; large; from the lateral aspect of the pons; sends three branches to the nose, eyelids, face, tongue, and muscles of the jaw

Abducens (VI)—motor; small; posterior to the pons; to the muscles of the eyeball

Facial (VII)—mixed; on the medulla; lateral to the abducens; to the facial muscles

Auditory (acoustic) (VIII)—sensory; posterior to the facial nerve on the anterolateral aspect of the medulla; from the inner ear

Glossopharyngeal (IX)—mixed; from the side of the medulla; to the tongue and pharynx

Vagus (pneumogastric) (X)—mixed; from the side of the medulla; passes into the thoracic and the abdominal cavities to the pharynx, larynx, heart, lungs, and stomach

Spinal accessory (XI)—motor; from the lateral surface of the medulla and the spinal cord; to the muscles of the neck

Hypoglossal (XII)—motor; from the ventral surface of the medulla; to the muscles of the tongue and neck

Medical students for generations have used the following mnemonic aid (with variations) to help them remember the order of the cranial nerves: "On Old Olympus' Towering Tops A Finn And German Viewed Some Hops." The first letter of each word stands for the initial letter of a nerve.

Sagittal Section of the Brain

On half-sections of preserved brain, find the (1) gray and white matter; (2) corpus callosum—cut section, curved; (3) corpora quadrigemina—between the cerebrum and cerebellum; (4) arbor vitae—white fibers, tree-shaped, in the cerebellum; (5) third ventricle—cavity above the optic chiasma; and (6) fourth ventricle—small cavity with a very thin roof, dorsal in the medulla, under the cerebellum.

Identification

Be able to identify and give the functions of the various parts of the central nervous system.

EXERCISE 22G
Respiratory System

Recall how passageways for air and food cross in the pharyngeal cavity (see Figure 22-13). Locate again the **epiglottis** and note how it closes the **glottis** (open end of the larynx) when food is being swallowed.

The **larynx** is a cartilage-reinforced cylinder that contains the vocal cords. Displace the epiglottis and look into the glottis (laryngeal opening) to see the

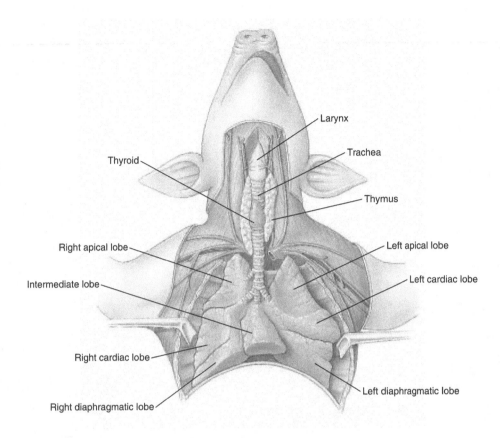

Figure 22-28

Respiratory system of a fetal pig, ventral view. Which lung is larger, the left or right? _____ In what structure are the vocal cords found? _____ What gland is important for regulating growth, development, and metabolic rate? _____

vocal folds (cords). These are folds of flesh directed downward, each with a slitlike opening. Open the larynx ventrally to see them better.

The **trachea** (Figure 22-28) is stiffened by a series of C-shaped cartilage rings, which are incomplete dorsally where the trachea lies against the esophagus.

Lungs are unequally paired, the larger right lung having four lobes and left lung two or three lobes. The right lung has an **apical lobe,** a **cardiac lobe,** a **diaphragmatic lobe,** and an **intermediate lobe,** which is median and notched to surround the postcava. The apical and cardiac lobes are usually fused on the left lung. Lungs are spongy and highly elastic.

Bronchi are branches of the trachea that extend into the lobes of the lungs. These branch repeatedly in the lungs to form, finally, microscopic **respiratory bronchioles,** which give off **alveolar ducts,** each of which terminates in a cluster of aveoli, or air cells.

 Remove the heart and large vessels, leaving stubs of the pulmonary vessels attached to the lungs. Remove the larynx, trachea, and lungs. Slit the larynx and trachea and follow the bronchi as far

into the lungs as possible. Trace a blood vessel into the lung tissue. Cut a thin section from a lung and examine with a hand lens or dissecting microscope.

Demonstration

The *butcher's pull.*[*] Examine the fresh lungs, trachea, and heart of a small sheep. Use a blowpipe to expand a lung. Trace one of the bronchi into the lung and follow some of its branches as far as possible into the lung tissue. Identify the pulmonary vessels. Trace a blood vessel as far as possible into the lung tissue. Why is the tissue so highly vascular? _____ Cut a cross section from a large artery and a large vein and contrast their walls. Contrast the trachea with the esophagus. Where do you find the cartilage? _____ Of what advantage is the cartilage? _____
_____
_____

_____
*The butcher's pull is referred to as the sheep pluck in the Carolina catalog (22-8830).

NOTES

PHOTO CREDITS

Part Openers

1: © William C. Ober; **2, 3:** Cleveland P. Hickman, Jr.

Chapter 1

Figure 1-1: Courtesy of Leica, Inc.; **1-5:** © Carolina Biological Supply Company / Phototake; **1-6A:** Cleveland P. Hickman, Jr.; **1-6B:** Courtesy G.E. Palade, The Rockefeller University, New York; **1-7A:** Courtesy Orci, L.J. 1971. Ultrastruct. Res. 35.1, Academic Press; **1-8A:** J.P. Revel, Calif. Institute of Technology; **1-8B:** From R.G. Kessel and R.H. Kardon, Tissues and Organs: A Text-Atlas Scanning Electron Microscopy, 1979, W.H. Freeman and Co.; **1-9:** © S.L. Flegeler / Visuals Unlimited

Chapter 2

2-1: © Carolina Biological Supply Company / Phototake; **2-2:** Courtesy Morgan, C.R., and Jersild, R.A. 1970; **2-3:** Courtesy G.E. Palade, The Rockefeller University, New York; **2-4, 2-5:** Courtesy of Charles Flickinger, from Flickinger. C. et al., 1979, "Medical Cell Biology", W.B. Saunders; **2-8:** © C.H. Rieder / Biological Photo Service; **2-9, 2-10:** © Carolina Biological Supply Company / Phototake

Chapter 3

3-5A-C, 3-6A-C, 3-9A-L: © Carolina Biological Supply Company / Phototake

Chapter 4

4-1A,B: Cleveland P. Hickman, Jr.; **4-2A,B, 4-3:** © Ed Reschke / Peter Arnold, Inc.; **4-4A,B, 4-5, 4-6A:** Cleveland P. Hickman, Jr.; **4-6B:** © Manfred Kage / Peter Arnold, Inc.; **4-7:** Cleveland P. Hickman, Jr.; **4-9:** © Carolina Biological Supply Company / Phototake; **4-11:** © David M. Phillips / Visuals Unlimited; **4-12:** © Biophoto Associates / Photo Researchers, Inc.; **4-13, 4-14, 4-15B-D:** Cleveland P. Hickman, Jr.; **4-16:** © Ed Reschke / Peter Arnold, Inc.; **4-17:** Cleveland P. Hickman, Jr.; **4-18:** © Carolina Biological Supply Company / Phototake; **4-19:** © R. Calentine / Visuals Unlimited; **4-20A:** © Carolina Biological Supply Company / Phototake; **4-20B:** © Cytographics / Visuals Unlimited

Chapter 6

6-1: © Carolina Biological Supply Company / Phototake; **6-7:** © David M. Phillips / Visuals Unlimited; **6-9:** © Eric V. Grave / Photo Researchers, Inc.; **6-12:** Cleveland P. Hickman, Jr.; **6-14:** From A. Wilcox, "Manual for the Microscopial Diagnosis of Malaria in Man", Public Health Service Publication No. 796. U.S. Government Printing Office, Washington, D.C. 1960; **6-16:** © Karl Aufderheide / Visuals Unlimited; **6-18:** © Phil A. Harrington / Peter Arnold, Inc.; **6-19, 6-20:** © Walker England / Photo Researchers, Inc.; **6-22:** © David M. Phillips / Visuals Unlimited

Chapter 7

7-2: Cleveland P. Hickman, Jr.; **7-5:** © Stanley Flegler / Visuals Unlimited; **7-6A,B:** Frances M. Hickman; **7-7A,B:** © William C. Ober

Chapter 8

8-2: © DRK Photo; **8-4A,B:** © D.P. Wilson / Eric & David Hosking; **8-5:** © Robert Brons / Biological Photo Service; **8-8A:** © William C. Ober

Chapter 9

9-1A: © Carolina Biological Supply Company / Phototake; **9-6A:** © Cabisco / Visuals Unlimited; **9-7A,B:** Cleveland P. Hickman, Jr.; **9-8:** © Stan Flegler / Visuals Unlimited

Chapter 10

10-4: © Robert Calentine / Visuals Unlimited; **10-6:** Frances Hickman

Chapter 11

11-1, 11-6: Cleveland P. Hickman, Jr.

Chapter 12

12-2A: © Daniel W. Gotshall / Visuals Unlimited; **12-2B:** © William C. Ober; **12-4:** © G.L. Twiest / Visuals Unlimited; **12-5A:** © Carolina Biological Supply Co. / Phototake; **12-5B:** Cleveland P. Hickman, Jr.; **12-6:** Cleveland P. Hickman, Jr.

Chapter 13

13-3: Cleveland P. Hickman, Jr.

Chapter 15

15-4: © Larry S. Roberts

Chapter 16

16-1: © D.P. Wilson / Eric & David Hosking; **16-2:** Cleveland P. Hickman, Jr.; **16-5A,B, 16-7:** © William C. Ober; **16-9A,B:** © R. Harbo

Chapter 17

17-2, 17-4, 17-5: Cleveland P. Hickman, Jr.

Chapter 18

18-5A: © C. Stehr / Visuals Unlimited

DEFINITIONS

Regional and Directional References

anterior Pertaining to the front or head end; cephalic; cranial.

posterior Pertaining to the tail or hind end.

dorsal Referring to the back or uppermost side.

ventral Referring to the belly side.

lateral Pertaining to the side of a body; situated to either side of the midline.

medial At or near the middle or midline of a body or organ, in contrast to lateral.

cephalic (cranial) Pertaining to the head end. The opposite of caudal.

caudal Pertaining to the tail end.

proximal Toward or near the point of attachment. The opposite of distal.

distal Away from the base or point of attachment.

longitudinal Pertaining to the long axis of the body; lengthwise.

peripheral Referring to parts away from the center; external to.

superficial On or near the surface.

oral Pertaining to the mouth or the region around the mouth.

aboral Pertaining to a region away from or most distant from the mouth.

Terms That Indicate Planes of Section

sagittal section Longitudinal section through the median vertical plane that bisects the body into right and left halves; or any section parallel to it.

parasagittal section Section to one side of the midline, separating right and left portions of unequal size.

frontal section Longitudinal section made at right angles to a sagittal section. It is parallel to the dorsal and ventral surfaces. Same as coronal section.

transverse section Any section made through and at right angles to the longitudinal axis.

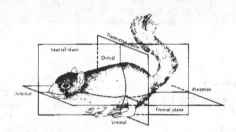

median plane Vertical longitudinal plane that extends from the dorsal to the ventral surface and passes from the anterior end to the posterior end through the middle of the body. This kind of plane produces the sagittal section.

Kinds of Symmetry

symmetry Correspondence in size, shape, and relative position of parts that are on opposite sides of a dividing line or median plane.

spherical symmetry Condition in which any plane passing through the center point will divide the body into like halves. Rare in life; usually associated with floating forms.

radial symmetry Condition in which any plane passing through the longitudinal axis will divide the body into similar halves. Best suited to sessile forms.

bilateral symmetry Condition in which only a sagittal plane (through the longitudinal and dorsoventral axes) will divide the body into like halves. The most common type of symmetry.

biradial symmetry Essentially radial, but only two planes through the longitudinal axis create truly similar halves.

Analogy and Homology

analogous Similar in function and superficial structure (e.g., the wings of a bird, bat, and insect are analogous).

homologous Basically similar as a result of similarity in embryonic origin and development (e.g., the forelimbs of a bird, bat, horse, and human are homologous).